Glencoe Science

Blueprints for Success

SCIENCE CLASSROOMS THAT WORK

ConnectED

LOOK INSIDE TO FIND:

A. CLASSROOM AND LABORATORY MANAGEMENT AND SAFETY
B. DIFFERENTIATED INSTRUCTION
C. ENGLISH-LANGUAGE LEARNERS
D. LANGUAGE ARTS AND LITERACY
E. MATHEMATICS SUPPORT
F. SCHOOL-TO-HOME CONNECTION
G. PERFORMANCE ASSESSMENT

McGraw Hill Education

Photo credit: page iv: Meg Krsacok

Credits: The Probeware information in Tab A was reviewed and edited by Vernier Software and Technology.

The McGraw·Hill Companies

 Education

Send all inquiries to:
McGraw-Hill Education
8787 Orion Place
Columbus, OH 43240-4027

ISBN-13: 978-0-07-891485-0
MHID: 0-07-891485-X

Printed in the United States of America.

2 3 4 5 6 7 8 9 10 REL 15 14 13 12 11 10

Table of Contents

Classroom and Laboratory Management
and Safety.. Tab A

Differentiated Instruction .... Tab B

English-Language Learners (ELL)............................. Tab C

Language Arts and Literacy...................................... Tab D

Mathematics Support .... Tab E

School-to-Home Connection .... Tab F

Performance Assessment .... Tab G

To the Teacher

"Blueprints is the essential resource for any teacher who wants to keep up with the latest insights and best teaching practices in education. I love the *Classroom Scenarios*, as well as the practical application of strategies found in the *Differentiated Instruction*, *ELL*, *Language Arts and Literacy*, *Math Support*, and *Performance Assessment* sections. **Blueprints** gave me the tools to provide authentic learning opportunities that met the needs of all my students and made me successful in increasing student performance and achievement in my science classroom!"

Steve Federman, middle school science teacher in Loveland, Ohio

Consultants

Douglas Fisher, Ph.D., is a professor at the Department of Teacher Education at San Diego State University and is a teacher at Health Sciences High & Middle College. He is the recipient of an International Reading Association Celebrate Literacy Award, as well as a Christa McAuliffe Award for excellence in teacher education. He has published numerous articles on reading and literacy, differentiated instruction, English-Language Learners, and curriculum design, as well as books such as *Improving Adolescent Literacy: Strategies at Work* and *Checking for Understanding: Formative Assessment Tools for your Classroom*.

Viken "Vik" Hovsepian is a Senior National Mathematics Consultant to McGraw-Hill and is an author of several of its mathematics programs. Professor Hovsepian holds an elementary teaching credential in mathematics as well as life (secondary) credentials in mathematics, chemistry, and physics from the University of California at Los Angeles. He has been teaching for more than 25 years. Professor Hovsepian is a member of NCTM and CMC-South and is invited periodically to present "Math is Fun" to both organizations.

Classroom and Laboratory Management and Safety

Table of Contents

A Classroom Management Plan..4

Classroom Rules..6

Classroom Arrangement..9

Attendance and Absences..11

Activity Transitions..14

Class Materials and Assignments..15

Interactive Instruction...17

Peer Partners...20

Cooperative Learning..21

Multiple Learning Styles..30

Accommodations and Modifications..32

Manage Laboratory Sessions..34
- Before a Lab Session..34
- During a Lab Session..36
- After a Lab Activity...37

Manage Laboratory Work Outside the Classroom.................................38
- Home Lab Work..38
- Field Trips..38
- Dealing with Emergencies..41

Review Laboratory Safety Guidelines..43
- Present Safety Guidelines to Students..44

Review General Laboratory Procedures...45
- Overview of Laboratory Equipment..45
- Laboratory Safety Techniques and Procedures...................................45
- Assessing Students' Readiness for Lab Tasks.....................................51

Maintaining an Environmentally Safe Laboratory..................................52
- Waste Disposal Guidelines...52
- Sterilization Procedures...53

Manage Laboratory Materials Storage...55
- Material Safety Data Sheets (MSDS)...55
- Storage Procedures..60

Chemical Incompatibility Reference..64
- Inventory Practices..66
- Waste Disposal Policies..66

Prepare Live Exhibits..69
- Aquariums..69
- Terrariums..69
- Plants...70

Check Facilities and Equipment..71
- Facilities Specifications...72
- Safety Equipment Specifications..74
- Safety Requirements for Investigation Equipment..............................78

Emergency Response...80
- Very First Steps..81
- First Steps in Detail...81
- Using Accident Response Equipment..83
- Giving First Aid..84
- Cleaning Up Hazardous Spills..87

A

Advantages of Small-Scale Chemistry 89
Why Use Electronic Data Collection? 91
Data Collection Hardware and Software 92
Collect Data Using Probeware 94
Tips for Successful Data Collection..95
Sample Probeware Lab 96
Electronic Data-Collection Providers..99
Sample Student Laboratory and Safety Guidelines Handout..................101
Sample Student Laboratory Cleanup Checklist 102
Student Lab Safety Form...103
Sample Teacher Observation Form. 104
Phone List for Local Resources 105
Sample Guardian/Learning Partner Letter Regarding Home Lab Work..106
Sample Guardian/Learning Partner Letter Regarding Field Trips 107
Sample Permission Form for Field Trips 108
Sample Medical Emergency Form...109
Sample Accident Report Form 110
Sample Letter to Guardian or Learning Partner....................................111
Sample Letter to the Principal..112
Note to the Substitute Teacher 113
Safety Symbols..114
SI Conversion Table 117

A

Digital Resources for Teachers

Professional Development — **mhpdonline.com** *These PD modules address both teaching strategies and science content.*

- ✓ Literacy Strategies: Reading, Writing, Listening, and Speaking
- ✓ Differentiate Instruction
- ✓ English-Language Learners
- ✓ Standards-Based Instruction
- ✓ Assessment Strategies and Rubrics
- ✓ Teaching Energy
- ✓ Teaching Mitosis and Meiosis
- ✓ Teaching Moon Phases
- ✓ Teaching Photosynthesis
- ✓ Teaching Physical and Chemical Change
- ✓ Teaching Weather Concepts

TEACHING TODAY — **teachingtoday.glencoe.com** *A no-fee professional development Web site where you will find resources for:*

- ✓ Lesson plans with downloads for newsletters, parent conference letters
- ✓ Teaching tips
- ✓ How-to articles sorted by discipline, grade level, and instructional type
- ✓ Math support
- ✓ Demonstration videos

A Classroom-Management Plan

In this section, you will explore a classroom management plan that includes strategies and techniques for engaging students in active learning. Beginning the school year with a management plan in place can help you create a positive learning environment and can help minimize disruptions and behavioral problems. When students, parents, and administrators understand your rules and expectations, you can focus class time on instruction rather than on discipline.

What is it?

A classroom-management plan is a teacher-created document that describes the rules and procedures that he or she will use to govern the classroom. Many principals require that all teachers submit a classroom-management plan each year so that administrators and families understand each teacher's classroom philosophy and expectations. Writing a thoughtful and well-constructed plan is an appropriate first step in a proactive approach to classroom management and can curtail problems later (Kounin, 1970). After you construct a classroom-management plan, you can produce a student-friendly version for students and a letter to send home for families.

What do I do?

A good classroom-management plan reflects the aspects valued by a teacher and, therefore, should be unique. "Canned" plans (those that someone else wrote but are available to the public) are unlikely to meet the unique needs of your situation. However, it can be productive to review a variety of these before you write your first plan. This will help you determine what you want to include. Ask your colleagues to share their plans with you. From them you can gain a sense of what people at your school expect. In addition, there are many resources available on the Internet.

Now you try it!

A basic classroom-management plan should include the following elements:

- **A Statement of Your Teaching and Learning Philosophy**
  What are your views and beliefs about how teaching and learning should occur in your classroom? What are your beliefs concerning community and diversity in the classroom? Your statement should be no more than a few sentences long, yet should be clear enough for administrators, students, and families to understand your teaching philosophy.

- **Classroom Rules** Your rules should serve as a clear message about your expectations of student behavior in your classroom. Authorities recommend limiting the number to three to five positively stated rules.

- **Classroom Procedures** Every environment needs a set of procedures in order to ensure a smooth-running situation. When creating your classroom-management plan, consider how students will perform basic tasks, such as turning in homework, sharpening pencils, asking for help, and entering and leaving the room. This section addresses a number of procedures.

- **Discipline Procedures** How will you address disruptions in the classroom? How will students resolve disputes? Clearly stated discipline procedures can prevent misunderstandings with students, families, and administrators. Again, be sure to consult your school district's discipline plans to ensure you are in compliance with these regulations.

- **Room Arrangement** Once you have outlined your classroom rules and procedures, you can plan the physical layout of the room, if it can be altered. Most teachers designate specific areas of the room for academic, social, and storage purposes. In addition, you will want to ensure that traffic patterns are logical, particularly if you have any special-needs students, and that you can easily see each student in the room (Wong & Wong, 2001).

- **Student Absences** This section of your plan should contain the school district's policy for absences, as well as your methods for catching up work that students miss when they are absent. These methods might include an absence notebook, note-taking, and homework buddies. This section discusses all of these in more detail later.

- **Communication Plan** After you create your plan, you will need to consider how you will share it with students and families. Secondary teachers often create a syllabus, which they review with students on the first day of class. Some successful teachers require a parent's signature on the syllabus. Middle-school teachers are more likely to generate a simplified plan. In addition, they might send a letter home to families during the first week of school and review their procedures during the first parent-teacher meeting.

Classroom Rules

What is it?

Effective teachers regard classroom rules as an essential element for maintaining a smooth-running learning environment. Well-written rules communicate a teacher's expectations for the class as they relate to a learning climate and student performance (Wong & Wong, 2001, 1998). It is important to note that once you create rules, you must explicitly explain and reinforce them. Two studies of efficient classrooms found that in all cases, teachers reinforced the rules daily during the first week of school using discussion, modeling, and demonstrations (Evertson & Weinstein, 2006; Emmer, Evertson & Anderson, 1982; Evertson & Emmer, 1980).

What do I do?

Establish the rules. There are two decisions you will need to make as you develop rules for your classroom. First, you will need to decide whether you intend to create your own rules or collaborate with your students to develop the rules for the year. Advantages of writing class rules with students include building more "buy-in" because students have had input, as well as conveying an expectation that the class will operate as a community. This can lead to a sense of autonomy as students learn that they are responsible for their behavior (Kohn, 1996). Remember, however, that you are the leader of this community and can establish the rules that you deem necessary.

Beginning teachers might prefer to create their own rules without student input. During the first few years of professional practice, teachers experiment with what does and does not work for them. One advantage of writing rules in this manner is that you can address the aspects you deem important.

The second decision you will need to make is whether to state the rules for your classroom using specific or general terms. Examples of specific rules include:

- Raise your hand to speak in class.
- Enter the classroom quietly and put away your belongings.
- Keep hands and feet to yourself.
- Speak in a quiet voice.

A disadvantage of using specific rules is that it can lead to the "loophole defense" by students who violate classroom norms that are not explicitly stated. ("The rules don't say I can't have a messy desk!") For this reason, some teachers prefer to use a few general rules that encompass many possible concerns that might arise throughout the year. An example of a set of general rules might look like this:

- Take care of yourself.
- Take care of each other.
- Take care of this place.

In the student situation discussed earlier, the teacher could cite the third rule as a reason for cleaning up the offending desk. In either case, the rules should be few (three to five is advisable) and positively stated. Be aware of rules that all begin with the word "no" because these do not tell students what they should do, only what they should not do. In the absence of clearly stated rules, you leave students to guess about what is acceptable.

Post the rules. After you and/or your students develop classroom rules, post them in the classroom in a place where everyone can see them. Posted rules also allow classroom visitors and substitute teachers to adhere to and reinforce the expectations for the class.

Teach and rehearse the rules. As stated earlier, this is a critical component for ensuring an efficient classroom. Teach students the rules during the first week of school, and revisit them occasionally throughout the remainder of the year, especially after school breaks. Model each rule so that students can learn what the rules look and sound like. For example, if one of the rules is to take care of each other, you can model examples of how students should speak to each other in class. Examples of inappropriate behavior can also be useful, but be sure you do not ask a student to model such examples—this should be for you to perform.

Determine what will occur when a rule is violated. This is perhaps the trickiest part of your classroom-management plan, because you do not want to have to write a book of "if-then" scenarios. Likewise, you want to avoid correcting students for minor infractions. This can serve as a greater distraction from the lesson than the offending behavior. You do, however, want to respond consistently to disruptions and rule-breaking without causing an escalation of the behavior. Grossman (2004) advises you to intervene when any of the following situations occur:

- **Harmful Behavior** When someone is likely to physically or emotionally injure someone else, or when a student might destroy something, you need to intervene.
- **Distracting Behavior** If a student's behavior interferes with the education of other students, you must intercede.
- **Testing Behavior** A student might test the system to see whether you will follow through. You must follow through and enforce your rules.
- **Contagious Behavior** Some disruptive behaviors can spread through a classroom quickly. Intervene before other students become involved.
- **Consistent Behavior** If a student exhibits a pattern of misbehavior, develop a consistent response to it.

Misbehavior does not always warrant an immediate response. You can deal with some behaviors later. Grossman (2004) suggests these considerations when you decide when to respond:

- **Immediate Response** If the misbehavior is harmful, disruptive, or likely to be contagious, deal with it as quickly as possible. These types of misbehavior can escalate quickly.
- **Delayed Response** Sometimes you might not have all the facts, as when one student tattles on another. In such situations, it is better to delay your response until you investigate the situation. Other situations might warrant a delayed response because the timing is just not right. For example, if a student is very upset, or if your intervention will embarrass the student in front of peers, wait until you can speak to the student privately.

Many effective teachers find that developing various discipline procedures gives them the flexibility to make sound judgments regarding the nature of the situation. The goal is to re-engage the student in the learning situation as quickly as possible, not to mete out punishments.

- **Move Closer** Proximity control works wonderfully well for some misbehavior. Often the nearness of a teacher is enough to get a student back on task.
- **Signal** A look or gesture can be an effective tool for ending misbehavior.
- **Redirect** Speaking quietly to the student, restate what it is that he or she should be doing.
- **Replace** Look for a competing behavior that makes the misbehavior impossible to perform. For example, a student cannot daydream when he or she has to distribute papers to the class.
- **Reduce** You can minimize some misbehavior by reducing the task demand. A student who is having difficulty getting started on an assignment can often benefit from having the task divided into smaller segments.
- **Relocate** If the environment seems to be contributing to the misbehavior, relocate the student. Other students' conversations might distract some learners. These learners might work better in a quiet location. Keep students who have had a verbal or a physical altercation separated until they can respond calmly to each other.
- **Ignore** Not every misbehavior needs your attention. If it does not meet any of the criteria listed (harmful, distracting, and so on), it might be one that you should ignore.

Now you try it!

Draft a set of rules that might be useful for your classroom. Consider the developmental level of your students so that the rules reflect language that is meaningful and that they will understand. Discuss your draft rules with a colleague in order to get constructive feedback.

Classroom Arrangement

What is it?

The physical environment of your classroom greatly affects your students' ability to learn. Emmer, Evertson, and Worsham (2002) advise teachers to consider visibility, proximity, accessibility, and safety when arranging a classroom. Each classroom is unique; your academic needs and student considerations will influence your classroom arrangement. Keep in mind that a student with special needs might need a particular placement in the classroom to increase visibility or to minimize distractions.

What do I do?

Use these guiding questions to develop a room arrangement that works well for you and your students.

- **Visibility** Are there areas of the classroom from which students cannot easily see the board or screen? If so, consider using these areas for other purposes, including small-group work or storage.

- **Proximity** The physical distance between you and a student, or proximity, is a useful tool for increasing student engagement. Look at the pathways for your movement in your classroom. Can you easily reach each student in the room to provide extra instruction or behavioral support? Can you circulate during whole-group teaching to monitor learning? Jones (2000) suggests that you arrange student desks to provide both an interior loop and an exterior loop in the classroom (see **Figure A.1**). This gives you proximity to all students and decreases off-task behavior in your classroom. Keep proximity among students in mind as well. Engaging classrooms use partner arrangements throughout the day. Be certain that students can easily move into partner groups at your direction.

- **Accessibility** An orderly learning environment enables students to easily reach materials and areas of the classroom. Students sharpen pencils, throw away trash, enter and exit the room, and choose books from the classroom library. How will students accomplish these tasks in your room? When planning your room arrangement, consider patterns of movement in these high-traffic areas. For example, many teachers often locate the wastebasket next to their desks. Instead, place the wastebasket in an area of the room that is convenient for students and does not bring them near your desk, where confidential materials are easily accessible.

- **Safety** Above all, students must be safe in your classroom. All schools have specific requirements for maintaining unobstructed exits in case of fire. Be sure to consult these regulations when you plan your room arrangement. Next, catalog the items that can pose a threat to student safety. Is there laboratory equipment stored in your classroom? If so, place it in a secure area.

Now you try it!

Measure your classroom space and map it to scale on graph paper. Be sure to note the locations of windows, doors, electrical outlets, computer stations, and other fixed objects. Cut out scaled shapes for the furniture you have available in your room, and place the shapes on the graph paper. Remember to pay attention to visibility, proximity, accessibility, and safety concerns.

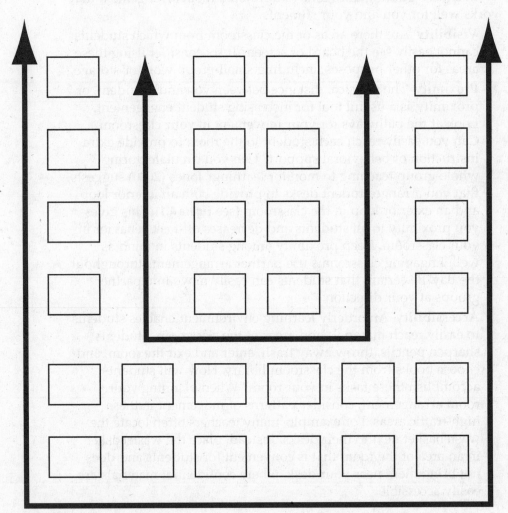

Figure A.1 Arranging desks for proximity

Attendance and Absences

What is it?

Taking attendance daily is one of the many important clerical responsibilities of a classroom teacher. A teacher must report absences, tardy students, and attendance in an accurate and timely manner in order to fulfill the legal obligations of the school. Student safety is also a consideration, especially when students fail to appear at school. Schools are *in loco parentis,* a legal term that means the school assumes supervisory responsibilities of students during school hours.

What do I do?

Establish an attendance procedure. Teachers usually take attendance at the beginning of each school day or class session, which is one of the busiest times of the school day. You need a system to gather attendance information quickly and accurately. Here are several ideas for collecting attendance.

- **Use bellringers.** An effective way to establish an orderly environment at the beginning of class is to use the daily practice of responding to bellringers—prompts or questions posted on the board or shown using an overhead projector. After students become accustomed to this procedure, they will begin writing responses as soon as they are in their seats. Teachers typically instruct students to do the writing activity until the bell or timer rings for class to begin. While students are writing, you have an ideal opportunity to record attendance data and focus on any other immediate details or issues that need attention. Additionally, bellringers activate student thinking and prepare students for the lesson's content.

- **Appoint a student attendance monitor.** You can assign a student to gather attendance information each class period. You can assign classroom jobs like this one (there can be many) by using a chart. Students can read the chart to learn their assignments for the week. The attendance monitor for each period completes an attendance grid and gives it to the teacher. Because attendance forms are legal documents, however, the teacher must verify the accuracy of the information before signing the forms.

- **Assign seats and maintain a seating chart.** This procedure is especially effective during the first weeks of school because you can quickly scan the classroom to identify the names of students who are absent. Keep a reproducible chart handy to record changes in seat assignments.

A

Throughout the school year, students will be absent from school due to illnesses, family emergencies, or travels. When students return from absences, they probably will need to catch up on their assignments. A student's return can be a disruption because you must take time from instruction to inform the student about what he or she has missed. You can establish several procedures in your classroom to ensure that students receive materials and assignment information for days missed.

- **Absence Notebook** An absence notebook is an efficient method for keeping track of materials a student will need when he or she returns. The student attendance monitor can also maintain the notebook. Whenever you distribute handouts and informational flyers, the attendance monitor should gather extra copies for students who are absent. In addition, he or she should note assignments and due dates on a log kept in the notebook. A blank version of this log appears in **Figure A.2** on the following page. When absent students return, they can go to the notebook to collect the materials and assignment information they missed. The notebook is also useful for students who were present but forget some important information.

- **Note-Taking** Many teachers require students to take notes during lectures. These lecture notes are useful to students when they complete homework assignments and review for tests. To ensure that absent students have access to missed lectures, assign a student to take notes for absent students. You can photocopy these class notes and include them in the absence notebook. If you use overheads during your lectures, you can also place copies of them in the absence notebook. If you use PowerPoint or other electronic notes during class time, make these notes available to students by posting them on a Web site, e-mailing them, or copying them onto disks that students can borrow. These are also effective accommodations for a student with special needs who cannot generate his or her own notes.

- **Assignment Partners** Assignment partners are pairs of students that provide information for each other. Each student serves as a point of contact for the other to clarify information about homework and assignments. He or she also can review details of class assignments for the absent partner. Because this is meant to be a peer support strategy, it is best to assign partners rather than to allow students to choose their own partners. This eliminates the possibility of hurt feelings at being left out and encourages students to communicate with classmates who are not in their usual social networks.

- **Teacher Meetings** During the rush of the day, it is easy to forget about the student who has returned from an absence. Establish a routine in your schedule, perhaps near the end of the class or the school day, to consult with returning students about what they missed.

Now you try it!

Decide how you will take attendance in your classroom, and add that decision to your notes for developing your classroom management plan. It is important to have a procedure in place so that the task of collecting attendance information does not interfere with the level of student engagement in your classroom. Also familiarize yourself with your school district's policy on student absences. After adding this information to your classroom management plan, outline your procedures for dealing with student absences in your class.

While You Were Out

Here is a list of this week's assignments.
Be sure to copy them into your assignment notebook.

Date	Assignment	Details You Should Know	Due Date	Who to Ask for Extra Help

Figure A.2 Absence notebook log

Activity Transitions

What is it?

Increasing the amount of time that students have for an academic task is directly linked to learning outcomes (Paik, Wang, & Walberg, 2002). Effective educators use procedures that promote smooth transitions between classroom events, leading to fewer disruptions and more time spent on course work.

What do I do?

The following ideas can help make transitions from one activity to the next smoother.

- **Chalkboard Countdown** Students working in small groups need assistance in monitoring their pace in order to complete assigned tasks. A chalkboard countdown is a simple way to accomplish this. When giving students directions about a learning task, discuss time allotment. Then, as students work, periodically post the remaining time on the board.

- **DVD** Use your students' knowledge of the controls on a DVD player to signal transitions. Review the DVD commands on a remote control:

   Play: Begin your work.

   Pause: Stop briefly to listen for further instructions.

   Fast forward: Increase the pace of your work.

   Stop: The time to work on this task has ended.

   Rewind: Go back to check the work you have completed.

- **Musical Interludes** Play recorded music while students return supplies, hand in assignments, and return desks to original positions. Students should finish by the time the music stops. Good music selections include the theme song from the *Jeopardy!* game show or Chopin's "Minute Waltz" (which is closer to two minutes long).

Now you try it!

Identify times in your daily schedule when you and your students need an activity transition procedure. Introduce your procedure during one transition, and practice it each day until students are proficient.

Class Materials and Assignments

What is it?

Throughout the day, a teacher distributes and collects materials and assignments. Procedures for handling papers and equipment shorten transition times during a lesson and decrease the likelihood that misbehavior will occur. In addition, these procedures reduce lost materials.

What do I do?

Most teachers distribute papers by counting out the appropriate number and handing the pile to the first person in each row. In turn, students take one and pass the remainder to the students behind them. The process reverses for collecting papers, beginning with the last student in the row. This can become an opportune time for students to talk because they take their eyes off the teacher. To reduce the risk of misbehavior, distribute and collect papers across rows, as illustrated in **Figure A.3.** Below are other tips for distributing and collecting materials.

- **Magnetic Clips** Attach a magnetic bulldog clip to the side of each desk. Throughout the day or class period, students clip papers to turn in. When directed, students then remove and place all the papers in the proper container(s). This minimizes the number of times students must walk around the room to turn in papers.

- **Classroom Equipment** Scientific items, such as microscopes and scales, are costly and sometimes impossible to replace. For this reason, some teachers might be disinclined to give students easy access to them. However, this defeats the purpose of having them in the classroom. To prevent loss, number items with an indelible marker or label maker, and place the same number on the shelf or storage container. When a student borrows an item, he or she is given an index card with the number that corresponds to his or her place in your roll book. The student then places the card on the shelf when removing an item. You will be able to identify missing items at a glance, as well as determine who last used the item.

- **Student Folders** Students submit several assignments each day. This quickly results in many papers that need to be graded and returned. To keep papers organized, set up two plastic file crates and label them "Completed Work" and "Graded Work." Place a hanging file for each student—labeled with his or her name and student number—in each file crate. At the beginning of class, students can place their homework in one file crate and collect their graded work from the other. This system also allows you to easily distinguish whether a particular student turned in an assignment.

Now you try it!

Determine what procedures you will use to distribute and collect materials, and add these procedures to your classroom-management plan. Make a list of organizational materials you need—magnetic clips, file crates, a labeling device—and check with your school's facilities manager for availability. Although you might need to purchase some items, it is wise to find out what you can obtain for free at your school site.

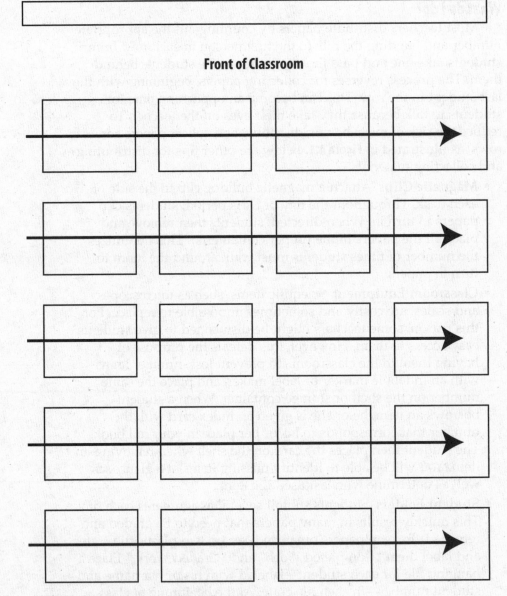

Front of Classroom

Figure A.3 Plan for distributing and collecting papers.

Interactive Instruction

What is it?

Good instruction demands that every teaching event involve students as active participants in their own learning. During interactive instruction, students have the opportunity to say, to write, and to do things. They also have opportunities for collaborating and sharing ideas with one another. When you use multiple modalities of learning in each lesson, you reinforce the skills you are teaching and increase the likelihood that students will be able to apply information later (Ellis, Semb, & Cole, 1998).

What do I do?

Use the Say-Write-Do strategy. This strategy refers to the elements of engagement necessary in every lesson. During all instruction phases, students need to speak in order to repeat new vocabulary, answer questions, and apply new information. You can also reinforce and apply key concepts and skills during the lesson by having students write. In addition to speaking and writing, students must do things during lessons to engage in active learning. This is particularly important in the science classroom.

- **Say** During group instruction, you can signal students to repeat a key phrase by first asking a question, signaling the class to get ready for a group response, pausing for thinking time, then signaling again to respond in unison.

  Another method for fostering student responses during group instruction is to invite each student to share his or her response with a partner. Teach students that your signal to turn to a partner is their cue to answer the question that was just posed.

- **Write** You can instruct students to write words or statements directly in their notebooks while you circulate to check for accuracy. Instruct students to put their pens or pencils down after they write their answers so you can properly pace the lesson.

  Response boards are particularly effective for monitoring what students write. Each student has a small whiteboard and washable board marker at his or her desk. Throughout the lesson, you instruct students to write answers to questions and hold up their response boards. This provides an opportunity to assess the knowledge of the class and to clear up misunderstandings.

- **Do** This is an essential component of the science classroom. Labs and experiments not only offer students opportunities to develop investigational skills, but also act as another modality through which students can access and apply lesson content. The next section of this book provides information about lab management and safety.

Learners also can use a series of hand signals during lectures to indicate their responses to questions. The most basic is the "thumbs up, thumbs down" signal to dichotomous choices. More complex questions can be answered using "fist to five." Students use the appropriate number of fingers to indicate their level of agreement or disagreement with a particular statement.

Fist—I need more information before I make a choice because this topic is new to me.

One finger—I completely disagree with this statement and can offer several reasons to support my position.

Two fingers—I disagree with this statement and can offer one reason to support my position.

Three fingers—I am unsure of where I stand on this issue and am interested in hearing from others.

Four fingers—I agree with this statement and can offer one reason to support my position.

Five fingers—I completely agree with this statement and can offer several reasons to support my position.

Use the Tell-Help-Check strategy. Evidence on the effectiveness of student collaboration for learning has been well-documented in research literature (Johnson, Johnson, & Maruyama, 1983; Slavin, 1996). However, some students might be unsure of how to work together to support one another's learning. They can benefit from a structure such as the Tell-Help-Check pattern for reviewing material to reinforce their learning. Periodically during a lesson, ask students to restate or review important concepts to one another using this pattern. For example, during a lecture on atomic structure, the teacher asks students to name and summarize information.

- **Tell** Partner 1 turns to partner 2 and recalls the information without using notes or textbooks.
- **Help** Partner 2 listens carefully and asks questions and gives hints about any missing or incorrect information.
- **Check** Both partners consult notes, textbook, or handouts to confirm the accuracy of information.

Use the Think-Pair-Share strategy. Think-Pair-Share is an instructional technique that encourages increased participation during classroom discussions (Lyman, 1981). In addition, it is intended to foster higher-quality responses by allowing a student to try out his or her answers on a partner before sharing them with the whole class. This lowers the risk for learners while raising accountability and engagement because it actively involves every student. The four steps to the Think-Pair-Share process are:

- **Ask** Invite discussion by first posing a thought-provoking question that requires an extended response.
- **Think** Prompt students to think quietly about their answers. This is similar to the brainstorming phase of a group discussion.
- **Pair** After the wait time, students turn to their partners to offer their responses and to listen to the ideas of their peers. After both students have shared, they should ask each other questions and discuss the topic.
- **Share** Signal students to finish their discussion and focus their attention on you. Ask them to share their responses and those of their partners. This exchange of ideas should serve as the next step in your whole-class discussion of the topic.

Peer Partners

What is it?

One of Russian psychologist Lev Vygotsky's central theories was that experiences within a learner's zone of proximal development support him or her (Vygotsky, 1978). Further, Vygotsky suggested that learners attain access to this zone, defined as a level of skill just beyond the learner's independent level, through socially meaningful interaction with an adult or a peer at a higher skill level.

The benefits for peer partnerships extend to the more skilled student as well. Studies have shown that peer partnerships provide opportunities to review material and enable a deeper understanding of newly acquired skills and concepts (Gautad, 1993; Moody, Vaughn, & Schumm, 1997). Students working in peer partnerships are more likely to engage in academic risk-taking, perhaps because neither is the expert (Kalkowski, 1995).

What do I do?

Students work in a variety of peer partnerships in the engaged classroom. Keep in mind the following quality indicators when using peer instructional arrangements.

- **Partnerships are heterogeneous in nature.** Partner work is an ideal opportunity to group students in mixed-ability (heterogeneous) pairs. This grouping practice ensures that no partnership is without a member skilled enough to successfully complete the task.
- **Partnerships are brief in nature.** Students should have experiences with a variety of classmates throughout the school year. Change partners frequently to foster a sense of community and expand the social and academic skills of your students.
- **Students learn effective partnering skills through instruction.** Successful teachers do not leave quality partnerships to happenstance. They give specific instructions of what occurs within the partnering activity before students work together. They also revisit these instructions throughout the school year.
- **Assign numbers to partners for ease of instruction.** Number students in pairs as partner 1 or partner 2 so you can give directions quickly and efficiently. Predetermine which number will represent the more skilled students so you can assign them the modeling roles as needed.
- **Monitor partnerships and intervene when difficulties arise.** Circulate and listen to the working conversations that happen in partnerships. Some partnerships work better than others. If there is conflict between two students, be sure to intercede and help them resolve their difficulties.

Cooperative Learning

What is it?

It is not enough for science students to learn only subject matter. They also must learn the skills that they will need when they enter the working world—how to listen, respond, agree, disagree, clarify, encourage, and evaluate. These cooperative learning skills are necessary for team members to work together productively and to succeed in today's team-oriented workplaces. Because of the increasing importance of interaction, it's essential that educational strategies include cooperative learning. Unlike traditional learning, the teacher supports rather than directs cooperative learning, as described in the table below.

Teacher's Role	
Cooperative Learning	**Traditional Learning**
supports	directs
redirects questions	answers questions
teaches social skills	makes rules
manages conflict	provides discipline
structures interdependence	encourages independence
helps students evaluate group work	evaluates individuals
helps students solve controversies	directs recitation and discussion
provides resources	serves as a major resource

Cooperative learning is not traditional group work. The teacher serves as a facilitator for student-directed learning, and not as the central force for organizing and motivating the students. Because students are not segregated into groups determined by academic skill levels, they learn to work with others of all abilities. Under the basic elements of cooperative learning, a student

- must perceive that the group "sinks or swims" together;
- is responsible for himself or herself and everyone else in the group to learn the assigned material;
- must see that all members in the group have the same goals;
- must share the tasks and responsibilities equally with other group members;
- will be given one evaluation that will apply to all members of the group;
- shares leadership while he or she acquires skills for collaborating during learning;
- will be accountable for material worked on in cooperative groups.

Cooperative learning prepares students for the growing diversity of our schools, communities, and workplaces. One aspect of diversity is the different ways in which students learn. Cooperative groups can take advantage of the different learning styles of group members.

Cooperative Learning	Group Work
purposeful selection of small teams, usually two to five members	self-selected or randomly selected groups; often larger than five members
maximization of heterogeneity of team	prevalence of group homogeneity
groups remain together for extended periods of time within the classroom setting	groups meet sporadically for short periods of time, often outside of class
team members alternate assigned roles and responsibilities	work is unstructured
positive interdependence; strategies encourage and create group identity	no commitment to group's success; learning is passive
attention to development of social skills	no regard to development of social skills
equal sharing of workload	unequal sharing of workload
team accountability—group and individual grading	independent grades
joint achievement; "we all sink or swim" mentality	individual achievement emphasized
teacher as facilitator	teacher as authority

Many techniques or methods exist for incorporating cooperative learning into the classroom, and teachers might create new techniques suited to their own particular needs. Read the list and descriptions below to learn more about some well-known techniques that educators developed, researched, and documented.

Teams-Games-Tournaments (TGT) David L. DeVries and K.J. Edwards at Johns Hopkins University devised this method to incorporate academic games in order to aid learning, particularly for students who have difficulty responding to traditional tasks and rewards, such as grades on written assignments. In TGT, teams compete weekly in tournaments and hold practice sessions during the rest of the week. In addition, teacher-prepared newsletters that feature high-scoring players and a list of team standings encourage the teams. Students compete against students of similar academic skill; individual scores compile into team scores.

Student Teams Achievement Divisions (STAD) In Student Teams Achievement Divisions, a method developed by Robert E. Slavin, students of varying abilities and cultural backgrounds work in groups to review material that the teacher presented. They use various techniques to master the subject matter, including quizzing each other, discussing problems as a group, and studying worksheets. Students take the test individually, earning points for their teams based on individual progress.

One way to employ STAD in your classroom is to tell each group its base score or average to date. Divide groups into pairs and have each pair divide a set of review questions between them. Have partners ask each other questions and determine answers. They should share the questions and answers with the rest of the group after checking an answer key. Partners should continue asking and answering questions until everyone in the group can answer all of the questions. Give an individual test that includes many of the questions from the review. Award bonus points to groups whose average scores on the test are higher than their base scores.

Jigsaw and Jigsaw II These cooperative learning techniques, developed by Elliot Aronson and his students at the University of Texas and the University of California, are used in many schools in the form of the Jigsaw classroom.

In Jigsaw, narrative material is divided so that in every group, each member is responsible for one section. Each student devises a teaching plan that consists of objectives, concepts to present, notes, diagrams, and questions that test understanding for his or her section.

In Jigsaw II, a class divides into several groups. Members of the groups are responsible for learning sections of written material. Each group member studies one block of narrative. The experts for that section meet to review the material, then report back to their groups. Groups take a quiz on the material.

Group Investigation (GI) The Group Investigation model, developed by Sharan and Sharan at Tel-Aviv University in Israel, employs group research projects to develop cognitive skills. Students usually choose what topic or item to research. Then they work as a group to gather, process, and present information on that topic. Students develop high-level analytical skills by planning and working on a group project.

Creative Controversy (CC) This cooperative teaching method makes use of academic conflict to develop students' higher-level critical-thinking and problem-solving skills. According to its developers, David W. Johnson and Roger T. Johnson at the University of Minnesota, the process for this technique involves five steps:

1. Organize information and derive conclusions.
2. Present and advocate positions.
3. Create uncertainty by challenging opposing views.
4. Reverse perspectives.
5. Reconceptualize, synthesize, and integrate positions.

Unlike traditional classroom debates, creative controversy demands that students consider both sides of an argument and come to a group consensus after engaging in respectful discussions.

Complex Instruction (CI) Elizabeth G. Cohen developed this application of organizational theory to classroom instruction. It calls for students to carry out cooperative activities according to the students' pace, not the teacher's. Students form heterogeneous groups and use one another as academic resources to complete high-level tasks. The teacher relinquishes the role of direct supervisor and instead delegates authority to students, providing peripheral guidance and specific feedback as the students work.

What do I do?

Form cooperative learning groups. Cooperative learning groups are very different from groups formed for group discussion or group projects. Cooperative learning groups or teams must be formed deliberately. Select two to five students for each team. These group members will work together, interdependently, to accomplish a well-defined learning activity or task. The formation of the group—its size and heterogeneity—is extremely important to the success of the cooperative learning effort.

Deliberate selection involves teaming students of different skill levels and learning styles, students from both genders, and students with varying cultural, social, and economic backgrounds. The point of deliberate group selection is to maximize the positive effects of small-group learning. Studies show that differences among team members encourage productivity and achievement. Heterogeneity increases tolerance and teaches students about differing points of view and consideration for others' thoughts and feelings. Diversity can be a catalyst for creativity and productivity. Each person on the team— in spite of or because of differences—has something to contribute.

Arrange your classroom. Students in cooperative learning groups should face each other as they work together. It is helpful to number tables or blocks of desks so you can refer to the groups by number. Alternatively, each group can choose a name.

Prepare your students for cooperation. Preparation is a critical step. Tell students about the rationale, procedures, and expected results of cooperative learning. Students need to know that you are not trying to force them to be friends, but rather that you are asking them to develop working relationships with others for a specific purpose. Point out that they will need to do this in the workplace. Explain that using cooperative skills might feel awkward at first. Emphasize that it will take time to learn the necessary cooperative skills, but that it will be worth it.

Explain the three basic rules of cooperative learning:
- Stay with your group.
- Ask a question of your group before you ask your teacher.
- Offer feedback on ideas, but avoid criticizing other people.

You might want to post these rules in your classroom. Consistently enforce the first rule, in particular, until students become comfortable with their groups. Have students get acquainted. Students who know each other are more comfortable working together. Have students complete several "getting-to-know-you" activities to become more comfortable with students they don't know.

Explain the day's lesson. At the start of each activity, write the following headings on the chalkboard or a transparency and display it:

Fill in the action plan by following the guidelines below:

Topic of the Day: general academic topic

Task: work that students would complete, such as a practice page or model

Goal: the academic objective

Cooperative Learning: the targeted cooperative learning skill or strategy

Special Instructions: method of evaluation or other information specific to the activity

Introduce the cooperative skill or strategy for the lesson. Each activity should include a cooperative learning skill or strategy that students focus on during their group work. Some skills and strategies you might wish to use are

- acknowledge contributions;
- speak quietly;
- take turns and share;
- show agreement or disagreement;
- remain on task;
- encourage participation;
- deal with distractions;
- help without giving answers;
- honor individual differences.

Discuss the cooperative learning skill or strategy to be used.

When introducing a skill or strategy, ask the following questions, filling in the blanks with the name of the skill or strategy: Using the three questions listed, the students take ownership of the learning process.

1 *What is _____?*

2 *In any group, why is it important to use _____?*

3 *How will _____ improve your group's working relationships?*

Model the skill for students by asking the class what the skill should look and sound like in action. Write appropriate examples on the board for students to reference while they work.

A

Monitor student use of skills and strategies. Students will not work cooperatively automatically. When you first use cooperative learning, observe groups very closely to see that things are off to a good start. Move about the room and listen to make sure that students realize that communication matters and that you are aware of their progress. Use the **Teacher Observation Form** found on page 104 to record the number of times you observe the use of expected skills on a particular assignment for each group. In the beginning, do not try to count too many different behaviors. Occasionally, you might want to try having a student make the group observations.

Provide assistance with the task. Clarify instructions, review concepts, or answer questions, but avoid interfering in the cooperative process. It is especially important to let groups make decisions on their own. Students must be allowed to make mistakes and evaluate themselves to see where they went wrong. Because of their past experiences, when students see you hovering nearby they will automatically start asking you questions. Your first response should be, "Have you asked everyone in your group?" You might ask groups to appoint one student from each group to be the "spokesperson" or "liaison" between you and the group. That group member should be the only one from the group allowed to speak with you.

  Your role will be to support groups rather than to supervise them directly. Help a group that is stuck by asking a few open-ended questions. Ask group members to think of strategies for managing their own conflicts.

Group Behavior	Suggested Teacher Response
Use of cooperative skill	Encourage with specific compliments.
Quick completion of task	Ask questions requiring deeper analysis.
Off task	Have group members suggest methods to keep members on task.
Questioning the teacher	Ask, "Have you asked everyone in your group?"
Difficulty with the resolution of a problem	First ask, "What have you done so far to resolve the problem? What could you do next?"

Intervene to teach cooperative skills. Some groups might have more difficulty learning cooperative skills. You might wish to intervene, asking groups to identify their problem areas and propose solutions. Reject inappropriate suggestions, such as ignoring the problem.

Provide closure for the lesson. You should ask students to summarize what they have learned and relate it to what they have previously studied. You might want to review the main points and ask students to give examples and answer final questions.

Have students conduct self-evaluations. In order for a group to be aware of its progress, the members should evaluate how they are working together. Give students a few minutes at the end of a lesson to decide whether they achieved the objectives you set for that lesson. Everyone should participate in the evaluation. Sometimes, you might wish to incorporate evaluations into the overall grade for the activity. Make sure that students do not skip or rush through the evaluations. Vague responses such as, "We cooperated." or "We did okay." are too superficial to be beneficial to the group. Most of the time, you will want students to do one evaluation for the whole group, though occasionally, it is beneficial to have students reflect on their individual contributions to the group.

Evaluate student academic learning. As with any student learning, assessment and evaluation of cooperative groups are necessary and important steps. The following are some tips and suggestions for evaluating students' work.

- **Cooperative Tests and Quizzes** Even though students work together in cooperative learning, individuals are accountable for their own learning. Do not incorporate group grading until students are comfortable with cooperative learning. Evaluation tools should include traditional tests and quizzes.

  To determine a group score, average all group members' scores, or have one student from each group take the test. You select the student to take the test on the day the test is administered. Students should not know ahead of time who you will choose to take the test. All other group members will get the grade earned by the test-taker.

  Some experts suggest basing the group score on the improvement of individual scores. In this way, others suffer no penalty if a group member's initial achievement level is low. To receive maximum credit, all group members should score higher than they did on the previous test.

  You might also wish to award extra-credit points to everyone in a group if all members achieve a certain score on the test. For example, if everyone scores more than a 90 percent, the group gets 10 bonus points. You could also award group or class improvement points using this system:
  - 3 points if everyone in the group scores 10 or more above their base or average;
  - 2 points if everyone in the group scores 5–9 above their base; and
  - 1 point if everyone in the group scores 4 below to 4 above their base.

  The group receives the sum of its members' individual improvement points. Using this system, the group members who improve the most will be of great value to the group. Often these students have low motivation and skills and, as a result of their new importance, will develop higher self-esteem and better work habits. The improvement points can be recorded on a large bar graph for individual groups or on a thermometer-type graph for the entire class.

A

What to do with bonus points is an issue on which experts disagree. Some teachers like competition among teams; others feel that competition is opposed to the principles of cooperative learning. Also in question is the subject of material rewards for points. Some teachers feel that payment for learning lowers the motivation and pleasure of learning for its own sake. Most experts agree that a limited use of rewards enhances the classroom experience. There is a list of suggested rewards on page 29.

For a change of pace, give a group test. Tell each student to prepare one 3" × 5" notecard of information. Allow group members to share notecards during the test. Have students who do not prepare a notecard take the test individually. Use group tests infrequently as individual mastery and learning is the ultimate goal.

• **Cooperative Assignments** For written assignments such as lab reports, research papers, and worksheets, students can work together or cooperatively and earn a group grade. You can base grades on combined answers, or each group can submit a paper for a group grade. You might let students select which paper they think is most representative of the group's work, or you might select the paper without giving the group advance notice of which one you will choose.

• **Cooperative Projects: Skits, Debates, and Other Group Projects** In order to provide individual assessment of group projects, you might want to combine a group score with an individual score based on effort and participation. You might ask group members to numerically evaluate the contributions of members and justify the scores. Another method of assessing individual contributions to a group project is to give the group the combined total of all their scores and allow the group members to divide the points fairly among themselves.

Many students do well evaluating their own group products, such as reports and presentations, if they have a list of grading criteria. One advantage is that students perceive grades they assign themselves as being fair. You might wish to involve students in establishing the grading criteria. This method also helps them perceive the overall grading process as being fair.

• **Cooperative Contracts** After group members have been working together for some time, they will learn each other's strengths and weaknesses. You might want them to fill out a **Student Agreement** and award points for achieving contracted goals. To implement the use of a contract, first ask students to list what their groups do well. Tell them to be specific. Also, ask them to list the specific things they need to do to improve their group work. They should focus on the behaviors that need to be changed, not on the individuals. Beside each item they should indicate how each group member could help in making the change. Discuss each group's contract with your students and tell them how many points you will award if they can "fix things" by the selected date. You may give groups with bigger problems more points. Ask students to evaluate their progress each day on a scale of 1–10.

- **Commendations and Awards** Most students respond positively when recognized for achievement. Suggestions for recognition and rewards are given in the table below. Many businesses are willing to provide free passes or coupons. In addition, you might want to use handmade certificates.

Recognition	Privileges	Rewards
certificate	free time	free passes: dance, athletic event, movie, skating rink
smile	excused from homework	
display of work	early lunch	treat for class; movie, pizza
standing ovation	music during class	
message to parents	time for game playing	gift certificates: fast food, hair styling
quarterly recognition ceremony	library time	points earned toward prize, popcorn party, or free pass to athletic event
personal note from teacher to student	computer time	
	use lab equipment	
list of group achievement points on a posted chart	help other students or teachers	
list of class achievement points on a posted chart		

- **Change groups periodically.** Some teachers keep groups together for a week, a quarter, or a thematic unit. The only necessary criterion is to have groups stay together long enough to experience success as a group. The advantage of changing groups periodically is that students have more opportunities to deal with a variety of classmates.

If your school has not used cooperative learning previously or recently, you might wish to explain the method to your colleagues and use the **Sample Letter to Guardian or Learning Partner, Sample Letter to the Principal, Note to the Substitute Teacher** found on pages 111–113.

Multiple Learning Styles

What is it?

In 1983, Harvard psychologist Howard Gardner introduced a model of multiple learning styles he called "multiple intelligences" or MI. Gardner's model was not the first to indicate that we are all smart in different ways, however it was the first to support such an idea with scientific evidence. Gardner backed his model with extensive research in the fields of cognitive and developmental psychology, animal physiology, neuroanatomy, and more. The MI model focuses on discovering what a student does best.

It is a way for teachers to rethink who a student is and what possibilities he or she holds.

What do I do?

Students learn in different ways. Multiple learning styles help students approach problems and solve them in a way that makes sense to them. The way students learn, however, isn't always the way they're taught. You can address these differences in learning for what they are—just differences. As a science teacher, you might want to use scientific methods and observe your students. Watch their best and worst behaviors. Find out how they spend their free time. These observations will provide you with clues about your students' learning styles so you can encourage them to learn and achieve in their own ways.

Learning Style	Characteristics	Suggested Activities
Verbal/Linguistic	reads regularly, writes clearly, and easily understands the written word	• notes • reports • written descriptions or stories
Logical	enjoys using numbers, logic, and critical-thinking skills	• science fair projects • puzzles • write-ups of lab experiments
Visual/Spatial	thinks in terms of pictures and three-dimensional objects	• diagrams • mock-ups • collages, drawings, and paintings
Auditory/Musical	has "good ear" and readily produces rhythms and melodies	• music and lyrics • audiotapes of performances • discographies
Kinesthetic	learns from touch, body movement, and the manipulation of objects	• role-playing • demonstrations • classroom theater
Interpersonal	understands and works well with other people	• peer and group reports • community service projects • simulations
Intrapersonal	has a realistic understanding of own strengths and weaknesses	• journals • goal setting • progress charts
Naturalist	distinguishes among, classifies, and uses features of the environment	• environmental projects • plant/animal classification and interaction • pattern recognition

A

You might find that applying students' best learning styles to interactive and cooperative learning activities can enhance their stronger skills and help them improve other skills. For example, you might assign students with different strengths to one group, allowing them to demonstrate those strengths. At other times, you might assign students to tasks that will help them strengthen their weaker skills. You also could pair students so that one person who is stronger than the other in a particular learning style can help the second student expand his or her abilities.

Avoid forming groups in which all of the students are weak in a particular learning style. Likewise, avoid forming homogeneous groups. Interactive and cooperative learning strategies provide many ways for students to reinforce their strengths and improve on their weaknesses. The chart on the next page details some characteristics and suggested activities for different learning styles.

Accommodations and Modifications

What is it?

Educators use accommodations and modifications to ensure that students with special needs can access the core curriculum in mainstream classrooms (e.g., Castagnera, Fisher, Rodifer, Sax, & Frey, 2003). An accommodation is a change in the teaching or testing procedures to provide a student access to information and to create an equal opportunity to demonstrate knowledge and skills. Accommodations do not change the instructional level, content, or performance criteria for meeting the standards. Examples of accommodations include enlarging print, using Braille or oral versions of tests, and using calculators. A *modification* is a change in what the teacher expects the student to learn and/or demonstrate. Although a student might be working on modified course content, the subject area remains the same as that for the rest of the class. Modifications vary according to the situation.

What do I do?

Four modification techniques are:

- **Same—Only Less** The assignment remains the same, but you reduce the number of items. The items you select should be representative areas of the curriculum. For example, you could modify a science test that consisted of multiple choice questions with five possible answers each so that the number of possible answers is two.

- **Streamlined Curriculum** You reduce the assignment in size, breadth, or focus to emphasize key points. For example, a student could outline the chapter rather than write a summary of the chapter's contents. Alternatively, a student with special needs could focus on identifying the themes of the chapter and create a display to support his or her writing on those main ideas.

- **Same Activity with Infused Objective** The assignment remains the same, but you incorporate additional components, such as IEP (Individualized Education Plan) objectives or identified skills. Teachers often do this in conjunction with other accommodations and/or modifications to ensure that all IEP objectives are addressed. For example, if a student has an IEP objective to answer factual and inferential questions, you might need to remember to ask these types of questions so that the student can practice this skill in a natural setting.

- **Curriculum Overlapping** The student might complete the assignment in one area during another time. Some students work slowly and need more time to complete assignments, whereas others need to explore the connections between various content areas. For example, if a student participated in a poster project in his or her cooperative learning group, the student could also use the poster during a lesson in another subject.

Deciding which technique to use depends on the type of assignment and the student. You might need only to reduce in size one assignment for a student to succeed, whereas for another, you might need to incorporate infused objectives. Keep in mind that you do not always need to modify the curriculum—even when you consider students with more significant special needs. When you provide multi-level instruction, you might not need to change a lesson. For additional information on differentiated instruction, go to Tab B.

For more information on Differentiated Instruction visit

Mc Graw Hill **Professional Development**

at **mhpdonline.com**

Introduction

This section provides basic information about lab and field management and safety. It is intended to help you foster students' confidence regarding their laboratory and field skills and to encourage a life-long interest in science. Preparedness promotes safety in the classroom, the laboratory, and the field. This preparedness should be for all students, including those with special needs.

The publisher makes NO claims to the completeness of this section's discussion of laboratory and field safety, chemical storage, and first aid. The material presented is not all-inclusive, nor does it address all of the hazards associated with handling, storing, and disposing of chemicals or with laboratory management. Local, state, and federal laws strictly regulate chemical disposal. Consult these laws before attempting to dispose of any chemicals. The following resource provides more information about handling and disposing of chemicals: *Prudent Practices in the Laboratory: Handling and Disposal of Chemicals.* Washington, DC: National Academies Press, 1995.

Manage Laboratory Sessions

Before a Lab Session

Before students begin a lab session, familiarize yourself with the activity so that you know how to set up the lab and which materials you need. If you are not familiar with the activity, perform a trial run so that you are better able to help students conduct it. Also be prepared to enforce all safety rules and allow sufficient cleanup time.

Remember the following as you conduct your trial run:

- Always read/re-read an investigation carefully.
- Analyze the investigation for appropriateness for your students.
- Determine approximately how long the investigation will take an average student to perform.
- Anticipate what could go wrong during a typical laboratory activity and take steps to address those concerns.
- Perform the activity yourself so that you can determine where students might have trouble.
- Consider substitute chemicals or procedures if they will be safer to use. Refer to the Material Safety Data Sheet (MSDS) and the Chemical Incompatibility Reference Sheet for each substance you plan to use to be sure that the substitution will be safe and will work as planned. See a sample of Material Safety Data Sheets on pages 56–59.

Lab and Materials Setup

Use the following checklist as a guide as you set up your lab and materials.

- Make sure that the safety and evacuation guidelines are posted and clearly visible.
- Be sure that all safety equipment (pages 74–77) is accessible and working properly.

A

Copyright © Glencoe/McGraw-Hill, a division of The McGraw-Hill Companies, Inc.

- Arrange the lab in such a way that equipment and supplies are clearly labeled and easily and safely accessible.
- Set up only the equipment and materials that are needed to complete the assigned activity. (Note: This practice helps eliminate the problem of students performing unauthorized investigations.)
- Check that all lab equipment is in good condition (no cracks in glassware, no frayed electrical cords, and so on; see pages 74–77).
- Set up beakers or wide-mouthed jars and droppers for any solutions and reagents that will be used. **WARNING:** *Remind students to use a separate dropper for each solution. Do NOT return leftover chemicals to their original containers.*
- Arrange for proper disposal of wastes prior to the lab (see pages 66–68).
- Know all actions and reactions that should occur between the chemicals you and your students will use, and investigate unexpected reactions if they occur. Refer to the MSDS for each substance that you and your students will use. Highlight all safety concerns about the substance. See pages 56–59 for a sample MSDS with safety issues highlighted.
- Use dilute solutions of chemicals whenever possible.

Prepare Kits

If you are planning a series of lab activities that use similar materials, you might wish to set up kits for students using containers for the materials, such as plastic tubs or cardboard shoeboxes. Each kit should contain a materials checklist for the students to use, such as the one that follows.

| Group/student | | Date |
Quantities	Description	Breakage
2	beaker (25 mL)	
2	beaker (50 mL)	
1	graduated cylinder (25 mL)	
1	burner	
2	collecting bottle	
2	dropper	

Date kit checked out _____   Date kit checked in _____

Give each team of students the responsibility of filling out and returning the equipment checklist to you at specific intervals. These checklists will enable you not only to keep track of materials and breakage, but also to assess students' proficiency in keeping their equipment organized and in good shape.

Label and store equipment and specimens that are used only a few times during the course in containers in a storage area separate from students' kits (see page 60).

During a Lab Session

Getting Students Started

Before students begin a lab activity, be sure they know the proper procedures to follow if an accident occurs (see page 101). Remind them to fill out the **Student Lab Safety Form,** page 103, and to follow safe practices, and explain the harm or injury that can occur if they do not. Also remind them that class rules about behavior will be enforced.

Discuss any particular safety concerns regarding the lab, and describe the protective equipment that students should use, such as goggles, aprons, or gloves. Demonstrate the proper use of any special devices that the lab requires, and review procedures for using the devices properly. Explain to students that they must carefully follow the steps of the investigation and not take shortcuts. Shortcuts can lead to unsafe conditions and unsuccessful investigations.

After you answer students' questions regarding the lab and its procedures, make sure students are wearing appropriate clothing and using the protective equipment indicated. Check to see that students' hands and work areas are dry and that students have in their work areas only those items needed for the assigned lab. Finally, review students' laboratory designs and setups before giving them permission to start.

As Students Work

Monitor the lab and the students continuously in order to foster safe learning. Work with students to correct any procedure or action that is not safe. If accidents do occur, follow school/district guidelines for first aid and reporting the accident (see pages 80–87 and 110).

After a Lab Activity

Post-Lab Work

Discuss lab results with the class, encouraging students to explain any unexpected observations or outcomes. As students describe what happened, correct any misconceptions that might exist regarding the lab.

Cleanup Procedures

Distribute to students the **Student Laboratory Cleanup Procedures Checklist** found on page 102. Direct students to clean up their work areas and to inspect all equipment for problems as they do so. Make sure the equipment is clean and dry before storing it. Also make sure chemical containers are clean and properly labeled before returning them to storage. Clean work surfaces after each class. If active cultures of microorganisms spill, use a solution of 10 percent household bleach and 90 percent water to disinfect the area. Sterilize reusable scalpels and dissecting instruments before and after investigations. Follow appropriate procedures for the removal of wastes (see page 52). Know and follow your district's and state's regulations for proper disposal of all lab wastes.

Manage Laboratory Work Outside the Classroom

Lab work outside the classroom falls into two categories—home assignments and school-sponsored field trips. Both require thoughtful preparation and planning.

Home Lab Work

Periodic assignments might require students to perform investigations at home. These should not require unusual or expensive materials. Likewise, they should not include materials or chemicals that require adult supervision or special handling or disposal. You should provide clear written and verbal instructions for students to follow. Assume that you, as the teacher, will be held accountable for materials you might supply the student for the investigations. This pertains to science fair projects as well as course work. At the beginning of the school year, you might wish to send a letter to inform parents and guardians of the purpose of home investigation assignments. You can find a sample letter on page 106.

Field Trips

Field trips provide wonderful opportunities for students to observe and make discoveries about the natural world around them. Just as in the classroom laboratory, safety is of primary importance. The next few pages provide checklists for planning safe and successful field trips as well as information on what to do in the case of an emergency. You can find a sample letter to parents, a permission form, and a medical emergency form on pages 107–109. Note: You must follow your school's and/or district's policies regarding field trips. These pages are intended only as a guide.

Planning Procedures

Planning and communication are key to taking a safe and successful field trip. Before you can take your students out of the school setting, you need to coordinate with administrators and parents, as well as with transportation services and the field site. The following checklists and suggestions can serve as a guide to planning your excursion.

School Officials

- Notify and obtain approval from your school administration.
- Reconcile the costs of the field trip with budget constraints.
- Determine how the timing of the field trip will affect students' attendance in other classes. Notify the teachers involved.
- Determine whether substitute teacher(s) will be needed.
- Verify that the field trip relates to and augments your course of study. Will it also augment other courses?
- Confirm whether there are school regulations that would restrict some students, such as those with discipline problems, from taking part in a field trip. What arrangements will you need to make for those students on the day of the field trip?
- Determine the length of time you will spend at the site for the activities you have planned. Also allow time in your plan for relaxation and cleanup.

A

- Determine the number of chaperones you need for the number of students you are taking on the field trip.
- Identify and recruit the number of chaperones you will need. Ask parents or guardians to help.
- Make a list of students who are going, and leave it and the students' permission forms with a school official.
- Make arrangements for taking investigation materials (magnifying lenses, test tubes, and so on) with you.
- Make arrangements for taking personal safety equipment (goggles, gloves, and aprons) with you.

The Field Site

- Visit the site ahead of time to be sure it is appropriate for your needs.
- Obtain permission from the proper officials at the site for your field trip.
- **WARNING:** *Consider any health concerns of your students that might be affected by conditions at the site.*
- Learn what requirements you and your students must meet to obtain permission to visit the site. Determine how these requirements will affect your plans.
- Find out whether the site charges admission fees and if so, how much they are.
- Choose an alternate site in case there are too many obstacles to using the original site.
- Set a date for the field trip. Select an alternate date in case of inclement weather.
- Check to see whether guides, forest rangers, or site personnel will be required.
- Determine what kind of restroom and lunch shelters/facilities are available. Will students need to bring their own lunches?
- Verify the location of a first aid station or other emergency services at the site.

Regarding Transportation

- Determine which type of reliable transportation is available.
- Confirm the cost of transportation and how it is to be paid—school or students—or plan another way to raise money to pay for the transportation.
- Determine the length of travel time, including loading and unloading.
- Provide parents with details regarding transportation.
- Determine whether additional insurance is needed for field trips.
- Make a contingency plan in case a vehicle breaks down.
- Find out whether transportation permission forms are needed.
- Make sure there is fire safety equipment on board the vehicle(s).
- Make sure there will be a well-stocked first aid kit available on the transportation vehicle(s).

Parents

- Decide whether you need to have a meeting with the parents.
- Write a letter to parents and guardians regarding the purpose of the field work. (See page 107 for sample letter.)
- Make your expectations of the students clear to parents and guardians.
- Inform the parents and guardians what costs are to be shared by them and the students.
- Inform parents of your contingency plans should unexpected bad weather occur.
- Send home a permission form with a date by which it must be returned. (See page 108.)
- Send home a medical emergency form with a date by which it must be returned. (See page 109.)

Students

- Verify that students have the background necessary to be successful in the planned field work.
- Plan activities that will engage students actively in learning.
- Inform students of the purpose of the field work.
- Establish how you expect students to behave and inform them of the consequences of unsafe actions.
- Give students the information for parents and the necessary permission forms to take home. Make clear the due date for the forms to be returned.
- Instruct students regarding dangerous plants or animals they might encounter. Present visuals to help students recognize these.
- Inform students of the type of clothing they should wear.
- Notify students regarding needs for insect repellent and sunscreen.
- Inform students if they need to bring their own lunches and drinking water.
- Make research assignments to help students gain background for the planned activities.

On-Site Supervision

Consider the following suggestions for an easily managed trip.
- Take mobile phones in case of an emergency.
- Make sure well-stocked first aid kits are readily available.
- Take students' medical emergency forms with you.
- Follow school and local regulations regarding the handling of students' medication—prescriptions and over-the-counter medicines recommended by physicians—that students might need for medical conditions and for emergency allergic reactions.

- Designate study teams and safety partners.
- Inform students who the supervisors/chaperones are and where they will be.
- Assign specific tasks to the chaperones.
- Identify the boundaries within which students must stay.
- Clearly inform students of what is expected of them, both in conduct and in their observations and investigations. Make clear the timetable and signal for returning to a pre-selected spot.
- Explain how the field work will be evaluated.
- Distribute materials needed for the investigation (magnifying lenses, plastic test tubes, collecting bottles, and so on).
- Provide students with goggles, gloves, and aprons when necessary.
- Tell students to notify you or a chaperone immediately in case of an emergency. Establish evacuation or other necessary procedures.
- Designate an easy-to-find meeting spot where students can wait if they become separated from the group.
- **WARNING:** *Some substances, while harmless to many, can pose serious threats to others. Be prepared to deal with these threats.*
- **WARNING:** *Inform students NOT to eat berries or other vegetation or food items they encounter and to use gloves when handling items they are investigating.*
- **WARNING:** *Remind students that when they get home, they need to change clothing and wash with soap and water to lessen the chance of irritation from their exposure to plants and wildlife.*

Dealing with Emergencies
Student Accidents
- If the accident is serious, you should administer first aid while someone else calls for emergency services. Notify the parents or guardians. (See pages 84–87 for basic first-aid procedures.)
- If the accident is not serious, you should administer first aid and then notify parents or guardians.
- When you return to school (or at another appropriate time), file an accident report. (See page 110 for a sample form.)

Transportation Accidents
- Call emergency numbers immediately and administer first aid. (See pages 84–87 for some basic first-aid procedures.)
- Follow local regulations regarding vehicular accidents.
- File necessary reports with the police or fire departments.
- When you return to school, file the appropriate accident report with your school's administration. (See page 110.)

A

Weather Emergencies

Flash Floods

- **WARNING:** *Get to higher ground if rising water is threatening.*
- **WARNING:** *Do NOT drive through flooded intersections or stretches of road. Avoid canyons, small rivers or streams, and dry riverbeds.*
- **WARNING:** *Do NOT try to walk through flowing water that is more than ankle-deep.*
- **WARNING:** *Keep students away from drainage ditches, storm drains, viaducts, and other flooded areas.*

Tornado Conditions

- **WARNING:** *If possible, go to a basement or interior room at ground level.*
- **WARNING:** *Avoid large expanses of glass.*
- **WARNING:** *Move from large open areas such as cafeterias, gymnasiums, and auditoriums, but remain indoors.*
- **WARNING:** *Crouch down and cover your head with your hands and with coats, blankets, or pillows, if they are available.*
- **WARNING:** *Leave motor vehicles and find other shelter.*
- **WARNING:** *If shelter is not available, lie down in a low area and cover your head with your hands.*
- **WARNING:** *Do NOT seek shelter under an overpass. Overpasses are prone to wind-tunnel conditions.*

Lightning Conditions

- **WARNING:** *Avoid tall, isolated objects, including trees, bodies of water, fences, open doorways and windows, and open vehicles.*
- **WARNING:** *If you are outdoors, find safe shelter immediately. A hard-top car or a bus with the windows up offers protection if you cannot find a building.*
- **WARNING:** *If you are in a boat or are swimming, return to shore and seek shelter immediately away from the water.*
- **WARNING:** *If you are in a wooded area, crouch down under a thick growth of the smallest trees.*
- **WARNING:** *If you feel your hair standing on end, squat down with your head between your knees. Do NOT lie down.*

Review Laboratory Safety Guidelines

Whether you are a first-time or an experienced teacher, it is important to review safety guidelines at the beginning of each school year. This section deals with behaviors and actions that foster a safe learning environment. Because you serve as the role model for the behavior in the laboratory that you expect from your students, first review the safety guidelines for teachers. Then, on the first day of classes, introduce or review the safety guidelines that are the students' responsibility to follow.

Teacher Safety Guidelines

- Do not eat, drink, or store food or beverages in the laboratory. This includes gum-chewing and smoking.

- Wear appropriate clothing. Remove outerwear jackets and scarves. Avoid wearing shirts with long, loose-fitting sleeves that can drag through chemicals or flames or that can knock things over. Wear sturdy, closed-toe shoes to protect feet from spills and accidents. Protect cuts and abrasions with waterproof bandages and pull back long, loose hair.

- Thoroughly review your local and/or state safety regulations. Modify any activities to comply with these regulations. For example, open flames are not permitted in some states and communities.

- Be trained in first aid and CPR.

- Be aware of students with allergies or other medical conditions that might limit their participation in activities or require special protective equipment, such as face masks.

- Have a list of substances to be used in lab activities made available to the doctor of any pregnant teacher or student so that limitations can be determined beforehand.

- NEVER leave students unattended in a classroom or field setting.

- NEVER be alone or out of earshot of someone when you prepare lab activities or equipment.

- Always wash your hands with soap and warm water when entering the laboratory, after handling live cultures, after cleaning up, and before removing safety goggles.

- NEVER perform an investigation on any animal that might cause pain or suffering to the animal or be a health hazard to humans. Even small animals, such as laboratory rats or mice, can bite or scratch. Never bring captured wild animals into the classroom. They can be a source of human diseases. For example, some species of turtles are contaminated with salmonella bacteria that cause illness in humans.

- Use protists and simple invertebrates for lab or field activities involving animals when possible. Protists represent a wide variety of organisms and can be obtained in large quantities.

- A qualified adult supervisor who has had training in the proper care and handling of laboratory animals must assume responsibility for the conditions of any activity that involves living vertebrates. NO activity/investigation should be conducted that

Classroom and Laboratory Management and Safety | 43

involves drugs, organisms that are pathogenic to humans or other vertebrates, ionizing radiation, surgical procedures, or carcinogens unless the procedures have been approved by and will be performed or supervised by a qualified biomedical scientist.

- Have students notify you beforehand if they plan to bring a pet to class for observations. See page 63 regarding precautions for such events.
- Instruct students about the hazards involved with wild animals and your school's policy and local and state laws regarding their capture and use in the classroom/laboratory. **WARNING:** *Wild animals might exhibit unpredictable behaviors, can become dangerous as they mature, and if declawed, might not be accepted by zoos and will probably die if released into the wild.* **WARNING:** *There is the potential of contracting rabies from any infected warm-blooded animal.*
- It is recommended that you purchase fumigated, steam-sterilized materials.

WARNING:

- *Owl pellets can be a source of salmonella.*
- *Bird nests contain many organisms that can cause diseases.*
- *Bird eggs, even if disinfected when first acquired, will decay after a few days from gases building up in them. Rotten eggs produce noxious odors.*
- *Some insects carry serious diseases that can be transmitted to humans.*

Present Safety Guidelines to Students

Discuss with students the use and location of safety equipment, evacuation guidelines, and first-aid procedures at the beginning of the school year. Refer to fire-drill regulations and a chart of emergency procedures, which should be posted in a prominent place in the laboratory. Assign safety partners and explain their role in helping during emergencies.

Next, distribute and discuss the **Student Laboratory and Safety Guidelines** (see page 101). Emphasize proper attitudes for working in the laboratory and field, and review or present school rules regarding the consequences of misbehavior. Stress the need for safe practices on the part of everyone involved. Review safety guidelines with students at least once a month.

Discuss safe disposal of materials and laboratory cleanup policies at the beginning of the school year (see page 52). Distribute and review the **Safety Symbols Reference Sheet** (see page 114), and post laminated copies of the reference sheet at student work stations and near stored chemicals and equipment for quick reference. Explain to students that if they have any questions about how to handle a substance properly, they should always discuss these with you before they obtain, use, or dispose of the substance.

Finally, preview the planned science activity with students at the beginning of each lab session. Discuss the specific safety issues involved with each activity and describe the protective equipment that should be used. Refer to pages 45–51 for information about managing safe laboratory sessions.

Review General Laboratory Procedures

Knowledge of general laboratory techniques and procedures will foster students' success in the lab. As students become more familiar with the proper use of laboratory equipment, they can focus their attention on completing the activity at hand, making observations, and analyzing results. Following proper techniques in the lab also helps prevent accidents and cuts down on the cost of replacement materials and equipment. To facilitate students' success in the classroom laboratory, first orient students to the laboratory setting. This includes reviewing equipment and correct handling procedures, reviewing the use of SI units, and assessing students' readiness for work in the laboratory.

Overview of Laboratory Equipment

Identify the various devices that students will encounter in your lab and explain their uses. Name the parts of each device, especially stressing the importance of knowing the parts of a microscope. Quiz students on the names and parts of devices by asking students to identify each device/part based on your descriptions.

Laboratory Safety Techniques and Procedures

Review the following material on general laboratory techniques. Discuss this information with students, and at the appropriate times, demonstrate to students the techniques for using laboratory equipment and materials properly.

Using Heat Sources

- Use smooth-surfaced hot plates as a heat source when possible, especially if any flammable liquid is involved. Clean the cooled plate surface after each use. Hot plates remain warm for a period of time after they are turned off. **WARNING:** *Hot plates should be placed out of reach to avoid accidental contact.*

- Hot plate thermostats should be set to the correct temperature for the experiment—NOT to the maximum temperature.

- Alcohol burners are NOT recommended. However, if you must use them, check for cracks or chips and fill prior to student use. Use a plastic squeeze-type bottle to refill with alcohol or burner fuel, making sure the burner has cooled before adding fuel. Add a pinch of table salt to pure alcohol in the burner so the flame may be seen. Be sure a fire extinguisher is nearby. **WARNING:** *Some fluids contain heavy metals, such as lead compounds, and are NOT recommended for use in alcohol burners due to by-products produced from burning.*

- Match the burner to the type of gas available (i.e. natural, artificial, or L.P. gas).

- Sparkers or strikers are recommended for lighting burners. **WARNING:** *Matches tend to litter the lab as well as pose a fire hazard if not handled properly.*

- Bunsen or gas burners should be operated at a sensibly low level.

- Hot water baths should NOT be boiled unless absolutely necessary.

- NEVER leave an open flame unattended. When a burner is not in use, turn it off.
- Do NOT reach across an open flame.
- Light bulbs used in experiments should be the lowest wattage possible.

Heating Objects/Substances

- Always wear goggles when heating substances in the lab. Where possible, heat substances in a fume hood.
- Use a hot plate, rather than a gas burner, when evaporating liquids.
- Objects should NOT be held in a gas-burner flame for an excessive period of time.
- Always point the open end of a test tube away from yourself and others. **WARNING:** *Some chemicals can boil out of the test tube violently and unexpectedly when they are heated.*
- Heat-generating chemicals should be mixed slowly.
- NEVER heat chemicals in a closed container such as a corked test tube. **WARNING:** *The expanding gas inside will cause the test tube to explode or turn the stopper into a projectile with considerable force.*
- Do NOT use bare hands to pick up a container that has been heated or hand a heated container to someone. Hold the back of your hand near the container and check for heat before handling. If you can feel heat, use a mitten or tongs to pick up the container.
- NEVER reach across a hot apparatus to perform an experiment. The apparatus should be placed so that if hot liquids are spilled, they will fall onto the laboratory table, not onto a person.
- Watch heated objects constantly, and shield them from accidental contact.
- Limit air flow from open doors and windows when working with flammables.
- Limit the quantity of flammable and combustible chemicals in the work area to the amount actually necessary to complete the task at hand. For example, do NOT leave the can of alcohol nearby after you fill the alcohol burners.

Using Electrical Apparatuses

- Make sure that all electrical cords are in good condition and are not frayed or cracked. **WARNING:** *Do NOT use any electrical equipment that needs repair.*
- Make sure that circuits are not overloaded.
- Turn off all power sources when you set up circuits or repair equipment.
- Check all circuits set up by students before the power is turned on.
- When you assemble circuits, connect the live portion last. When you disassemble them, disconnect the live portion first.
- Do NOT use or wear metal articles, such as rulers, metal pencils or writing pens, or jewelry when working with electrical equipment.

- When disconnecting electrical equipment, pull from the plug and not from the cord.
- Use caution when handling electrical equipment that has been in use. The equipment might be warm or hot from being used.
- Keep electrical equipment away from water.
- NEVER connect, disconnect, or operate a piece of electrical equipment with wet hands or while standing on a wet floor.
- Use precautions to prevent spills on electric equipment or electrical outlets.

Working with Chemicals

- Read labels twice before using any chemical.
- Work carefully with oxidizing agents. **WARNING:** *Chlorates, nitrates, or peroxides and other oxidizers should NOT come into contact with combustible substances.*
- Discard any glove with holes or cracks. **WARNING:** *Some chemicals can diffuse through a glove, increasing exposure when the glove holds the chemical against the skin.*
- When removing gloves, peel the gloves off your hand, starting at the wrists and working toward the fingers. Keep the outside surface of the gloves from touching the skin during removal.
- Match the correct glove to the substance you are going to use. Refer to the labels on the glove boxes. **WARNING:** *Some kinds of gloves can dissolve when they are in contact with a solvent.*
- Use extra precaution with acids and bases. **WARNING:** *Always pour acid into water. Do NOT pour water into acids.*
- Wash an acid or base from your skin immediately.
- Use a pipette bulb. NEVER pipette liquids using your mouth.
- Do NOT pour extra chemicals back into the original containers. This causes contamination of the chemicals and can produce incorrect results in future investigations.
- NEVER use the same spatula to remove chemicals from two different containers. Each container should have its own spatula.
- When removing a stopper from a bottle, do NOT lay it down on the lab table, but place the stopper between two fingers and hold the bottle so that the label is in the palm of your hand. Both the bottle and the stopper will be held in one hand.
- Replace all stoppers and caps on the correct bottles as soon as you have finished using them.
- Do NOT model a volcano using ammonium dichromate. **WARNING:** *Ammonium dichromate produces chromium(III) oxide, a carcinogen.*

Working with Minerals

- Avoid identifying minerals by tasting. **WARNING:** *Tasting any substance is NOT recommended. Even if the substance is safe, the container might not be. Some semimetals, such as arsenic, antimony, and allemontite, are poisonous.*

- In the event that you work with uranium ores, minimize risks by using the smallest sample for the shortest amount of time possible. **WARNING:** *Avoid direct contact with the ore—use tongs or forceps and sealed samples.*

Using Thermometers

- NEVER use a mercury thermometer.
- NEVER hold the thermometer bulb in an open flame.
- Wrap a strip of tape around thermometers. Leave a protruding piece to keep the thermometers from rolling off work surfaces.

Using Batteries

- Check batteries to be sure they are charged and not leaking. Properly dispose of all leaking batteries (see page 80 regarding the safe disposal of batteries)
- Clean with soap and water all places a leaking battery has contaminated.
- **WARNING:** *Do NOT try to recharge any battery not specifically designed to be recharged. An explosion can result.*
- **WARNING:** *Do NOT try to heat a battery to make it work better. It might explode.*
- **WARNING:** *Do NOT store loose batteries in drawers where they can roll around. The rolling action could cause the batteries to leak.*

Using Lasers

- The laser beam should be at waist-level or below whenever possible.
- Use laser goggles and disinfect them after use. (See pages 53 and 74.)
- NEVER point the laser at anyone.
- NEVER stare at the laser beam or view the reflected beams.
- Block off the beam past the target. (A sheet of rough wood or a flat piece of carbon available at industrial lighting stores works well.) The target and any objects in the beam area should be nonreflective.
- NEVER leave the laser unattended. Prevent unauthorized access.
- Be sure the laser cord is grounded.
- Set up prisms and mirrors in advance to avoid unexpected reflections when you use a laser. Avoid other accidental reflections when using a laser by removing jewelry, wall mirrors, and other reflective surfaces.

Using Centrifuges

- Make sure the centrifuge is securely anchored in a place where its vibrations will not cause bottles or equipment to fall.
- Always close the centrifuge lid during use.
- Do NOT walk away from a running centrifuge until full operating speed is reached and the machine is running smoothly without excess vibration.

- Immediately stop the centrifuge if it starts to vibrate. Check that tubes are loaded symmetrically and contain approximately the same amounts of liquid.
- Regularly clean the buckets, centrifuge tube cushions, and rotors. **WARNING:** *Glass shards or other substances in the cushions are a common cause of tube breakage.*
- Do NOT touch a centrifuge while it is spinning.

Using Glassware

- **WARNING:** *Glass cools slowly. Do NOT touch glass that has been heated unless you have allowed sufficient time for cooling. Hold your hand over the glass to feel for heat emanating from it before touching. Always place hot glass on a heat-proof pad, never on a metal or a wooden desktop.*
- Heat and cool glass slowly. Do NOT set a hot beaker on a cold or damp surface, as this can cause the beaker to crack or shatter.
- When heating glassware, use a wire or ceramic screen to protect the glassware from the flame.
- NEVER use glassware that is scratched or chipped—failure and breakage can result.
- Wrap or strip glassware with masking tape if it is to be used under vacuum or pressure. This will prevent flying pieces of glass in the event of an implosion or explosion.
- Reduce scratches in glassware by using rubber-tipped stirring rods and coated clamps and by cleaning glassware immediately after use.
- NEVER eat or drink from laboratory glassware.
- NEVER heat pipettes, volumetric flasks, or burettes; they can change volume as a result of expansion.
- Clean glassware thoroughly before you store it.

Working with Glass Tubing

- Always protect your hands with several layers of cloth when you insert glass tubing into or remove it from rubber stoppers.
- Lubricate glass tubing or thermometers with glycerin, water, or stopcock grease before you insert them into a rubber stopper. Use a turning motion on the glass tubing when you insert it into a rubber stopper or rubber tubing.
- Remove glass tubing or thermometers from rubber stoppers as soon as possible in order to prevent the rubber or cork from adhering to the glass. If the tubing or thermometer does stick to the stopper, only a teacher should attempt to separate the two. The teacher should wear gloves and goggles, and may be able to release the frozen area by running a stream of hot water over it. Using a strip of paper between ground joints, frequently lubricating stopcocks, or taking apart the equipment for storage will help limit the problem. It is advisable to cut the rubber stopper when a thermometer is involved to avoid breaking the thermometer.

- Commercially made glass-tube cutters work well for cutting tubing. Wear safety goggles and protective gloves when cutting glass.
- After cutting glass tubing, always fire-polish the ends to remove any sharp edges. When bending glass tubing or fire-polishing cut-glass tubing, NEVER hand the hot end of the tubing to anyone until it has cooled.

Using Fume Hoods

- Work as far inside the hood as possible, at least 16 cm from the front edge.
- Work with the sash in the lowest position possible. NEVER work with the sash higher than chin level. The sash must be low enough to protect the head and upper body in case of an explosion.
- Even though the sash to the fume hood separates your face from the apparatus and materials under the hood, you also MUST use the personal safety equipment required for the activity.
- The sash must be kept in place except when setting up an activity. Do NOT conduct the activity until the sash has been returned to its proper safe position.
- Close the sash when the hood exhaust system is not operating.
- While preparing to use or while using the fume hood, keep the interior light on so that the working area has proper illumination.
- Place blocks under large objects so that there is proper air flow under the objects.
- NEVER store chemicals or materials in the hood.
- NEVER place electrical apparatuses or items that can produce a spark in the fume hood.

Using Electron Beams

- Cathode ray tubes and microwave tubes should be used with extreme care—operated at the lowest possible current and voltage with the operating time kept to a minimum. It is recommended that these tubes be used only by the teacher for demonstrations and that the students stand at least 2.5 m away from the tubes when they are in use. **WARNING:** *These tubes can produce X-rays.* **WARNING:** *The glass in any vacuum tube becomes brittle with age and can implode.*
- Infrared/ultraviolet goggles or an approved welders' face shield should be worn when these light rays are used. **WARNING:** *Infrared radiation and ultraviolet rays damage the eyes.*
- Eye protection is required for protection from mercury light sources. **WARNING:** *Mercury light sources can emit ultraviolet rays.*
- Using the Sun as a light source for lenses and prisms is NOT recommended. **WARNING:** *There is NO safe way to look directly at the Sun.*

Working with Biological Samples

- Consider substituting films, videos, and computer simulations for dissection activities.
- Carefully remove specimens from preservative solutions. Wear gloves and use tongs or forceps. **WARNING:** *Formalin solutions are carcinogenic. Any specimen kept in a formalin solution should be soaked in a water bath in a fume hood and then thoroughly rinsed in running water for several minutes. Preferably, these specimens should be replaced with ones stored in safer solutions.*
- When placing a blade onto a scalpel, leave the blade in the original package and hold the blade securely with the cutting edge away from your fingers. To remove the blade, use tweezers or forceps and always push the blade away from your body.
- During dissection, do NOT hold the specimen in your hand. Cut down into the specimen, NOT up toward your body.
- Most insects can be anesthetized by freezing them in a jar for up to an hour.
- Most insects may be killed by placing them in an airtight container in a freezer for 48 hours.
- Do not perform investigations with syringes with needles.

International System of Units (SI)

Emphasize to students why it is necessary to use compatible units when carrying out investigations. Explain that not only should all units of measure be in SI units, but also that all of the measurements used in an equation should be in the same units. For example, if some units of measurement in a relationship are in millimeters and some in centimeters, you must convert the amounts in centimeters to millimeters or the amounts in millimeters to centimeters. For further discussion, provide students with the **SI Reference Sheet** found on page 117.

Assessing Students' Readiness for Lab Tasks

Before students begin work on assigned investigations, foster a climate of safety and proper equipment use by assessing the knowledge and proficiency of the skills required. This is especially important for students new to the science laboratory or who are new to your school.

You might wish to set up various stations in the classroom, having a small group of students demonstrate their skills in performing certain tasks and using the appropriate devices at each station. For example, have students observe plant cells with a microscope. You should watch to see that they focus the lens and handle the microscope and sample properly. Rotate the groups through the stations until you have assessed the skills of each student. Rate each student's performance and provide additional instruction to those students who need it.

Maintain an Environmentally Safe Laboratory

Waste Disposal Guidelines

This section deals with daily cleanup needs and temporary storage of waste products. See pages 66–67 for information regarding waste reduction measures and major reorganization and cleanup of old and excess quantities of chemicals.

Work with your custodial department to develop safe ways to store wastes. Identify a safe place to store waste after it leaves the classroom laboratory. Keep school administration and local officials, such as the fire department, informed about the location of waste stored temporarily and your waste disposal procedures. **WARNING:** *Most states place a limit on the volume of chemicals that can be stored in school facilities. Know your state and local regulations regarding safe chemical storage.*

Use separate containers for different kinds of waste—paper, trash, broken glass, biohazardous materials, sharp objects contaminated with biohazardous fluids, toxic or caustic waste, and so on. **WARNING:** *Waste that contains both safe and hazardous substances is considered hazardous waste.* Equipment supply companies sell proper waste containers. Make sure the containers have the proper labels with safety icons and that students recognize the labels. **WARNING:** *Do NOT stack the containers; leaks must be visible to ensure prompt corrective action.*

Broken Glassware

Clean up broken glassware immediately. Set aside gloves, a brush, and a dustpan for that purpose. Wet cotton balls are effective for picking up tiny pieces of glass.

Batteries

Batteries can contain caustic substances and should be kept separate from other types of trash. **WARNING:** *Do NOT incinerate batteries. They are explosive.* Some newer types of batteries must be recycled in some communities. Find out about recycling regulations in your area.

Other Chemicals

Some chemicals can be washed down the sink. For example, almost all sodium compounds can be washed down the drain. Refer to water treatment officials for guidelines—they probably recommend that all liquid waste be adjusted to a pH between 5 and 8.

Any waste that must not be washed down the drain should be kept in safe containers. Empty reagent bottles with a plastic coating are suitable for most liquid waste. Solid waste can be discarded in empty chemical jars. Only similar, compatible wastes should be collected in a single container (see page 61 for information about chemical compatibility). **WARNING:** *All stored waste MUST be labeled. Waste disposal costs rise for unknown substances. Unknown substances may NOT be disposed of in the water or land.*

Biological Contamination

Place biological specimens and bandages, towels, and gloves used in cleaning up blood and other bodily fluids in the red biohazard containers and dispose of properly. Place sharp items such as needles and scalpel blades in a red biohazard container made especially for sharp objects. Glassware and glass microscope slides can be sterilized and reused.

Sterilization Procedures

Clean glassware is necessary to keep from contaminating an experiment and to provide safe equipment for students to use. Clean eyewear after each use.

Goggles

Germicidal ultraviolet (UV) cabinets are available for sterilizations. If used, follow the manufacturer's instructions. Check the UV intensity yearly with a UV meter. Clean the lamp often (weekly), as dust and dirt affects the intensity of the lamp. One drawback to the UV cabinet is the time it takes for sterilization to occur. The following alternative method may be used if a UV cabinet is unavailable or inconvenient to use.

1. Clean the goggles, frame, and lenses with liquid detergent on a paper towel. Rinse the goggles with water and partially dry with a paper towel. Use a separate paper towel for each pair of goggles.

2. Dip the goggles into a solution of one tablespoon of household bleach and one quart of water or wipe the goggles with a gauze pad or cotton ball soaked with a 70 percent isopropyl alcohol solution. Note: Make the bleach solution fresh daily.

3. Let the goggles air-dry.

4. In case of an infection, the goggles should be soaked in the bleach solution for 10 minutes following washing with a liquid detergent. This bleach solution should be used only for one pair of goggles and discarded immediately afterward.

Glassware

Glassware should be washed immediately. If immediate washing is not possible, soak the glassware until it can be washed. Most glassware can be cleaned with detergents and brushes. The glassware should be washed thoroughly with detergent and rinsed several times, with a final rinse of distilled water. (If all the detergent is not removed with the rinsing, the detergent will react with acids to form a grease coating on the glassware.) **WARNING:** *Do NOT use worn brushes with exposed metal that can scratch the glass.*

Various methods may be used to sterilize glassware.

- *Dry heat.* Larger pieces of heat-resistant glassware (petri dishes, beakers, graduated cylinders, test tubes) can be sterilized by placing them in an oven at a temperature of 350°F for 2 h. Glassware should be loosely wrapped in aluminum foil and placed on a metal tray or cookie sheet. Put them in a cold oven and turn on the heat to reach a setting of 350°F. Leave the glassware in the oven for two hours after it has reached the proper temperature. After this time, the glassware can be removed from the oven. Remember to use heat-proof gloves to remove the tray and place it on a heat-proof surface to cool.

- *Steam under pressure.* Place media or glassware in a pressure cooker or autoclave for 15 minutes. **WARNING:** *Do NOT open the cover until you turn off the heat source and allow the pressure to return to normal.*

- *Boiling.* Smaller pieces of glassware (droppers, stirring rods, and so forth) can be sterilized by boiling them in water for 30 minutes.

- *Using chemicals.* Culture dishes can be soaked in a 10 percent solution of household bleach and then rinsed with water, finishing with a rinse with distilled water. **WARNING:** *Wear rubber gloves to avoid burns when using strong disinfectants.* **WARNING:** *Some residues are not affected by detergents.* Discard glassware that cannot be properly cleaned. In many cases, plastic one-time use materials can be used. Petri dishes, for example, are available in plastic forms. If contaminated with a harmful organism or substance, even plastic Petri dishes must be sterilized before they are discarded.

Manage Laboratory Materials Storage

It is your responsibility to be informed of the local, state, federal, and district/school rules that govern the storage and disposal of materials used in your classroom/laboratory. This section discusses Material Safety Data Sheets, storage factors such as the nature of hazardous materials and chemical incompatibility, storage and handling procedures, inventory practices, and waste disposal. Refer to pages 61–63 regarding factors involved in the construction of storeroom facilities.

Material Safety Data Sheets (MSDS)

You should keep an MSDS file for all the chemicals you use and store in your classroom/laboratory. Manufacturers provide MSDS for each chemical they produce. An MSDS includes the following information:

- the name of the chemical
- manufacturer's name and address
- physical and health hazards, including organs it would affect
- first aid measures
- CAS number assigned by the Chemical Abstract Service
- chemical formula
- molecular weight for compounds, the atomic weight for elements
- common name of the chemical
- purity of the substance
- lot numbers
- supplier's name and address

See page 56 for a sample MSDS. Note that the sample is for a solution of sodium chloride (table salt), a common substance not considered hazardous. Even so, there are several safety issues concerning this table salt solution (indicated by the highlighted portions of the MSDS).

MATERIAL SAFETY DATA SHEET

Sodium Chloride 25%
90175

SECTION 1—CHEMICAL PRODUCT AND COMPANY IDENTIFICATION

MSDS Name: Sodium Chloride 25%
Catalog Numbers: 99150
Synonyms: None
Company Identification: [Manufacturer's name and address go here]
For information, call: [Manufacturer's phone numbers]
Emergency Number:
For CHEMTREC assistance, call:
For International CHEMTREC assistance, call:

SECTION 2—COMPOSITION, INFORMATION ON INGREDIENTS

CAS#	Chemical Name	%	EINECS#
7647-14-5	Sodium Chloride	25%	231-598-3
7732-18-5	Water	75%	231-791-2

SECTION 3—HAZARDS IDENTIFICATION

EMERGENCY OVERVIEW
Appearance: colorless
CAUTION! May cause respiratory tract irritation. May cause eye and skin irritation. May cause digestive tract irritation with nausea, vomiting, and diarrhea.
Target Organs: none
Potential Health Effects
　　Eye: May cause eye irritation.
　　Skin: May cause skin irritation.
　　Ingestion: Ingestion of large amounts may cause gastrointestinal irritation. Ingestion of large amounts may cause nausea and vomiting, rigidity or convulsions. Continued exposure can produce coma, dehydration, and internal organ congestion.
　　Inhalation: May cause respiratory tract irritation.
　　Chronic: No information found.

SECTION 4—FIRST AID MEASURES

Eyes: Flush eyes with plenty of water for at least 15 minutes, occasionally lifting the upper and lower lids. If irritation develops, get medical aid.
Skin: Get medical aid if irritation develops or persists. Flush skin with plenty of soap and water.
Ingestion: If victim is conscious and alert, give 2 to 4 cupfuls of milk or water. Never give anything by mouth to an unconscious person. Get medical aid if irritation or symptoms occur.
Inhalation: Remove from exposure to fresh air immediately. If not breathing, give artificial respiration. If breathing is difficult, give oxygen. Get medical aid if cough or other symptoms appear.
Notes to Physician: None
Antidote: None reported

SECTION 5—FIRE FIGHTING MEASURES

General Information: As in any fire, wear a self-contained breathing apparatus in pressure-demand, MSHA/NIOSH (approved or equivalent), and full protective gear.
Extinguishing Media: For small fires, use water spray, dry chemical, carbon dioxide, or chemical foam.
　　Auto-ignition: Temperature: Not available
　　Flash Point: Not available
　　NFPA Rating: Not published
　　Explosion Limits, Lower: Not available
　　Upper: Not available

SECTION 6—ACCIDENTAL RELEASE MEASURES

General Information: Use proper personal protective equipment as indicated in Section 8.
Spills/Leaks: Flush spill area with water.

SECTION 7—HANDLING AND STORAGE

Handling: Wash thoroughly after handling. Use adequate ventilation. Avoid contact with skin and eyes. Avoid ingestion and inhalation.
Storage: Store in a cool, dry place. Store in a tightly closed container.

SECTION 8—EXPOSURE CONTROLS, PERSONAL IDENTIFICATION

Engineering Controls: Good general ventilation should be sufficient to control airborne levels.

Exposure Limits

Chemical Name	ACGIH	NIOSH	OSHA—Final PELs
Sodium Chloride	None listed	None listed	None listed
Water	None listed	None listed	None listed

OSHA Vacated PELs:
Sodium chloride: No OSHA Vacated PELs are listed for this chemical.
Water: No OSHA Vacated PELs are listed for this chemical.
Personal Protective Equipment
Eyes: Wear appropriate protective eyeglasses or chemical safety goggles as described by OSHA's eye and face protection regulations in 29 CFR 1910.133 or European Standard EN 166.
Skin: Wear appropriate gloves to prevent skin exposure.
Clothing: Wear appropriate protective clothing to minimize contact with skin.
Respirators: Follow the OSHA respirator regulations found in 29 CFR 1910.134 or European Standard EN 149. Always use a NIOSH or European Standard EN 149 approved respirator when necessary.

SECTION 9—PHYSICAL AND CHEMCIAL PROPERTIES

Physical State: Solid
Appearance: Colorless
Odor: Odorless
pH: Not available
Vapor Pressure: Not available
Vapor Density: Not available
Evaporation Rate: Not available
Viscosity: Not available
Boiling Point: Not available
Freezing/Melting Point: Not available
Decomposition Temperature: Not available
Solubility: Soluble in water
Specific Gravity/Density: Not available
Molecular Formula: Solution
Molecular Weight: Not available

SECTION 10—STABILITY AND REACTIVITY

Chemical Stability: Stable
Conditions to Avoid: High temperatures
Incompatibilities with Other Materials: Reacts with most non-noble metals such as iron or steel, building materials (such as cement), bromine, or trifluoride. Potentially explosive reaction with dichloromaleic anhydride + urea. Electrolysis of mixtures with nitrogen compounds may form explosive nitrogen trichloride.
Hazardous Decomposition Products: Chlorine, toxic fumes of sodium oxide.
Hazardous Polymerization: Has not been reported.

A

SECTION 11—TOXICOLOGICAL INFORMATION

RTECS#:
    CAS# 7647-14-5: VZ4725000
    CAS# 7732-18-5: ZC0110000
LD50/LC50:
    CAS# 7647-14-5: Oral, mouse: LD50 = 4 gm/kg; Oral, rat: LD50 = 3 gm/kg.
    CAS# 7732-18-5: Oral, rat: LD50 = >90 mL/kg.
Carcinogenicity: Sodium chloride—Not listed by ACGIH, IARC, NIOSH, NTP, or OSHA.
    Water—Not listed by ACGIH, IARC, NIOSH, or OSHA.
Epidemiology: No information reported
Teratogenicity: An experimental teratogen
Reproductive Effects: Human reproductive effects by intraplacental route: Terminates pregnancy; Experimental reproductive effects
Neurotoxicity: No information reported
Mutagenicity: Human mutation data reported
Other Studies: No information reported

SECTION 12—ECOLOGICAL INFORMATION

Ecotoxicity: No information found
Environmental Fate: No information reported
Physical/Chemical: No information found
Other: No information found

SECTION 13—DISPOSAL CONSIDERATIONS

Dispose of in a manner consistent with federal, state, and local regulations.
RCRA D-Series Maximum Concentration of Contaminants: None listed
RCRA D-Series Chronic Toxicity Reference Levels: None listed
RCRA F-Series: None listed
RCRA P-Series: None listed
RCRA U-Series: None listed
Not listed as a material banned from land disposal according to RCRA.

SECTION 14—TRANSPORT INFORMATION

US DOT: No information available
IMO: No information available
IATA: No information available
RID/ADR: No information available
Canadian TDG: No information available

SECTION 15—REGULATORY INFORMATION

US FEDERAL
TSCA:
    CAS# 7647-14-5 is listed on the TSCA inventory.
    CAS# 7732-18-5 is listed on the TSCA inventory.
Health & Safety Reporting List:
    None of the chemicals are on the Health & Safety Reporting List.
Chemical Test Rules:
    None of the chemicals in this product are under a Chemical Test Rule.
Section 12b:
    None of the chemicals in listed under TSCA Section 12b.
TSCA Significant New Use Rule:
    None of the chemicals in this material has a SNUR under TSCA.
SARA:
Section 302 (RQ): None of the chemicals in this material has an RQ.
Section 302 (TPQ): None of the chemicals in this product has a TPQ.

CHEMICAL SARA Codes
    CAS# 7647-14-5: acute
    Section 313: No chemicals are reportable under Section 313.
Clean Air Act:
    This material does not contain any hazardous air pollutants.
    This material does not contain any Class 1 Ozone depletors.
    This material does not contain any Class 2 Ozone depletors.
Clean Water Act:
    None of the chemicals in this product is listed as Hazardous.
Substances under the CWA: None of the chemicals in this product is listed as Priority.
Pollutants under the CWA: None of the chemicals in this product is listed as Toxic *Pollutant under the CWA.*
<u>*OSHA:*</u>
    None of the chemicals in this product is considered highly hazardous by OSHA.
<u>*STATE*</u>
    Sodium chloride is not present on state lists from CA, PA, MN, MA, FL, or NJ.
    Water is not present on state lists from CA, PA, MN, MA, FL, or NJ.
    California: No Significant Risk Level; None of the chemicals in this product is listed.
<u>*European/International Regulations*</u>
European Labeling in Accordance with EC Directives
    Hazardous Symbols: Not available
    Risk Phrases:
    Safety Phrases:
<u>*WGK (Water Danger/Protection)*</u>
    CAS# 7647-14-5: 0
    CAS# 7732-18-5: No information available
<u>*Canada*</u>
    CAS# 7647-14-5 is listed on Canada's DSL/NDSL List.
    CAS# 7732-18-5 is listed on Canada's DSL/NDSL List.
    WHMIS: Not available
    CAS# 7647-14-5 is not listed on Canada's Ingredient Disclosure List.
    CAS# 7732-18-5 is not listed on Canada's Ingredient Disclosure List.
Exposure Limits

SECTION 16—ADDITIONAL INFORMATION
MSDS Creation Date: 5/14/1996
Revision #1 Date: 9/02/1997

The information above is believed to be accurate and represents the best information currently available to us. However, we make no warranty of merchantability or any other warranty, express or implied, with respect to such information, and we assume no liability resulting from its use. Users should make their own investigations to determine the suitability of the information for their particular purposes. In no way shall [the manufacturer] be liable for any claims, losses, or damages of any third party or for lost profits or any special, indirect, incidental, consequential or exemplary damages, howsoever arising, even if [the manufacturer] has been advised of the possibility of such damages.

Storage Procedures

Factors that affect how you store materials in your storeroom include the properties of hazardous materials, patterns of storeroom organization, and proper procedures for storing and handling various materials. Computer software programs that contain chemical storage patterns are available.

To help keep your storage room organized, you might wish to code each shelf area by group or type of substance. Mark that code on the label of the substance with a waterproof marker to help ensure that the substance is returned to the correct shelf after use. Also enter the code in your inventory record. **WARNING:** *Do NOT return unused substances to the original container. Contamination can cause unwanted reactions.*

The Nature of Hazardous Materials

Follow regulations for storing hazardous materials. (Check your MSDS file.) Follow all precautions when handling hazardous materials. Note that some materials might pose more than one type of hazard. Types of hazardous materials include:

- **Corrosives** Materials called corrosives can injure body tissues or damage metal by direct chemical reaction. Examples of corrosive acids are sulfuric, acetic, hydrochloric, and nitric acids. Examples of corrosive bases are sodium hydroxide and aqueous ammonia. Other corrosive substances include iodine, bromine, and ferric chloride.

- **Flammable Liquids and Solids** Liquids usually do not burn, but they often produce vapors that do. Examples are solvents such as acetone, ethanol, toluene, and glacial acetic acid. **WARNING:** *Vapors from flammable solids are as dangerous as those from liquids.*

- **Toxic Substances** Such substances enter the body by ingestion, skin contact, or inhalation. Acute effects of a toxic substance occur suddenly or within a few hours. For example, methyl alcohol can cause blindness or death if even small amounts are swallowed or inhaled. Chronic effects result from repeated exposure to a toxic substance over months or years and are dose dependent—calling for using the smallest amounts possible and following all precautions. Examples are benzene and formaldehyde.

- **Oxidizers and Reactives** These chemicals can explode, violently polymerize, form explosive peroxides, or are pyrophoric. Pyrophoric substances can ignite spontaneously when exposed to water or oxygen. Examples of oxidizers include nitric acid, hydrogen peroxide, and potassium nitrate and nitrite. Examples of substances that form hazardous polymers on aging include acrylonitrile and butadiene. Substances that can form explosive peroxides within a few months, include aldehydes, ethers, ketones, and vinyl compounds. Pyrophoric substances include calcium carbide, sodium, and magnesium powder.

- **Pathogens WARNING:** *All human, animal, and plant specimens present a potential hazard from pathogens.* Be selective in choosing microorganisms for laboratory activities. Reputable suppliers will list known or suspected pathogens in their catalogs. Today, most suppliers will not sell pathogens to schools. Purchase biological specimens in preservatives with low toxicity. Formaldehyde or formalin are no longer recommended as preservatives. Obtain an MSDS from suppliers for their holding and shipping fluid. Ethylene glycol is a significant ingredient in most nonformaldehyde preservative preparations. **WARNING:** *Ethylene glycol is toxic when ingested, even in small amounts. Use precautions. Thoroughly rinse specimens, wear gloves, and ensure good ventilation.*

- **Radioactive Materials** Radiation naturally occurs in some ores. Radioactive ores are largely regulated by the individual states. Overexposure to radiation can cause burns and cancer. Evaluate ores before use. They should not subject an individual to radiation levels of more than 5 millirems during an hour. Use ores for demonstration only. Do not allow students to handle radioactive ores.

Chemical Compatibility

A major factor in storing and handling chemicals is knowing which chemicals work with other chemicals. Chemical compatibility describes how stable a substance is when mixed with another substance. If substances do not change when mixed, they are considered compatible. If substances form a chemical reaction when mixed, they are considered incompatible. For example, acids and bases react when mixed and are therefore considered incompatible. Acids should be stored together in a separate area from bases.

General Storage Patterns and Procedures
The procedures that follow pertain to all areas, including earthquake-prone areas. For additional information, suppliers describe storage patterns in their catalogs. All items should be labeled with the name of the substance, its source, its acquisition and/or expiration date, hazard information, and necessary first aid steps to follow in the event of an emergency involving the substance. Chemicals should have chemical formula and concentration listed. Following are some additional suggestions for storing chemicals safely.

- Students should NOT have access to the storeroom area.
- **WARNING:** *Do NOT store hazardous substances above eye level and NEVER on the floor. Follow regulations regarding the storage of hazardous materials.*
- All storage shelves and cabinets should be securely attached to the walls. **WARNING:** *Do NOT place hazardous materials in unstable containers or in an apparatus that is not properly secured.*

- Larger equipment and larger chemical containers should be stored on lower shelves only.
- **WARNING:** *Do NOT store materials in direct sunlight.*
- Substances should be stored at the correct temperature.
- Storeroom temperature should be monitored on a regular basis.
- Poisons should be kept locked in a cabinet.
- Keep all containers of biological specimens in locked storage.
- Keep all syringes and scalpel blades in locked storage.

Handling Radioactive Materials

Follow all regulations regarding how to handle radioactive materials. All sources should be shielded, handled, and transported in a manner to prevent anyone from being exposed to unnecessary radiation. Normally, "Caution: Radioactive Area" signs are posted when radioactive materials are present. However, NO school should have enough radioactive material (5 millirems) to warrant such a sign.

WARNING: *Dinosaur fossils might be radioactive and should NOT be in a classroom laboratory unless they test at safe levels of radioactivity.* Keep dinosaur fossils in sealed containers, and wash them before being handling (with gloves).

Storing Chemicals

Store chemicals in a separate, dedicated room different from the preparation/equipment storeroom. Allow sufficient room to store chemicals according to compatible chemical families. A partial list of incompatible reagents can be found on pages 64 and 65. Store according to the guidelines that follow only those chemicals you intend to use.

- Separate chemicals by reaction type. Store acids in one place and bases in another. Oxidants should be stored away from easily oxidized materials.
- Peroxide production in aldehydes, ethers, ketones, and vinyl compounds can be slowed by storing them in full containers, by closing containers as soon as possible, and by tightly closing the containers' lids or caps, which limits exposure of the container's contents to oxygen.
- Some pyrophorics are stored with a layer of mineral oil or kerosene over them to prevent contact with the air.
- Store any source of ignition separately from combustible materials. Ignition sources include sparkers, strikers, lighters, matches, lenses, and parabolic mirrors.
- Store water-reactive chemicals (metals) where they will remain dry.
- Store chemicals in an upright position and place them no more than two containers deep.
- **WARNING:** *Do NOT store chemicals in fume hoods.*

- Refrigeration might be required to minimize decomposition or volatility of certain substances. Use only spark-free refrigeration in laboratories, storage rooms, and preparation areas for storing flammable chemicals (see page 60). **WARNING:** *Do NOT use laboratory refrigerators to store edibles.*

- Store acids and corrosives in a nonmetal or coated-metal, vented cabinet. The acid cabinet should be vented to the outside to prevent a buildup of toxic fumes (see page 60). A separate nitric acid compartment or cabinet must be provided to separate nitric acid from other inorganic acids or readily oxidized substances.

- Store flammable reagents in the smallest quantities possible. Store flammable liquids in appropriate safety cabinets and/or safety cans. **WARNING:** *Do NOT store flammables in a household-type refrigerator. Instead, use an explosion-proof refrigerator (see page 60).*

- Chemical shelving should have restraints to contain the chemicals. One- to two-inch wooden edge lips are acceptable, or stretch cords or $\frac{1}{8}$-inch stainless steel rods can be anchored to the individual shelves and set about two inches above the shelf level. **WARNING:** *Use caution when removing containers from shelves with lips so that they do not catch on the lip and tip over and spill.*

- For more information, refer to the Chemical Incompatibility Reference Sheets on the next two pages.

Handling Live Animals

Animals require specific diets and living conditions. Check with reliable sources about an animal's requirements and ensure they can be met before bringing the animal to school. If you intend to keep an animal over the course of one or more school years, consider how the animal's needs, particularly those for space, will change over time as the animal grows. If the animal's needs cannot be met on an ongoing basis, then consider keeping a different animal or have a plan in place for what will happen to the animal when its needs can no longer be met in the classroom. Remember that because animals need full-time care, you must make arrangements for weekends and holidays.

Consider students' allergies before bringing animals into the classroom. Any pet brought to class should have a clean bill of health from a veterinarian and mammals should be vaccinated for rabies. Contact special events directors regarding the use and handling of animals in science fairs and other research projects. Remember above all to treat animals with care and respect.

Chemical Incompatibility Reference Sheet

Chemical	Not compatible with
Gasses	
Acetylene	Bromine, chlorine, copper, fluorine, mercury, silver
Ammonia (anhydrous) **WARNING:** *This chemical is deadly by itself.*	Bromine, calcium hypochlorite, chlorine, iodine, mercury
Hydrocarbons (such as butane and propane)	Bromine, chlorine, chromic acid, fluorine, sodium peroxide
Hydrogen sulfide **WARNING:** *This chemical is deadly by itself.*	Fuming nitric acid, oxidizing gases
Oxygen	Oils; grease; hydrogen; flammable liquids, solids, or gases
Liquids	
Acetic acid	Ammonium nitrate, chromic acid, ethylene glycol, hydroxyl compounds, nitric acid, perchloric acid, permanganates, peroxides
Acetic anhydride	Water
Acetone	Concentrated nitric and sulfuric acid mixtures
Aniline	Hydrogen peroxide, nitric acid
Flammable liquids	Ammonium nitrate, chromic acid, halogens, hydrogen peroxide, nitric acid, sodium peroxide
Hydrogen peroxide (6% or more)	Acetone, alcohols, aniline, chromium, combustible materials, copper, iron and iron oxides, most metals and their salt, organic materials
Mercury	Acetylene, ammoni
Nitric acid (concentrated)	Acetic acid, alcohol, aniline, brass, copper, flammable gases and liquids, heavy metals, hydrogen sulfide, phosphorus
Oxalic acid	Mercury, silver
Sulfides	Acids
Sulfuric acid	Carbohydates, most metals, potassium chlorate, potassium perchlorate, potassium permanganate and other similar compounds of light metals such as sodium or lithium, reducing agents
Toluene	Strong acids, strong oxidizing agents

Chemical Incompatibility Reference Sheet (continued)

Chemical	Not compatible with
Solids	
Alkali and alkaline Earth metals (powdered Al or Mg, Ca, Li, Na, K)	Carbon dioxide, chlorinated hydrocarbons, halogens, water
Aluminum metal	Ammonium nitrate; antimony trichloride; bromine vapor; any bromate, chlorate, or iodate
Ammonium nitrate	Acids, chlorates, flammable liquids, nitrites, powdered metals, sulfur, finely divided organic or combustible materials
Calcium oxide	Water
Carbon (activated)	Calcium hypochlorite, all oxidizing agents
Chlorates	Acids, ammonium salts, powdered metals, sulfur, finely divided organic or combustible materials, reducing agents
Copper	Acetylene, hydrogen peroxide
Cyanides **WARNING:** *This chemical is deadly by itself.*	Acids
Iodine	Acetylene, ammonia, hydrogen
Nitrates	Reducing agents, sulfuric acid
Nitrites	Acids
Potassium	Carbon dioxide, water
Potassium permanganate	Ethylene glycol, glycerol, sulfuric acid
Selenides	Acids, reducing agents
Silver	Acetylene, ammonium compounds, oxalic acid, tartaric acid
Sodium	Carbon dioxide, sulfur, water
Sodium nitrate	Ammonium nitrate and other ammonium salts
Sodium peroxide	Acetic anhydride, carbon disulfide, ethylene glycol, ethyl acetate, ethyl or methyl alcohol, glacial acetic acid, glycerin, methyl acetate

A

Inventory Practices

Use the following tips as a guide to cataloging and maintaining laboratory materials.

- A computer inventory program can simplify the process of finding a substance. An alphabetized printout, manual listing, or file card system also works well. Information should include all items on the label plus the type of substance (chemical, biological, radioactive, and so on), condition, amount, size of container, and location in the storage room.

- Conduct periodic (at least once a year) inspections and cleanup efforts. For your personal safety, two individuals (NOT students) should be involved. Safety devices, such as goggles, masks, aprons, and gloves, should be worn. The storeroom should be well-ventilated (see page 73).

- Check stored substances for signs of leakage, deterioration, loose labels, or other potentially dangerous conditions.

- Control the amount of substances you have on hand. Check regulations for your area to find out what the legal limit is.

- Reduce your inventory by ordering only those substances needed in the next year or so and use small-scale chemistry amounts if possible (see pages 89–90).

- Take steps to dispose of all outdated, contaminated, and unlabeled materials.

- Dispose of those substances that have not been used in the last year or two as well as hazardous materials that should not be used in a classroom/laboratory.

- If possible, purchase materials by school or school district to prevent duplication and to buy in bulk for lower prices. **WARNING:** *Substances purchased in bulk and then transferred to smaller containers for individual schools MUST be labeled properly and placed into proper containers. Follow all safety regulations in the transfer of the substances.*

Waste Disposal Policies

This section discusses issues involved in waste generated from wholesale cleanup of a laboratory and storage room and possible methods of disposal to include in your policies and waste disposal plans. **WARNING:** *If you store non-hazardous wastes with hazardous wastes, the entire contents of the storage MUST be considered hazardous waste.*

Reducing Waste

An important step in managing waste disposal is finding ways to reduce the amount of waste you generate. Reducing the amount of waste produced reduces the costs of disposal and fosters a safer environment in the science laboratory. Consider the following:

- Buy only the amount of chemicals you will need within the next one to two years at the most.

- Scale down the amount of chemicals you use in each activity. Refer to the section on small-scale chemistry on pages 89–90 for more information about how to reduce the amounts of chemicals used.

- Many chemistry labs contain chemicals that were purchased in bulk years ago and that either have degraded or are no longer needed. Any initial savings in bulk purchases will therefore be thrown away. Costs of waste disposal increase when the disposal involves old and unstable materials.
- Students should NOT work with hazardous chemicals, and it is expensive to dispose of them as regulated waste. When you discontinue use of a hazardous chemical, any amount remaining in the inventory will require legal disposal as a hazardous waste. Be sure not to order more. Substitute non- or less-hazardous chemicals for hazardous chemicals in experiments.
- Use cyclohexane in place of benzene in molecular weight determination and freezing point experiments.
- Store biological specimens in isopropyl alcohol, sodium citrate, or other preservative safer than formaldehyde.
- Use cyclohexane in place of carbon tetrachloride in halide-ion tests.
- A 40-percent glyoxal solution can be substituted for formalin (a 40-percent formaldehyde solution) in some demonstrations.

Chemical Disposal

Local, state, and federal laws regulate the disposal of chemicals. Consult these laws before attempting to dispose of any chemicals. Prior to chemical disposal, identify which chemicals need to be disposed of. These include

- out-of-date or contaminated chemicals;
- chemicals without legible labels;
- chemicals that are too hazardous for student use.

WARNING: *Some substances should NOT be removed from storage except by certified teachers. Some of these include benzoyl peroxide, carbon disulfide, diisopropyl ether, ethyl ether, perchloric acid, and potassium metal.* NOTE: *Picric acid is outlawed for school use—if any is found in a school lab, trained officials must be called.*

Store wastes in tightly closed, compatible containers. For example, do not store acid or caustic wastes in metal containers. **WARNING:** *Do NOT mix organic and inorganic wastes.* **WARNING:** *Do NOT mix halogenated and non-halogenated solvents.*

Where to Dispose of Chemicals

Federal, state, and local laws regulate the amount and kinds of chemicals that can be put in a landfill or into the sewage system. Check with your school district. It might have a waste management program to help teachers recognize hazardous waste and understand proper disposal. Then check with local officials regarding laws for disposing of unknown substances. Possible sources of places that handle chemical waste include

- commercial chemical disposal companies in your area;
- some local industries;
- colleges and universities that have facilities for disposal available for school use.

How to Dispose of Chemicals

There are several options for substance disposal, but each school or school district must make its own arrangements according to local restrictions of landfills, sewer systems, or other treatment works. **WARNING:** *Be sure you check your state and local regulations before you use any of the following methods:*

- carbon absorption
- oxidation/reduction
- precipitation and clarification
- biological treatment
- land disposal

Here are some additional things to remember when deciding how to dispose of unneeded chemicals:

- Usable chemicals might be accepted by colleges, researchers, industry, or other schools. Contact the local American Chemical Society for suggestions. This method works best if direct communication is made with someone known to the person making the contact.
- You might be able to consolidate your waste with that of other local schools for more efficient disposal.
- **WARNING:** *Follow state and local regulations regarding the transportation of chemicals.*
- SOME hazardous wastes can be treated so that they are non- or less-hazardous. For example, acids or bases can be carefully neutralized to a final pH range of 5–8 and then flushed down the drain with a 20-fold excess of water. Sodium bicarbonate is used to raise pH, and 1M hydrocloric acid is used to lower pH. **WARNING:** *Pouring certain chemicals down the sink or other drains may interfere with some chemicals that are used in water treatment processes.*
- Some waste disposal companies recycle chemicals and resell them.
- Recover laboratory wastes. Recovery of chemicals can be a learning tool for students, and can be presented as the final step in a chemistry experiment or as a project for more advanced students. University chemistry departments, the Internet, and the Environmental Protection Agency offer information about chemical recovery.

Prepare Live Exhibits

Aquariums and terrariums are useful for maintaining living organisms, such as small plants and animals, to study as a class. You can use any glass or plastic container (4 L or larger) with a cover as an aquarium or terrarium. Wash and rinse the container thoroughly before you use it.

Instructions follow for preparing aquariums and terrariums and for growing plants.

Aquariums

1. Place washed aquarium gravel on the bottom of the container to a depth of 4 cm.
2. Add aged tap water to a depth of 5 cm above the gravel. To age tap water, allow it to sit in an open container for three days so that any chlorine in it can dissipate.
3. Anchor aquatic plants, such as eel grass, in the gravel.
4. Fill the aquarium by pouring aged tap water over a saucer to avoid disturbing the gravel on the bottom.
5. Let the aquarium stand for one day.
6. Add guppies, goldfish, snails, duckweed, and other organisms. (Recall that adult guppies eat smaller fish, so keep young and adults separated.)
7. Suspend a thermometer in the water to monitor the temperature. Maintain a temperature of 20–25°C. A lamp or sunny window can supply light and warmth.
8. Cover the aquarium.
9. Ensure that the cover of the container allows for air circulation.
10. Add small amounts of high-protein baby cereal or special fish food daily. Snails will eat any food the fish do not consume.
11. Keep the plants pruned so they do not fill the tank.
12. Keep tap water aging to replace any water lost by evaporation.
13. If algae develop in the aquarium and turn the water green, do not discard the water. It is an excellent source of food for other organisms.

Terrariums

1. Place pebbles on the bottom of the container to a depth of 2 cm.
2. Add 1 cm of clean sand and then 3 cm of topsoil.
3. Place a layer of healthy green moss on top of the topsoil.
4. Plant several clusters of small ferns and liverworts. You can also add lichens.
5. Place interesting rocks and driftwood in the terrarium.
6. Cover the terrarium.
7. Place the terrarium in filtered light.
8. Keep the plants moist by sprinkling with water occasionally. The pebble and sand layers allow for drainage. If water accumulates in the pebble layer, do not add more water until there is no more standing water.

Plants

You can grow plants in the laboratory from seeds or from cuttings. Bean plants, coleus, geraniums, and philodendrons usually grow well and often can be obtained at relatively low cost from nurseries and local gardening centers.

1. Place packaged potting soil 5 cm deep in the bottom of a clean milk carton or plastic sandwich bag. Poke holes in the bottom of containers to ensure good drainage. Place containers on a plastic tray to catch water runoff.

2. Plant seeds or cuttings from other plants.

3. Keep the soil moist.

4. Many kinds of seeds germinate within two weeks. Radish and bean seeds grow especially quickly. Cuttings of many kinds of plants should root in two to four weeks. (Cuttings from plants like coleus and philodendron can be rooted in water alone.)

5. Place coarse sand or pebbles in the bottom of pots for drainage.

6. Transplant the seedlings or rooted cuttings into the pots. Place the pots on a tray to collect excess water.

7. Water occasionally. Do not over-water. Rotting stems and roots and yellow or brown leaves can indicate overwatering.

8. Place the plants in a warm, lighted area. Leaf-curling is a sign of too much heat. Dropping leaves often indicates a lack of humidity.

9. Add a weak solution of plant food every two to three months to supply nutrients.

Check Facilities and Equipment

Surveying your facilities and knowing what you have to work with is a very important step in managing the success and safety of your students. You'll need to keep in mind the number of students in each class and how many labs you'll be teaching.

If you are not the only teacher using the science classroom and lab facilities, you and your colleagues should complete the survey of lab facilities as a team. If you have more than one lab facility available, you might wish to consider setting up each one for a specific use. Your school can realize savings if you set up Earth science equipment in one lab, physical science equipment in another, and life science materials in a third.

You might find that a portable demonstration cart, as shown in **Figure A.4**, will add flexibility to your teaching. If each teacher has a cart, he or she can move his or her cart to a specific lab facility as needed, or use it for demonstrations in the classroom. The cart also can be used for small group activities. Demonstration carts are available from scientific suppliers. They usually contain a work space, sink, propane gas torch or burner, water reservoir, and storage cabinet. **WARNING:** *Do NOT store hazardous materials in the cart.*

Figure A.4

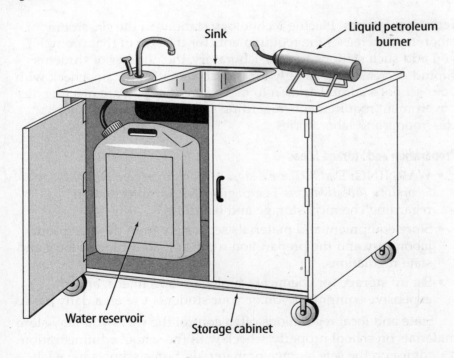

Sink

Liquid petroleum burner

Water reservoir

Storage cabinet

Facilities Specifications

This section presents information on various aspects of school science buildings, such as recommended amounts of space for student work areas and storage needs for a well-managed science classroom/lab. This section also gives basic specifications for built-in features for fire control and air quality.

Space Requirements Overcrowding is a leading cause of lab accidents, and it interferes with student learning. Space requirements include a minimum amount of space for student work areas and room for separate storage and preparation areas. Check with your school's administration to make sure that your laboratory area meets your local and state regulations regarding space requirments. Making sure that there is sufficient space for student's to work safely is an important consideration in setting up your laboratory area and your classrooms.

Student Work Areas Generally, state regulations stipulate a certain amount of square footage per student per instruction level or a certain number of students per laboratory. The net square footage includes exposed storage space, such as cabinets or shelving. The square footage does NOT include hallway space, storage closets, or preparation offices. Check these regulations to be certain that your space requirements comply.

Technology Stations Placing technology stations in the classroom laboratory increases the requirements for the size of that room. If you add such stations to your laboratory, the number of students should decrease accordingly for the lab activities. Again, check with your school's administration to make sure that you are meeting all government requirements regarding space allocations in your classrooms and laboratories.

Preparation and Storage Areas

- **WARNING:** *Do NOT use a storage room to prepare materials for laboratory investigations.* See pages 70–72for information regarding chemical storage and handling.
- Store equipment and materials separately from the classroom laboratory and the preparation room and according to local and state regulations.
- Set up storage for chemicals, biological specimens, and expensive equipment you or your students use on a daily basis.

State and local regulations often control the ways you may store materials on school property. Check with the school administration for advice on the safe storage of materials. Some schools have lab-prep personnel who help maintain science material inventories and who also help set up laboratory investigations. If your school employs these people, they should be aware of all government regulations. They are a good source of information about laboratory safety and the proper storage of science materials. There are also printed and internet sources of information that can guide you in the safe storage of materials.

Fire Control Features In the event of fire, science classrooms must meet minimum requirements set by the National Fire Protection Association (NFPA) and local fire officials. These include such requirements as:

- Each science room, preparation room, and equipment/materials storage room MUST have two clearly marked emergency exits. One of the exits in a ground-floor room may be a window if it is large enough for an adult to escape through.
- Fire extinguishers should be placed at eye level at every exit. See page 76 regarding specifications for fire extinguishers.
- All rooms should have a sprinkler system.
- All rooms should have a smoke alarm.
- There MUST be a general fire alarm system throughout the building.
- You MUST post and practice fire-drill procedures.
- Keep a fire blanket at eye level near each fire extinguisher. Clearly mark it, and make it easily accessible. See page 76 for more information on fire blankets.
- All utilities should have a master cut-off control switch. These should be easily accessible by teachers but not so handy to students. Label the controls clearly to mark to the room location and type of utility.
- **WARNING:** *Do NOT use stairways and hallways as storage areas.*
- **WARNING:** *NEVER block access to exits, emergency equipment, control switches, and so forth.*

Electrical Systems Apart from the danger of electrical shocks, fires in the classroom laboratory commonly result from misuse of electrical power and equipment. Follow local and state government building codes in all cases regarding sources of electricity and the kinds of outlets that are safe to use in laboratories. Give special consideration to laboratory areas that also have sources of water. An electrical contractor in your area will be aware of all building codes relating to the safe installation and maintenance of all electrical outlets. Make sure that you have a fire extinguisher that is rated for use in putting out electrical fires in any areas where people will be working with electricity.

Air Quality Control Science Classrooms, Laboratories, Fume Hoods, and Storage Areas Proper ventilation systems contribute to a safe environment for you and your students. These systems will vary depending on the use of the classroom and laboratories involved. Follow all government regulations that regulate ventilation equipment in any areas of your school that are used for science investigations, as well as for material storage. These areas will have different regulations than other parts of your school's building. In most cases, the class, laboratory, and storage areas need ventilation equipment that provides for a rapid exchange of air. These regulations are designed to prevent the toxic buildup of gases that laboratory work can produce. You can obtain additional safety information from American National Standards Institute (ANSI) Z9.5.

A

Remember, when dealing with things like fire control features, electical systems, and air quality control, your local fire officials can be one of your best sources of information regarding local requirements.

Safety Equipment Specifications

The same general guidelines for investigation equipment apply to safety equipment. You can group safety equipment according to use. You use one group of equipment for personal protection as a precaution. Another group contains the equipment you will need to deal with accidents if they occur. You can find details for the appropriate use of this equipment in the section titled "Emergency Response" on pages 80–83.

Personal Protection Equipment You MUST wear personal protection equipment if there is a chance of exposure to harmful substances. Some school districts require all individuals to put on goggles and aprons before they enter the laboratory.

Eyewear All lab activities, in the laboratory or out, require safety goggles. Check your local and state regulations for the preferred code. This code will appear on the frames and lenses. Several types of eyewear are available. They are NOT the same. The type of eyewear you and your students wear MUST be appropriate to the activity.

- Chemical safety goggles should be large enough to protect the eyes and form a seal around them. Chemical safety goggles should also be able to form a seal around eyeglasses without affecting the vision correction afforded by the eyeglasses. **WARNING:** *Contact lenses can trap chemicals (even vapors) against the cornea and cause damage. It is best not to wear contact lenses in a lab that requires chemical safety goggles.*
- Laser goggles are rated for the wavelength and power of a particular laser (see page 80). One type of goggles is NOT automatically usable with any type of laser. **WARNING:** *Chemical safety goggles are NOT suitable for work with lasers.*
- **WARNING:** *NO devices are approved to protect the eyes against direct viewing of the Sun.*

Gloves Wear gloves to protect hands against heat, sharp objects, chemicals, body fluids, and so forth. **WARNING:** *One kind of glove will NOT protect hands against all hazards. Certain gloves can dissolve when they come in contact with a solvent.* Make sure the glove type is appropriate for the activity. Supplier catalogs often include a list rating of the effectiveness of certain materials in protecting against particular substances. As an alternative, refer to the manufacturer's MSDS (see page 55) if there is a question regarding which type of glove to use with a certain chemical.

- *Polyethylene gloves* protect hands against light corrosives and irritants.
- *Latex gloves* protect against biological materials. Change them as soon as they show soil. **WARNING:** *Some people have an allergic reaction to latex.*

- *Hypoallergenic latex gloves,* while more expensive than regular latex, are available. You can also wear cotton gloves beneath latex, neoprene, and nitrile gloves to protect against irritation.
- *Natural rubber gloves* help protect against electrical shock and light corrosives.
- *Neoprene gloves* provide protection against mineral acids and alcohols.
- *Nitrile gloves* are resistant against solvents, punctures, and abrasion.
- *Oven mitts* should be used when dealing with heat sources and heated materials or extreme cold.

Clothing/Body Protectors Wear laboratory aprons and coats to protect skin and clothing from spilled materials that might be hazardous. Protective clothing comes in many types of material.

- Aprons and lab coats made of multiple layers offer protection from permeation.
- **WARNING:** *Check to be sure that the protective material is flame retardant.*
- Aprons should have bibs that tie closely to the lower part of the neck. They should cover the body at least to the knees. Wear them over clothing. Wear clothing in lab that covers the arms and fits closely.

Face Masks Face masks offer protection against dust, allergens, and vapors. Some people are allergic to odors that might not be classified as hazardous to most people. Masks are available that offer varying degrees of protection, depending upon the need.

Waste Disposal Containers Equip every lab with the proper containers for the various kinds of waste that you and your students might produce. For example, biohazardous sharp objects must be placed in a puncture-proof container. Properly label waste containers and place them in a location that is convenient but out of the way of heavy traffic. Waste containers require proper storage and ventilation.

Accident Response Equipment This section deals with the specifications for accident response equipment. See page 83 for procedures for using the equipment.

Eyewash Stations An eyewash station MUST be available where chemicals are used, including classrooms and preparation rooms. An eyewash station should be reachable within 10 seconds (or 25 feet) by anyone in the classroom who has been splashed. It is best practice to wash chemicals from the eyes as soon as possible. Plumbed fixtures that deliver large quantities of water quickly are generally more efficient than plastic squeeze bottles. Dilute the chemical in the eye or eyes as quickly as possible. You should follow all state and local guidelines when installing eyewash equipment.

A

Safety Showers Many schools have safety showers in their laboratories, especially in chemistry laboratories. These showers deliver a large amount of water to quickly wash chemicals that may have splashed or spilled on a person working in the laboratory. Like eyewash stations, safety showers deliver a large amount of water quickly. This large volume of water dilutes the chemicals that spilled. You should follow all government regulations regarding the installation and maintenance of saftey showers.

Fire Blankets Specially treated wool fire blankets should be available in all science laboratories where hazardous chemicals are used or stored.

Fire Extinguishers Every classroom and laboratory should have fire extinguishers. In cases of large areas, several fire extinguishers might be needed. Check with local authorities to make sure that your classrooms and laboratories comply with all fire department regulations. Using proper equipment is extremely important in fighting fires. There are several classes of fire extinguishers, and each one effectively quenches a specific type of fire. Fire extinguishers are labeled for the class of fire for which you should use them. Remember to check extinguishers at the beginning of the school year to make sure that the material in the extinguisher is still able to put out a fire. In many localities, a professional service or the local fire department inspects and labels fire extinguishers.

Table 1

Fire Class	Methods of Extinction		Precautions
Class A: ordinary solid combustibles (paper, wood)	Water	Dry chemical class ABC fire extinguisher	NEVER use water on class B, C, or D fires.
Class B: flammable liquids (acetone, alcohol, ethers, grease)		Class B or dry chemical class ABC fire extinguisher	
Class C: electrical or static charges		Class C or dry chemical class ABC fire extinguisher	The extinguishing material in a Class C extinguisher will not conduct electricity. C is always used with other letters on an extinguisher.
Class D: combustible metals (magnesium, postassium, sodium)	Dry, clean sand	Class D fire extinguisher	Dry, clean sand is suitable for small fires; NEVER use water on combustible metals—some might react violently with water.

Materials for Chemical-Spill Cleanup Cleanup materials should be items that quickly absorb liquids or substances that neutralize an acid or caustic spill. Cleanup materials are available from chemical supply companies. Follow state and local regulations for materials and procedures to follow for chemical spills.

First Aid Kits Keep first-aid supplies readily at hand. A capable person can give immediate aid while waiting for the school nurse or emergency squads. At a minimum, supplies should include the following (see page 84–87 for first aid procedures):

- Recommended items for first-aid kits:
  - disposable gloves (latex or plastic)
  - antiseptic
  - disinfectant
  - bleach (at time needed, prepare a solution of 1 part bleach to 10 parts water)
  - disposable towels
  - sterile gauze for covering open wounds
  - medical tape
  - scissors
  - adhesive bandages for covering small wounds
  - plastic bags for holding contaminated waste
- Items NOT recommended for first-aid kits
  - iodine **WARNING:** *Iodine can cause tissue damage.*
  - ice pack compress **WARNING:** *Swelling of soft tissues should be examined by a physician.*
  - ammonia inhalants **WARNING:** *If person is unconscious, get help immediately.*
  - tourniquet **WARNING:** *Use hand pressure until medical assistance is available. Wear protective gloves and a thick gauze pad to avoid contact with blood.*

Local authorities might recommend additional materials. Check with your local Red Cross for assistance. In many areas, they might be willing to conduct a survey of your classrooms and laboratories and make recommendations about appropriate first aid materials to keep on hand. Your school nurse or physician can also make suggestions about materials that you should keep readily accessible for emergencies.

A

Safety Requirements for Investigation Equipment

Following some basic precautions regarding laboratory equipment can greatly reduce common hazards. See pages 45–51 for safe techniques in the use of investigation equipment and materials.

General Equipment Guidelines

- Keep manufacturer's instructions for proper usage techniques as well as safety precautions for equipment.
- Protect equipment from dust, humidity, and extreme temperatures, especially electronic equipment and microscopes.
- In earthquake-prone areas, clamp equipment to the table top.
- All electrical equipment should be 110-volt approved by Underwriters Laboratory or other equivalent. Locate all outlets, surge protectors, and cords well above floor level.
- Work surfaces should NOT have cracks or areas inaccessible to cleaning.
- All work surfaces should be water-, heat-, and chemical-resistant.
- Control noise levels. Sustained noises above 80 decibels can cause or lead to hearing damage. **Table 2** shows guidelines regarding exposure to noise.

Table 2

Sound Level Limits			
Sound level (decibels)	Exposure limit	Typical source	Resulting hearing damage (after exposure limit)
150	0 s	jet plane taking off	ruptured ear drum
120	7 min 30 s	chain saw, live rock music	pain and serious damage
110	30 min	power saw, rock music	
105	1 h	snow blower	
100	2 h	woodworking shop	serious damage
95	4 h	electric drill	
90	8 h	tractor	damage
85	8 h	electric shaver	possible damage
80	None	mini-bike	

Specific Guidelines for Commonly Used Equipment

Heat Sources

- Hot plates with a flat surface (NOT coils) are recommended for heat sources. **WARNING:** *Hot plates stay hot after they are unplugged or turned off. Some hot plates have warning lights to show they are hot.* Be sure that you have an adequate number of outlets for the hot plates (one outlet per hot plate).

- A high temperature burner with a grid produces excellent results for bending glass. If your laboratory has gas burners, you and your students MUST use them with the appropriate type of gas. A manual central cut-off valve should be accessible to the teacher. **WARNING:** *NEVER use open flames when a flammable solvent is in the same room.*

- Alcohol burners are NOT recommended. **WARNING:** *Alcohol burners can explode in the event of a fire. If you must use an alcohol burner, see* page 45 *regarding proper procedures for doing so.*

Thermometers Digital thermometers are recommended. Some cities now prohibit the sale of mercury thermometers. If accuracy requires you to use a mercury thermometer, use one with a coating that helps contain the mercury even if the glass breaks. **WARNING:** *Mercury exposure to can cause nerve damage and developmental problems in small children.* (See pages 87–88 regarding the proper disposal of mercury thermometers and cleanup of mercury spills.)

Refrigerators Cold storage is often recommended for certain materials, such as biological specimens and some flammable solvents. Specifications for laboratory refrigerators include the following:

- An explosion-proof refrigerator is recommended for storing flammable materials. These refrigerators have modified internal wiring and sealed motors and switches to prevent sparks. **WARNING:** *Control switches and defroster heaters in a home refrigerator can spark, which can ignite flammable materials.*

- A refrigerator used for storing radioactive materials MUST have the standard symbol for radioactivity on the door. The refrigerator should be checked periodically for radioactive contamination. **WARNING:** *NEVER store food in a science storage refrigerator.*

- In earthquake-prone areas, refrigerators should have secure closing devices. Older magnetic locks have not always proved effective during earthquakes.

Glassware Most injuries in the classroom laboratory are cuts that result from broken glassware. Use the proper kinds of glassware in order to greatly reduce the chance of injuries. (See pages 49 and 53 for safe techniques and cleanup procedures.)

- Glassware should be heat-resistant.
- Glassware also should offer resistance to chemicals and accidental breakage.

Batteries

- Alkaline or dry-cell batteries are recommended for classroom use.
- Use storage batteries only when you need a larger DC current. **WARNING:** *Storage batteries contain acid and have the ability to deliver sufficient current to cause wire insulation to ignite.*

Lasers The Bureau of Radiological Health classifies lasers according to the amount of power they emit—Class I to Class IV. Those recommended for secondary schools are Class II and III-A lasers. **WARNING:** *Even low-powered lasers may cause eye damage.* (See page 74 for the proper type of goggles for use with lasers.)

Acceleration Models Two common types of acceleration models are rockets and steam engines. Following safety standards and procedures can reduce hazard levels, which include the possibility of hearing damage.

- **Rockets** Some common recommendations for rockets include the following:
  - Rockets should be made of lightweight materials.
  - The rocket, including the engine, should NOT weigh more than 453 g.
  - The engine should NOT contain more than 133 g of propellant.
  - Use only a solid propellant and a factory-made engine.
  - Remote-controlled launches in open areas are recommended; students should be at least 5 m from the rocket.

  WARNING: *Students should NOT rework or reload the engines; an explosion could result.*

- **Steam Engines** Steam engines with solid fuel burners are recommended for classroom laboratories. **WARNING:** *Alcohol fuel is NOT recommended. Pure alcohol burns with an invisible flame. If you add additional alcohol to the burner because it appears the flame has gone out, vapors and the stock can of alcohol can ignite.*

Emergency Response

Many of the tools and chemicals in the science laboratory can cause injury or allergic reactions if you use them without proper attention and care. Allergic reactions can be in the form of swelling or hives, muscle cramps, disorientation, unconsciousness, and death from shock or suffocation. Even with the best efforts at prevention, emergencies still occur. Therefore, along with practicing effective safety measures, you also must be prepared to act quickly according to the given situation.

Obtain medical help in every case of serious injury or illness, in all cases of injury to the eye, and whenever in doubt. **WARNING:** *A teacher should NOT diagnose or treat injury or illness, or offer medication, but should offer necessary first aid until medical help is obtained.* After you contain an emergency, file an accident report whenever there is any injury to a student and/or property damage, even if an accident report is not required (see page 110 for a sample form).

Very First Steps

In cases of emergency, seemingly different responses need to take place simultaneously—calling 911 or other emergency number, getting the school nurse, using the safety equipment, administering first aid, and so on. Memorize the following first steps as they pertain to different kinds of emergencies.

1 **Keep calm** in all cases and **call 911** or other emergency number.

2 **In case of injury,** send a student to get the school nurse, if available, or the principal.

* If the victim is not breathing, restore breathing if you have the training to do so.
* Stop any bleeding by applying a light pressure, wearing protective gloves. **WARNING:** *If an object is in the wound, do NOT remove the object.*
* Prevent shock. A clean fire blanket is useful for keeping an accident victim warm to help prevent shock (see pages 81–82).
* Contact the parent or guardian as soon as possible.

3 In case of fire, begin evacuation and sound the alarm immediately.

4 In case of chemical spill, place affected student in the safety shower or use eyewash station if the spill affects the eyes (see page 83).

First Steps in Detail

In Case of Injury If a student receives a wound that causes severe bleeding or if the student is unconscious, send for the nurse and call 911 or another emergency number. If the injury is severe but the victim is ambulatory, accompany the person to the nurse's office. The nurse should

* administer additional first aid;
* contact the injured person's parent or guardian;
* pursue additional treatment as needed;

If a nurse is not available, contact a parent or guardian and advise him or her of the accident's severity and obtain permission to proceed with treatment as needed.

If you cannot reach a parent or guardian, you must act in accordance with the seriousness of the situation. If an emergency medical form (see page 109) exists that grants permission for emergency health care to be administered, call a physician. On the physician's advice, seek treatment for the injured student.

In Case of Shock Causes of shock include electrical charges from equipment and outlets and from lightning, severe allergic reactions, and other illnesses. A person suffering from shock might be unconscious, dazed, weak, and/or confused, or might even stop breathing. If you witness a student going into shock, you should

* call for emergency medical aid immediately;
* check for breathing and pulse immediately;
* keep the injured person warm, quiet, and lying down;
* elevate the feet a few inches if there are no chest or head injuries;

A

- start CPR if necessary and if you are trained to do so;
- if the shock is from electricity, carefully separate the person from the electrical source. **WARNING:** *Make sure you have dry hands and are not standing on a wet floor.* **WARNING:** *Do NOT use a metal object or other conducting material to separate the victim from the power source.*
- use the master control switch to shut off the electricity;
- check for entrance and exit burns; treat burns as you would a thermal burn, keeping in mind that some burns might be large and below the skin.

See pages 86–87 for first aid measures.

In Case of Fire

- Evacuate the students, sound the fire alarm, shut off master switches in the classroom for gas and electrical power (if available), close windows and doors if possible, and then determine whether it is feasible to try to put out the fire. Be informed regarding which type of fire extinguisher to use (see page 76) and the proper use of fire blankets (see page 76). **WARNING:** *If the fire is spreading or could block the escape route, leave immediately and let professionals fight the fire.*
- You can use cloth towels or fire blankets to smother a small fire.
- Inform students of the priority to first stop, then drop, and then roll in order to put out clothing fires.
- **WARNING:** *Do NOT use a fire extinguisher on a person, as serious chemical burns or frostbite can result.*

In Case of Chemical Spills
If a chemical spill occurs in the laboratory or in the classroom, quick action can reduce the possibility of injury to a student or teacher. A chemical spill such as a liter bottle of hydrochloric acid breaking in the chemistry laboratory is considered a major spill.

- Immediately evacuate all students through the exits farthest from the spill. Fumes from a chemical spill can cause severe damage to the body.
- Immediately assist any person splashed with the chemical to the safety shower (see page 76).
- Turn on the emergency exhaust fan.
- Contain the spill wearing the proper protective clothing. **WARNING:** *Do NOT allow the spill to trap you.*
- Call for help. The school safety plan should contain the numbers of agencies or departments in your community that will assist in containment and removal of the chemical.
- For materials entering the eye, rush to the eye wash station. The first response prior to medical treatment for a student or teacher who has hazardous material in the eye is to flush with water to dilute chemicals, wash out debris, or irrigate the eyes. (See below for techniques for using the eyewash station.)
- In case of mercury spills, provide maximum ventilation and avoid all contact with skin, clothing, or shoes. See pages 87–88 for measures regarding cleanup.

- In case of biological contamination, use gloves during first aid and in cleaning up blood and other bodily fluids. See page 89 for instructions on the proper disposal of contaminated items.

Using Accident Response Equipment

Eyewash Stations

- Begin washing the face, eyelids, and eyes as soon as possible, and continue for at least 15 min. The eyelids should be open, rotating the eyes as much as possible so water can flow on all surfaces and in the folds surrounding the eyeballs to ensure removal of the chemical.
- **WARNING:** *Do NOT rely on spray bottles as a substitute for eyewash stations.*
- **WARNING:** *Contact lenses, if worn, should be removed immediately if at all possible. Begin flushing even if contacts cannot be removed.*
- If the injured person is lying down, gently hold the eyelids open and pour water from the inner corner of the eye outward. **WARNING:** *Do NOT allow the chemical to run into the other eye.*
- In the case of an alkaline burn or any other serious eye injury, immediately send for an ambulance so that first aid will not have to be discontinued during transport to medical facilities.

Safety Showers

- Begin use of the shower as soon as possible, removing any contaminated clothing while in the shower (have large towels or lab coats available for privacy).
- The victim should remain in the shower for a minimum of 15 minutes, washing the skin with water or with soap and water for some organic chemical splashes. Cool water is fine; it slows chemical reactions and is good first aid for burns.
- **WARNING:** *AVOID using neutralizing solutions unless recommended by medical personnel.*

Fire Blankets To use a fire blanket, follow the manufacturer's recommended technique of wrapping the victim to extinguish the fire. **WARNING:** *Incorrect use could hold heat near the body, increasing the possibility of burns.*

- For a folded fire blanket stored in a case, spread the blanket on the floor so that the affected person can wrap it around his or her body while rolling.
- For a fire blanket in a vertical wall case, the blanket will unroll from the case as the person wraps the blanket around his or her body. As soon as the blanket is out of the case, the person should lie on the floor to prevent a "chimney effect."

In both cases, hold the blanket tight at the neck to force flames away from the head.

First-Aid Kits Students should be aware of the location of the first-aid kit, but a teacher should be the one to administer first aid. Keep first-aid kits in a conspicuous place in the classroom or the laboratory. Mark this location clearly.

Giving First Aid

First aid is the first assistance provided to a person suffering an accident or a sudden illness. Persons giving first aid should seek NOT to treat the victim but rather to protect him or her until professional medical assistance arrives. Every teacher bears the responsibility for knowing how to help a student in the case of an accident or illness.

It is strongly recommended that teachers take a first-aid course with CPR training. Some states require that at least some teachers in a school be formally trained in first aid. Check school regulations regarding the training of students in using emergency equipment, such as the safety showers and eyewash stations. **WARNING:** *Anyone administering first aid should wear protective gloves.*

This section provides general procedures for injuries most commonly related to school laboratory work. Most injuries are minor cuts and burns to the hands. Many injuries occur when students are cleaning glassware. In addition to the possibility of injury from broken glass, there is the threat of injury from the cleaning solution or the chemical substance used with the glassware.

Cuts and Scratches

- Wash the injured area thoroughly.
- Place a compress on the wound to stop the flow of blood. **WARNING:** *Do NOT disturb blood clotting by removing saturated cloth, simply add more layers until bleeding slows or stops.*
- Replace a compress with a sterile bandage if the injury is minor. **WARNING:** *Do NOT use any topical medications unless advised to do so by a physician.*
- Accompany the student to the nurse's office if he or she has a moderate to severe injury.
- **WARNING:** *In case of severe cuts, do NOT use a tourniquet unless you are trained to do so and then only as a last resort.*
- Follow proper procedures to clean up blood (see pages 88–89).

Seizures, Fainting Spells, Concussions, and Shock

- Leave the person lying down. Loosen any tight clothing and keep crowds away. Call the nurse immediately.
- Call for emergency medical aid immediately.
- Check for breathing and pulse immediately.
- Keep the injured person warm, quiet, and lying down. Elevate the feet a few inches if there are no chest or head injuries.
- Start CPR if necessary.

Injuries from Chemical Spills

- Rush the injured person to the safety shower. Immediately drench the entire injured area with a continuous flow of water.
- Send a student to alert the school nurse or to get another teacher.
- Use a spill kit to contain and remove the chemicals.

Eye Injuries from Foreign Substances

- Rush the student to the dual eyewash station. Remember to guide the student as he or she will have difficulty seeing.
- Rinse the open eyes with a continuous stream of water for 15 minutes.
- Send a student to alert the school nurse or another teacher.

Exposure to Toxic Substances

- Rush the person to the nurse's office and call 911 or other emergency number. The person calling for medical assistance should know the victim's age and weight, the toxic substance involved, the amount taken, whether any first aid has been given, whether the victim has vomited, and how long it will take to get the victim to the hospital.
- The nurse should also contact the Poison Control Center immediately.
- If CPR is required, a mouth-to-mask resuscitator should be used to protect the person administering aid from being affected by the hazardous substance as well.
- **WARNING:** *Toxic substances can enter the body by inhalation, ingestion, injection, or skin contact.*

Inhaled Poisons

- Call for medical assistance.
- Carry the victim to fresh air if possible. If the victim is too large to carry, open all doors and windows.
- Begin CPR if the victim is not breathing, but only if you are trained to do so. **WARNING:** *Do NOT inhale victim's breath.*
- Treat the victim for shock until medical assistance arrives. (See page 84.)

Ingested Poisons

- Consult the MSDS (see page 55) filed in your department.
- Call for medical assistance.
- Maintain the victim's breathing.
- **WARNING:** *Do NOT administer syrup of ipecac to induce vomiting, or water or milk for dilution of the poison, unless advised to do so by a physician or the Poison Control Center.*
- Take the container of poison to the medical facility.

Skin Contact Poisons

- Remove contaminated clothing as soon as possible if contact is made with a plant poison (such as poison ivy oils). Wear rubber gloves if you are helping a student. Immediately wash all exposed areas with large quantities of soap and water.
- See section regarding the treatment of chemical burns of the skin and eyes (page 82).

Chemical Burns If the chemical is a strong corrosive, irritant, or is toxic, immediately send for an ambulance so that first aid will not have to be discontinued during transport to medical attention. This is especially important for strong alkali (such as sodium hydroxide) burns.

- Use rubber gloves to remove victim's clothing.
- As quickly as possible, place the student in the safety shower for at least 15 minutes.
- Call the nurse and 911.
- **WARNING:** *Do NOT attempt to neutralize the chemical unless approved by medical personnel and the chemical is first diluted with water.*
- Wash chemical burns to the eyes, eyelids, and face at the eyewash station for at least 15 minutes.
- Remove contact lenses if at all possible.
- Cover burns with a sterile dressing (NOT fluff cotton).

Thermal (Heat) Burns Identify the severity (whether first-, second-, or third-degree) of the injury to the body and follow the appropriate first-aid procedure.

First-Degree Burns These are the least severe burns, affecting the outer layer of the epidermis only. They are characterized by redness and heat and commonly cause itching, burning, and pain in the victim.

- Hold burn under cool running water for 5 minutes.
- Cover burn with a clean dressing.

Second-Degree Burns These burns affect deeper layers of the epidermis. They are characterized by mottled red skin and blisters. Second-degree burns cause considerable pain and the loss of bodily fluids through blisters. The victim is at risk for infection and might require hospitalization.

- Lay clean towels over the burned areas and pour cool water over the towels. **WARNING:** *Do NOT add ice or salt to the water.*
- Gently blot the area dry. **WARNING:** *Do NOT break blisters, remove tissue, or apply ointments, sprays, or salves.*
- Cover the burned area with a clean, dry dressing.
- **WARNING:** *If legs are affected, keep them elevated.*

Third-Degree Burns These are the most severe burns, affecting skin as well as deeper tissue. Third-degree burns appear white or charred and cause little pain due to the damage caused to nerve endings. The victim may lose internal fluids and is at high risk for infection, and usually will require extensive hospitalization.

- Call 911 or other emergency number.

- Call the school nurse.
- Treat for shock (see page 81).
- **WARNING:** *Do NOT remove burnt clothing.*
- **WARNING:** *Do NOT cover burns with dressing.*

Bites and Stings

- Wear gloves while attending bites. **WARNING:** *There is danger of infections and rabies from bites of all warm-blooded animals.*
- Identify the source of the bite or sting.
- If the bite or sting is from a venomous source, seek medical help immediately.
- Keep the victim calm and quiet. Keep injury area lower than the heart. **WARNING:** *Do NOT apply ice.*

Venomous Snake Bites **WARNING:** *Do NOT administer treatment unless a hospital is more than one hour away. If it is, then apply constricting bands. Check pulse to be sure blood flow has not stopped.*

- **WARNING:** *Incision and suction are NOT recommended.*
- If you have a field trip planned for an area where snakebite is possible and medical help will not be nearby, have a snakebite kit available and obtain training in its use.

Tick Bites Ticks should only be removed by parents or guardians. Contact them as soon as possible, and advise them to seek medical help, especially if the victim becomes ill within a week of the bite.

In Case of Allergic Reactions

- Get immediate medical help if the victim has a history of allergies. (See page 109 for a sample medical emergency form.)
- Keep the victim as quiet as possible.
- Use cold compresses (or ice wrapped in a cloth) to relieve swelling.
- If the allergic reaction was the result of an insect sting, remove the stinger with a scraping motion using a stiff card or fingernail to reduce toxin injection. **WARNING:** *Do NOT pull the stinger out.*
- Wash the bite area with soap and water. Apply calamine lotion (or a paste of water and baking soda).
- Treat for shock if the allergic reaction is severe.
- **WARNING:** *Any sting to the throat, mouth, or tongue requires medical help immediately.*

Human Bites

- Immediately notify parents/guardians of both parties. Medical records should be shared.
- Wash bite area with soap and water. Get medical treatment if the skin is broken.

Cleaning Up Hazardous Spills

Mercury **WARNING:** *Mercury thermometers are NOT recommended. If you still use them, and they break, use the following steps to clean up the spills. These are general guidelines for cleaning up a mercury spill. You should also* be aware of state and local regulations that apply in case a thermometer breaks and its mercury spills. You should ask students to leave the area of the spill before you begin your clean-up.

- A mercury sponge, which contains zinc fibers, is useful for final mercury cleanup. Wipe down all surrounding areas, as mercury tends to splatter.

- If preferred, the mercury may be sprinkled with zinc metal dust to form an amalgam which is more easily collected than elemental mercury. **WARNING:** *Take great care with zinc metal dust, as it expands when damp and can cause a container to explode.*

- If a commercial spill kit is not available,

  - On a hard surface, while you're wearing gloves, either use a stiff paper to brush the beads together or use a dropper to collect the beads. **WARNING:** *Do NOT sweep the mercury with a broom, as this creates more vapors and contaminates the broom.* Put all parts—the broken thermometer, the paper or dropper, and the beads of mercury—in a seamless polyethylene or polypropylene bottle or widemouthed jar for regulated disposal. Seal the container and place it in the toxic/caustic waste bin for proper disposal.

  - On a carpet, cut out and dispose of the mercury spill in a toxic/caustic container. **WARNING:** *Do NOT vacuum the mercury because it will cause the mercury to evaporate and become part of the atmosphere. Incinerating mercury also will cause it to become part of the atmosphere.*

- When you replace mercury thermometers with digital ones, dispose of the mercury thermometers as you would a mercury spill.

Other Chemical Spills If a chemical spill occurs in the laboratory or in the classroom, quick action by the teacher can reduce the possibility of injury to a student or the teacher. A chemical spill such as a liter bottle of hydrochloric acid breaking in the chemistry laboratory is considered a major spill.

- Immediately evacuate all students through the exits farthest from the spill. Fumes from a chemical spill can cause severe damage to the body. (See page 82 for treatment of injuries from chemical spills.)

- Turn on the emergency exhaust fan.

- Contain the spill wearing the proper protective clothing. **WARNING:** *Do NOT allow the spill to trap you.*

- Call for help. The school safety plan should contain the numbers of agencies or departments in your community that will assist in containment and removal of the chemical.

Biological Spills Biological spills that occur in a science laboratory or classroom can generate aerosols that can be dispersed in the air throughout the room. These spills can be very dangerous if they involve microorganisms that may be infectious. Any biological material, living or dead, that is a pathogen or disease-carrying organism is termed a biohazard. The biohazard symbol is universal and should be used on all potential pathogenic material. Any bodily fluids spattered during an accident or as a result of illness should be considered potentially infected. **WARNING:** *Blood spills should be cleaned by persons trained in the task. If an untrained person encounters a blood spill they should limit access to the area and call for assistance immediately.*

- **WARNING:** *AVOID direct skin contact with bodily fluids.*
- Use disposable gloves when direct hand contact with bodily fluids is necessary.
- Keep gloves in accessible locations.
- Wear mask and eye protection or face shield.
- Wear lab aprons or coats.
- Remove any contaminated clothing.
- Vigorously wash the exposed area with soap and water for one minute.
- Soak up the spill with paper towels.
- Place contaminated paper towels in a plastic bag for disposal. According to the Centers for Disease Control, infective waste should be either incinerated or autoclaved before disposal in a sanitary landfill. A school janitor should be familiar with the procedure for your district.
- Place sharp items such as needles and scalpel blades in a red biohazard container made especially for sharp objects.
- Glassware and microscope slides can be sterilized and reused. See pages 53–54.
- Clean any surface that has been in contact with the fluids with an EPA-approved disinfectant such as a freshly made 1:10 dilution of household bleach.
- After removing gloves, wash hands for 10 to 15 seconds with a disinfectant soap and running water.

Advantages of Small-Scale Chemistry

Several advantages result from scaling down the amount of chemicals used in investigations. By using small-scale chemistry, you will be able to do more experiments, save money, and have a safer working environment.

Economic Savings Reduced costs result from buying smaller quantities of chemicals and equipment. While buying a larger amount may make the unit price smaller, the total amount needed for small-scale chemistry will be greatly reduced, thus resulting in savings. Microscale glassware also will bring savings after the initial investment. For example, a microplate with 64 wells costs less than 64 test tubes and the test-tube racks needed to hold 64 test tubes.

Safety Using smaller quantities of chemicals results in smaller amounts of toxic vapors being released, smaller spills to clean up, and smaller amounts of vapors and materials that can contribute to fire hazards. Using plastic labware minimizes the hazards of glass. If a chemical reaction must be heated, hot water might provide the necessary heat. If greater heat is needed, use a hot plate. Microchemistry techniques rarely use open flames or burners.

Less Storage Space Microscale glassware and other equipment take up much less space than larger items. Having smaller amounts of chemicals and other substances saves shelf space in storage rooms and cabinets.

Less Waste Less hazardous waste is a great advantage to the environment. The cost of disposing of hazardous waste has been reduced.

Time Savings Using very small quantities of chemicals often reduces reaction times. For example, it takes less time to heat 20 mL to a desired temperature than it does to heat 200 mL.

The Microplate

The first item is a sturdy plastic tray called a microplate. The tray has shallow wells arranged in rows and columns. These wells are used instead of test tubes, flasks, and beakers. Some microplates have 96 wells; other microplates have 24 larger wells.

The Plastic Pipette

Small-scale chemistry uses a pipette made of a type of plastic that is soft and very flexible. The most useful property of the pipette is the fact that the stem can be stretched without heating into a thin tube. If the stem is stretched and then cut with scissors, the small tip will deliver a tiny drop of chemical. You may also use a pipette called a microtip pipette, which comes already stretched.

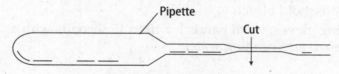

Cutting a stretched pipette

The pipette can be used over and over again simply by rinsing the stem and bulb in hot water between reagents. The plastic inside the pipette is non-wetting and does not hold water or solutions the way glass does.

The Microplate Template and Microplate Data Form

You should provide students with Microplate Templates and Microplate Data Forms whenever they carry out an activity that requires them.

To help with observations, students should place a Microplate Template beneath the 24-well or 96-well microplate. The template is marked with the correct number of wells, and labels on each row and column help guide the student with placement of chemicals from the micropipettes. The white paper background that the template provides allows the student to observe color changes and precipitate formations easily.

Use Microplate Data Forms to write down the chemicals used and to record observations of the chemical reactions that occur in each well.

Why Use Electronic Data Collection?

Electronic data-collection technology, or probeware, can greatly enhance learning experiences in the science classroom. This is not to say that stopwatches, metersticks, and spring scales no longer have a place in the classroom. Teaching students to use traditional measuring instruments is still important; however, teaching students to use probeware in our technology-filled world has become just as important. Below are some of the advantages electronic data collection can bring to the science classroom.

Probeware

- expedites data collection allowing students to spend more time analyzing results;
- provides more accurate readings and reduces student measurement errors when compared to traditional measuring instruments;
- allows students to perform experiments with instruments not previously obtainable in the classroom. Instruments include motion detectors, CO_2 gas sensors, accelerometers, and EKG sensors;
- permits students to continuously monitor experiments without requiring close attention. For example, a student may want to monitor CO_2 production from a plant over a 24-hour period;
- helps students directly measure values that were more indirectly measured in the past. For example, traditional experiments investigating the pressure/volume relationship in gases required students to infer the pressure from the amount of weight on a syringe. Using a gas pressure sensor, students can measure the pressure directly.

In addition, the use of probeware supports the shift from conventional teacher/student dialogue and teacher-centered instruction to a learning environment that is student-centered and inquiry-based.

According to the National Science Teachers Association (NSTA), technology should permit students to collect and analyze data as scientists do. Research shows that the use of probeware has a positive impact on student learning and achievement from elementary grades through college across all science disciplines. National organizations including NSTA, ISTE, ASTE, and IB call for the regular incorporation of technology, including probeware, in the science classroom. The National Education Technology Standards specifically recommend the use of scientific probeware with students when conducting real-time investigations of natural scientific phenomena.

Data Collection Hardware and Software

Although there are many electronic data-collection systems available, each system consists of four basic components—the computing platform, the data-collection software, the sensor interface, and the sensors. The newest systems combine these components, reducing the number of system pieces.

Computing Platform

The main component of a data-collection system is the computing platform. The computing platform can be a computer, a handheld computing device, or a graphing calculator.

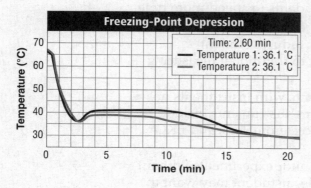

Freezing-Point Depression

Time: 2.60 min
Temperature 1: 36.1 °C
Temperature 2: 36.1 °C

Temperature (°C) vs. Time (min)

Data-Collection Software

The data-collection software provides control over the system. The software provides a way to monitor sensor readings, set data-collection parameters, initiate data collection, represent data graphically and numerically, and analyze data.

Sensor Interface

The sensor interface is a bridge between sensors and the computing platform. The main function of the interface is to control the data collection by providing power to the sensors, transferring sensor identification information to the data collection software, applying the data collection settings, and transferring the sensor readings to the data-collection software.

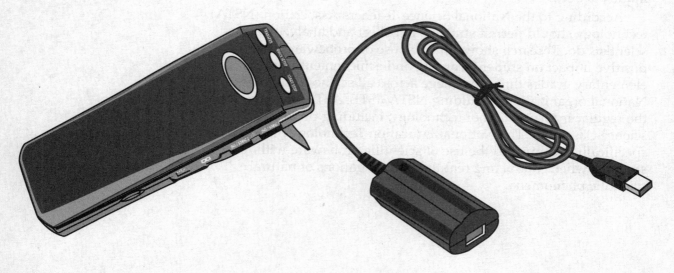

A

Sensors

Electronic sensors respond to changes in environmental conditions related to the physical attribute they are measuring. Many sensors include an integrated circuit chip that stores sensor identification and calibration information.

USB and Wireless Sensors

USB and wireless sensors have the sensor interface built into the sensor. These sensors connect directly to the computing platform or communicate with the platform wirelessly.

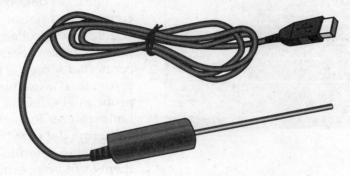

Stand-Alone Data Collection Systems

The newest data collection systems are all-in-one handhelds that include the computing platform, data collection software, and sensor interface. Many of these systems also include built-in sensors. While these systems have their own computing platforms, many can also be used with a computer.

Collect Data Using Probeware

Electronic data collection starts by connecting your data-collection system components together and launching the data collection software.

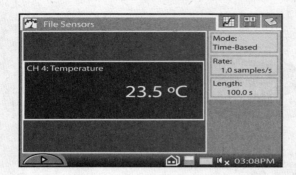

Setting Up Data Collection

For most data-collection systems, connecting a sensor is enough to enable you to collect data. Default data-collection settings based on the connected sensor(s) are set in the software. For example, a temperature probe might default to reporting temperatures in degrees Celsius and collecting data for 180 seconds. You can use the default settings or modify them to fit your experiment.

Sensor Settings

The sensor's displayed unit of measurement is the most commonly changed sensor setting. Other sensor setting options include zeroing and sensor calibration.

Data Collection Mode: Time-Based

The most frequently used data-collection mode is time-based. Use this mode for experiments where changes in the experimental variables occur over time. The settings associated with time-based data collection are described below.

- **Sample Rate** The number of data points collected each second. For some systems, the sample rate is entered as the time between samples. Acceptable sample rates depend on the sensor used and the sensor interface.

- **Number of Samples** The number of data points collected for each connected sensor. Depending on the data collection software, this value is either entered directly or is calculated based on the sample rate and experiment length. The maximum number of samples allowed depends on the available memory on your system.

- **Experiment Length** The time the system will be collecting data. Depending on the data collection software, this value is either entered directly or is calculated based on the sample rate and number of samples.

  Example: Consider the experiment in which you investigate changes in the temperature of 100 mL of room-temperature distilled water after adding an effervescent antacid tablet. Preliminary experimentation indicates that the reaction stops after two minutes. For this experiment, the time-based data collection settings could be:

  Sample Rate = 2 samples/second (0.5 seconds between samples)
  Number of Samples = 300
  Experiment Length = 150 seconds (2.5 minutes)

Data Collection Mode: Event-Based

Another data collection mode is event-based data collection. Event-based data collection allows you to manually control when each sample is collected. The sensor value reported is typically a single sensor reading but could be an average of several readings taken over time. The independent variable, representing the event, is entered manually, or it can be sequentially generated.

Example: Consider the experiment in which you want to investigate the pressure of a confined gas as it relates to the volume of the container. In this case, it is desirable to collect pressure measurements only after adjusting the container's volume. Since the changes in volume will not necessarily occur at equal time intervals, event-based data collection is used.

Collect the Data

Once the setup is complete, you are ready to collect data. Start data collection by interacting with the "Collect" or "Play" button or icon. Advanced start options such as triggering are available with some systems. Refer to your software documentation for details. A graph of the data is displayed during data collection.

Analyze the Data

You can analyze the collected data in many different ways. For many experiments, reading the information directly from the graph is enough. Other experiments require additional calculations, graph modifications, or modeling to interpret the data.

Tips for Successful Data Collection

The following are some tips that can help you use probeware successfully in your class.

Keep your system up-to-date.

To ensure you have the latest features and functionality available for your data-collection system, keep your data collection software up-to-date.

Know your sensors.

Here are some important things to know about the sensors you are using.

- **Sensor range:** the minimum and maximum values the sensor can measure
- **Response time:** the time it takes the sensor reading to show accurate measurements given a change in the measured quantity
- **Warm-up period:** the length of time a sensor must be powered before it will give accurate measurements
- **Damaging conditions:** conditions that would cause permanent damage to a sensor
- **Storage requirements:** conditions under which a sensor should be stored to ensure maximum life

Try it before you assign it.

This is especially important for anyone who is new to electronic data collection. Doing the experiment will help you identify places where students may encounter difficulty. Helping students avoid problems keeps the focus on the science and not the technology.

Troubleshooting

If you think that the probeware is in error, test the system in a more controlled way. For example, if you doubt the readings from a voltage sensor, connect it across a known DC source, such as a single AA battery. If it properly reads the voltage here, it is probably working in your experiment.

Sample Probeware Lab

On pages 97–98 you will find a sample probeware lab. All probeware labs include a Teacher Preparation page and the Probeware Activity pages.

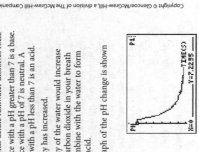

LAB Teacher Preparation
The Formation of Caves

Purpose
Students will learn how caves form when rainwater becomes acidic as it combines with carbon dioxide from the atmosphere and soil and then dissolves rock. They will use a probe to monitor the pH of water as they exhale into it with a straw, increasing the amount of carbon dioxide. By analyzing a graph showing changes in the water's acidity, students will understand the process that forms caves.

Time Requirements
one 45-minute class period

Advance Preparation
• Install the EasyData program on the graphing calculators.
• Check pH probes. If calibration is necessary, refer to the probe manual.

Safety Information
• This lab requires students to exhale through a straw for 30 seconds. Make sure students do not have a medical condition, such as asthma, that would prevent them from safely performing this activity.
• Under no circumstances should students use a straw that someone else has already used.
• Review all safety precautions in the lab and remind them to observe all laboratory rules.

Teaching Tips
• Lead students in a discussion about the definition of an acid. According to one definition, it is a substance that produces hydrogen ions in water.

• Prior to the lab, lead students in a discussion of the pH scale.
• Explain that several geological processes can form caves. This lab focuses on solution caves, formed when water rich in carbon dioxide seeps into cracks in carbonate rocks such as limestone. Water combines with carbon dioxide to form carbonic acid, which reacts with limestone.

$$H_2O + CO_2 \rightarrow H_2CO_3$$
$$H_2CO_3 + CaCO_3 \rightarrow 2HCO_3^- + Ca^{2+}$$

Extensions
Have students research how stalactites and stalagmites form in caves. Students can prepare a short report to present to the class.

Pre-Lab Answers
1. Rainwater becomes acidic as it combines with carbon dioxide from the atmosphere and soil. This acidic rainwater dissolves rock.
2. A substance with a pH greater than 7 is a base. A substance with a pH of 7 is neutral. A substance with a pH less than 7 is an acid.
3. The acidity has increased.
4. The acidity of the water would increase because carbon dioxide in your breath would combine with the water to form carbonic acid.

A sample graph of the pH change is shown below.

LAB Probeware Activity
The Formation of Caves

Many processes form caves. Powerful waves carve sea caves in rocks located next to the ocean. Lava flowing from volcanoes forms caves if the surface lava cools and hardens before the lava underneath stops flowing. The most common type of cave forms when underground layers of rock, such as limestone, are dissolved by acidic groundwater. In this process, rainwater absorbs carbon dioxide as it falls through the air. As the water seeps through the ground, it absorbs more carbon dioxide in soil pores. The rainwater becomes acidic because water and carbon dioxide form a weak acid known as carbonic acid. When this acidic water reaches bedrock, it seeps through cracks, dissolving the rock and creating open areas. Slowly, over many thousands of years, the water creates a cave in the rock. In this activity, you will demonstrate the effect of increasing the amount of carbon dioxide in water. The carbon dioxide in your breath will react with the water, similar to the way rainwater reacts with carbon dioxide as it falls to Earth and seeps through the soil.

What You'll Investigate
• How does an increase in carbon dioxide affect the acidity of water?
• How does the acidity of water lead to the formation of caves?

Goals
Predict how increasing the carbon dioxide in water will affect its acidity.
Measure the change in acidity of water as you exhale into it.
Analyze a graph to determine what chemical change has taken place.

Materials
CBL 2 or LabPro unit
TI graphing calculator
link cable
EasyData program
pH probe
timer
distilled water
600-mL beaker
wash bottle
plastic drinking straw

Safety Precautions
• Always wear safety goggles and a lab apron.

Pre-Lab Questions
1. Describe how rainwater can contribute to the formation of a cave.
2. Describe how the pH scale is used to determine whether a substance is basic or acidic.
3. Suppose you determine that a substance has a pH of 6. An hour later, it has a pH of 2. Has the acidity of the substance increased or decreased?
4. Predict how exhaling through a straw into water would affect the acidity of the water. Explain your answer.

Probeware Activity (continued)

Procedure

Part A: Preparing the CBL 2 or LabPro System

1. Set up the calculator and CBL 2 or LabPro unit, as shown in **Figure 1**. Plug the pH probe into channel 1 of the CBL 2 or LabPro unit. Start the EasyData application. Select ⌊File⌋ from the Main screen, and then select New to reset the application. The pH probe will be recognized automatically.

Figure 1

Straw   pH probe

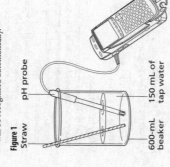

600-mL beaker   150 mL of tap water

2. Set up EasyData for data collection

   a. Select SETUP to set up the time interval between data points and the length of time data will be collected. Select ⌊Setup⌋ from the Main screen, then select **Time Graph...**

   b. Select ⌊Edit⌋ on the Time Graph Settings screen.

   c. Enter **5** as the time between samples in seconds.

   d. Select ⌊Next⌋.

   e. Enter **120** as the number of samples and select ⌊Next⌋.

   f. Select ⌊OK⌋ to return to the Main screen. One pH reading will be collected every 5 seconds for 600 seconds (10 minutes).

Part B: Collecting Data

1. Put 150 mL of tap water into the 600-mL beaker.

2. Remove the pH probe from the storage-solution bottle. Slide the cap and o-ring up the barrel of the probe to move them out of the way. Over a sink or empty beaker, use distilled water in a wash bottle to thoroughly rinse the probe. Set the solution bottle aside in a location where it will not be disturbed. Place the pH probe in the 600-mL beaker.

3. Allow the pH probe to remain in the water for one minute until the readings stabilize. During this time you will be able to see the pH reading on the screen.

4. Be sure the timer is set to count up. Select ⌊Start⌋ on the calculator to begin the 10-minute measurement. When you hear the tone indicating the measurement is beginning, start the timer.

5. When 30 seconds have passed, use the straw to exhale into the water for 30 seconds. Cup your hands over the beaker as you exhale to ensure that water doesn't splash out onto the calculator. Do not try to exhale continuously. Inhale through your nose and exhale through the straw at a natural pace.

6. After exhaling for 30 seconds, allow the pH probe to remain in the water, undisturbed for the remainder of the 10-minute measurement.

7. A graph showing changes in the water's pH during the measurement period will appear on the calculator screen. Sketch and label this graph in your Science Journal.

8. Use the right and left arrow keys to move the cursor along the data points. The time (x) and the corresponding pH (y) values will appear at the bottom of the screen. Write the selected values in the **Data Table**.

9. When you are finished, select ⌊Main⌋, then ⌊Quit⌋, then ⌊OK⌋.

Probeware Activity (continued)

Data Table: Selected pH Values

Time (s)	pH
0	
100	
200	
300	
400	
500	
600	

Cleanup and Disposal

1. Turn off the graphing calculator and disconnect the pH probe and the CBL 2 or LabPro unit. Rinse the end off the probe with distilled water and place the probe in the storage-solution bottle.

2. Follow your teacher's instructions for disposing of the contents of the beakers and returning all equipment to proper locations.

Conclude and Apply

1. Describe and explain what your graph looks like between 0 and 30 seconds. *During the first 30 seconds, the line is horizontal because the pH didn't change.*

2. Describe and explain the curve of your graph after 30 seconds. *Answers will vary. The graph should show a sharp drop at 30 seconds in response to exhaling in the water. This occurs because the carbon dioxide combines with water to form carbonic acid. The pH levels off when most of the carbon dioxide has reacted with the water.*

3. Explain how the results you obtained in this activity are similar to what happens when caves form. *In this activity, exhaling into water added carbon dioxide which caused the water's acidity to increase. Similarly, when rainwater falls through the atmosphere and then seeps through soil, it absorbs carbon dioxide which increases its acidity. This acidic water dissolves underground rock, forming caves.*

Electronic Data-Collection Providers

Vernier Software & Technology
13979 SW Millikan Way
Beaverton, OR 97005-2886
888-837-6437
info@vernier.com
www.vernier.com

Texas Instruments
Customer Support
P.O. Box 650311, MS 3962
Dallas, TX 75265
800-842-2737
ti-cares@ti.com
www.ti.com

PASCO Scientific
10101 Foothills Blvd.
P.O. Box 619011
Roseville, CA 95747-9011
800-772-8700
sales@pasco.com
www.pasco.com

Hewlett-Packard Company
Calculator Division
16399 W. Bernardo Dr.
San Diego, CA 92127-1899
800-HPINVENT (800-474-6836)
calceducation@hp.com
www.hp.com/calculators

Fourier Systems, Inc
9611 West 165th St., Suite 11b
Orland Park, IL 60467
877-266-4066
info@fourier-sys.com
www.fourier-sys.com

References

Flick, L., & Bell, R. 2000. Preparing tomorrow's science teachers to use technology: Guidelines for science educators. *Contemporary Issues in Technology and Teacher Education*, 1(1), 39–6

Metcalf, S. J., & Tinker, R. 2003. TEEMSS: Technology Enhanced Elementary and Middle School Science, Annual Meeting of the National Association for Research in Science Teaching, March 23–26, 2003, Philadelphia.

Mokros, J. & R. Tinker. 1987. The impact of microcomputer-based labs on children's ability to interpret graphs. *Journal of Research in Science Teaching*, 24(4) 369–383.

National Center for Educational Statistics. 2002. *Science Highlights: The Nation's Report Card 2000*. U.S. Department of Education, Jessup, MD.

National Science Teacher Association Board of Directors. 1999. NSTA Position Paper: The Use of Computers in Science Education. NSTA, Jessup, MD.

Weller, H. G. 1996. Assessing the Impact of Computer-based Learning in Science. *Journal of Research on Computing in Education*, 28(4), 461–484

Wetzell, David R., G. F. Varrella. 1999. Pre-Service Secondary Science Teachers' Concerns Regarding Use Of Calculator-Based Laboratory Scientific Probeware. September 26, 2007. Penn State, http://www.ed.psu.edu/CI/Journals/2000AETS/34wetzel_varrella.rtf

Sample Student Laboratory and Safety Guidelines Handout

You might wish to make a handout for students with safety information, like this example.

Regarding Emergencies

- Inform the teacher immediately of any mishap—fire, injury, broken glassware, chemical spills, and so on.
- Follow your teacher's instructions and your school's procedures in dealing with emergencies.

Regarding Your Person

- Do NOT wear clothing that is loose enough to catch on anything. Do NOT wear sandals or open-toed shoes.
- Wear protective safety gloves, goggles, and aprons as instructed.
- Always wear safety goggles (not glasses) when using hazardous chemicals.
- Wear goggles throughout the entire activity, including cleanup and handwashing.
- Keep your hands away from your face while working in the laboratory.
- Remove synthetic fingernails before working in the lab (these are highly flammable).
- Do NOT use hair spray, mousse, or other flammable hair products just before or during laboratory work where an open flame is used. (They can ignite easily.)
- Tie back long hair and loose clothing to keep them away from flames and equipment.
- Remove loose jewelry—chains or bracelets—while doing lab work.
- NEVER eat or drink while in the lab.
- NEVER store food in lab equipment or the lab refrigerator.
- Do NOT inhale vapors or taste, touch, or smell any chemical or substance unless your teacher instructs you to do so.

Regarding Your Work

- Read and complete the **Student Lab Safety Form** and have your teacher sign it before you begin the lab.
- Work ONLY on activities your teacher assigns.
- Use only those chemicals/substances your activity lists.
- Begin an activity only when your teacher directs you to do so.
- Handle equipment only when your teacher gives you specific permission.
- Remain in your own work area unless your teacher gives you permission to leave it.
- Point heated containers—test tubes, flasks, and so on—away from yourself and anyone else.
- Do NOT take any materials or chemicals out of the classroom.
- Enter storage areas only when your teacher instructs you to be there and supervises you.

- NEVER work alone in the laboratory.
- When using dissection equipment, always cut away from yourself and others. Cut downward, never stabbing at the object.
- Handle living organisms or preserved specimens only when your teacher authorizes you.
- Always wear heavy gloves when handling animals. If you are bitten, scratched, or stung, notify your teacher immediately.

Regarding Cleanup
- Keep work and lab areas clean.
- Limit the amount of easily ignitable materials you work with.
- Turn off all burners, including hot plates and other equipment, before leaving the lab.
- Carefully dispose of waste materials as your teacher instructs.
- Wash your hands thoroughly with soap and warm water after each activity.

Sample Student Laboratory Cleanup Checklist

A checklist such as this one can help ensure clean up after an activity is complete and safe.

_____ Promptly clean up your work area while still wearing your protective equipment.

_____ Turn off all hot plates or burners.

_____ Unplug electrical devices.

_____ Place all waste items in the proper disposal containers. NEVER wash anything down the sink drain unless your teacher instructs you to do so.

_____ Wash glassware with warm water and detergent. Then rinse the glassware several times with water, with a final rinse of distilled water.

_____ Wash the surface of your worktable.

_____ Return laboratory devices to their storage area as your teacher directs, carrying them properly.

_____ Wash your gloved hands with warm water and soap, being careful not to get water inside your gloves.

_____ Remove gloves by peeling them off your hands—start at the wrist and keep working toward the fingers. Do NOT let the outside surface of the glove touch the skin. Dispose of the gloves as directed by your teacher.

_____ After you remove your gloves, wash your hands in warm soapy water. Do NOT touch doorknobs, telephones, textbooks, your goggles, or other items until after you have removed your gloves and washed your hands.

_____ Remove your safety goggles after you have washed your hands.

_____ Wash and sterilize your goggles according to your teacher's instructions.

Student Lab Safety Form

Student Name: _____ Date: _____

Lab/Activity Title: _____

- Carefully read the entire lab and answer the following questions.
- Return this completed and signed safety form to your teacher to initial before you begin the lab/activity.

1. Describe what you will be doing during this lab/activity. Ask your teacher any questions you have regarding the lab/activity.

   _____

   _____

   _____

   _____

2. Will you be working alone, with a partner, or with a group?
   (Circle one.)

3. What safety precautions should you follow while doing this lab/activity?

   _____

   _____

   _____

4. Write any steps in the procedure, additional safety concerns, or lab safety symbols that you do not understand.

   _____

   _____

   _____

   Student Signature _____

Sample Teacher Observation Form

Form 1

Beginning Observations

Start by teaching one skill and recording each use of the skill with a mark. Later, you might want to record students' initials and observe more skills at the same time.

Cooperative Skill	Group							
	1	2	3	4	5	6	7	8

Form 2

Group Member Observation Form   Group #_____

Start by teaching one skill and recording each use of the skill by a group member with a mark. Later, you might want to observe more skills at a time. Or, keep the sheets and add new skills later.

Cooperative Skill	Group							
	1	2	3	4	5	6	7	8

Phone List for Local Resources

Keep the following phone numbers on hand in case of emergencies.

- **EMERGENCIES: 911**

- Fire Department _____

- Water Treatment Facility _____

- Poison Control Center _____

- Hazmat _____

- Hospitals _____

  _____

  _____

- American Red Cross _____

- School District Office _____

- Other: _____

  _____

  _____

A

Sample Guardian / Learning Partner Letter
Regarding Home Lab Work

[date]

Dear Guardian or Learning Partner:

Periodically your child/ward will be assigned lab activities to conduct at home. These activities have been tested by teachers and deemed appropriate for independent completion. We do, however, recommend that an adult supervise or work with the student to be certain that all safety precautions are being followed. The activities have been designed to use ordinary items found in the home.

If you have any concerns regarding the materials suggested or the advisability of your child/ward conducting the lab activities, please don't hesitate to call me at school between [hour] and [hour].

Sincerely,

[Teacher signature]

[Teacher name, printed]

[School name]

[School address]

[School phone number]

Sample Guardian/Learning Partner Letter Regarding Field Trips

[Teacher Name]

[School Name]

[School Address]

[School Phone Number]

Dear Guardian/Learning Partner:

A field trip is planned for [date] for science classes from [school name]. The [duration of trip] to [name of site] will be to study [purpose of study]. Students will observe and investigate such natural events and features as [list sample topics].

Departure time is approximately [time] at [location of departure (where students need to be taken if before usual school arrival time)]. Return time is approximately [time] at [location (if later than usual school dismissal time)]. Transportation will be provided by [type of transportation]. Travel time is estimated at [duration] to and from the site.

Lunch will [be provided at the site for a cost of $0.00/need to be brought by students as well as water or other beverage to drink].

Students should wear [type of clothing and shoes]. Please provide sunscreen and insect repellent for your child/ward. Investigation materials and safety equipment will be provided by the school.

Adult sponsors will accompany me to provide additional instruction and supervision. Students will be required to meet all verbal and written instructions regarding their lab work and their behavior.

Please read and sign the attached Permission Form and the Emergency Medical Form and return to me no later than [date]. Please send any needed medications with your child on the day of the field trip. I will carry the medication until needed. In an emergency, you may reach us by cell phone at [insert number]. In case the cell phone is out-of-range, the phone number at the site is [phone number] and the contact person there is [name].

We are very pleased about this opportunity for discovering interesting features of our world. If you have any questions regarding this field trip, please call me at school between [hour] and [hour].

Sincerely,

[Teacher's signature]

[Teacher's name, printed]

A

Sample Permission Form for Field Trips

[date]

After reading the letter informing me of the details of the field trip planned for [date] _____ to [name of site], I hereby:

❏ Give permission

❏ Deny permission

for my child/ward _____ to participate in the activity.

This permission extends to traveling via [form of transportation named in the letter]. I understand the time of departure is scheduled for _____. I agree to pick up my child/ward at [the time of arrival] (if it is after normal school closing) at [location at school].

_____

Parent/Guardian (print name)

_____

Parent/Guardian (signature)

_____

Date

Return this form to [name of teacher] no later than [date].

[School Name]

[School Address]

[School Phone Number]

Sample Medical Emergency Form

[Name of Teacher]

[Name of School]

[School Address]

[School Phone Number]

Date form to be returned to teacher: _____

- -

Name of Student _____ Date of Birth _____

Student Address _____

Name of Science Class _____ Class Period _____

Medical Conditions: _____

_____

_____

Known Allergies (include food allergies): _____

_____

_____

Medications Taken on a Regular Basis (include dosage and administering directions):

_____

_____

Medications Needed for Emergency Allergic Reactions: _____

_____

_____

Person to Call in an Emergency:

Name: _____ Phone Number (Daytime) _____

Name: _____ Phone Number (Evening) _____

Name: _____ Phone Number (Daytime) _____

Family Doctor: _____ Phone Number _____

In case of an emergency, I hereby authorize the physician selected
by school personnel to provide the necessary medical treatment for my child.

_____

Parent/Guardian (print)

_____

Parent/Guardian (signature)

_____

Date

A

Sample Accident Report Form

School _____ Date _____ Time _____

Student's Full Name _____

Student's Address _____

Phone_____ Age _____ Sex _____ Grade_____

Nature of the Accident (select from the following):
- Abrasion
- Burn
- Puncture or cut
- Ingested material
- Sprain
- Chemical contact
- Other _____

Region of the Body Injured (select from the following):
- Arm
- Eye
- Head
- Internal
- Leg
- Torso
- Other _____

Description of the Accident:
- How the accident occurred

_____

_____

_____

_____

_____

- Location where the accident occurred _____

- List of tools, equipment, or chemicals involved _____

- First aid treatment administered _____

- Who administered first aid? _____

- Time parent or guardian was notified_____

Student sent: _____ Home _____ Doctor _____ Hospital _____

Name of Hospital

_____ _____ _____
    Principal   Teacher   Nurse

Sample Letter to Guardian or Learning Partner

A

Dear Guardian/Learning Partner:

This year I will be implementing cooperative learning techniques in my science classes, along with traditional teaching methods. Cooperative learning is a thoroughly tested method of instruction in which students work in small groups toward a common goal while using specific cooperative skills.

Educational research shows the following benefits for students engaged in cooperative learning:

- greater academic achievement
- higher self-esteem
- use of higher-level thought processes
- increased time on task

Cooperative learning employs highly structured planning and clear goals for individuals as well as groups. Even though group products are evaluated, individuals are accountable for their own learning.

Please contact me if you have comments or questions. I am looking forward to a successful and exciting year in science.

Sincerely,

_____

Sample Letter to the Principal

Dear _____:

This year I will be implementing cooperative learning in my science classroom. I trust that this will meet with your approval. You probably know that cooperative learning is a thoroughly tested method of instruction in which students work in small groups toward a common goal while using specific cooperative skills, such as staying on task, dealing with distractions, and disagreeing in a congenial way.

In cooperative learning, members of heterogeneous groups share leadership, have positive interdependence, are responsible for each other's learning, produce a group product, and receive group rewards. The emphasis is not only on the scientific task, but also on good working relationships and communication—skills we know as necessary in today's workforce.

Educational research shows the following benefits for students engaged in cooperative learning:

- greater academic achievement
- higher self-esteem
- use of higher-level thought processes
- increased time on task

Cooperative learning employs highly structured planning and clear goals for individuals as well as groups. Research shows that students learn a significant amount of subject matter from each other. Rather than leave successful communication to chance, the cooperative learning method capitalizes on the importance adolescents place on interpersonal relationships. I will teach students cooperative skills in order to ensure productive group work. I will evaluate group products, but individuals will remain accountable for their own learning.

There are many worthwhile benefits of cooperative learning in any classroom setting, but current research shows that the low achiever has even more to gain, such as:

- improved attitude toward science and school
- improved attendance
- a lower drop-out rate
- reduced interpersonal conflict
- greater motivation

I would like you to visit my classes periodically and discuss your observations with me as the year progress. I shall keep you informed of our progress.

Sincerely,

_____

Note to the Substitute Teacher

Dear Substitute Teacher:

Students in my classes work in cooperative learning groups. This means they are responsible not only for their own learning, but for that of other group members as well. They "sink or swim" together. They divide a task and share responsibility equally. I use one evaluation when group products are produced, but students also are held accountable for their own learning.

Please use the attached transparency to explain today's lesson. Review the procedure on the student worksheet. As students work, encourage them to use the cooperative skills or strategy assigned to the lesson. When they ask you a question, before you give an answer, ask them whether they have asked everyone in their group. You might want to use the attached observation sheet to record students' use of cooperative skills as they work together.

For a brief overview of cooperative learning, please refer to pages 20–27 in Tab A: Classroom and Laboratory Management and Safety in the *Blueprints for Success: Science Classrooms that Work* booklet.

Thank you,

_____

A

SAFETY SYMBOLS

SAFETY SYMBOLS	HAZARD	EXAMPLES	PRECAUTION	REMEDY
DISPOSAL	Special disposal procedures need to be followed.	certain chemicals, living organisms	Do not dispose of these materials in the sink or trash can.	Dispose of wastes as directed by your teacher.
BIOLOGICAL	Organisms or other biological materials that might be harmful to humans	bacteria, fungi, blood, unpreserved tissues, plant materials	Avoid skin contact with these materials. Wear mask or gloves.	Notify your teacher if you suspect contact with material. Wash hands thoroughly.
EXTREME TEMPERATURE	Objects that can burn skin by being too cold or too hot	boiling liquids, hot plates, dry ice, liquid nitrogen	Use proper protection when handling.	Go to your teacher for first aid.
SHARP OBJECT	Use of tools or glass-ware that can easily puncture or slice skin	razor blades, pins, scalpels, pointed tools, dissecting probes, broken glass	Practice common-sense behavior and follow guidelines for use of the tool.	Go to your teacher for first aid.
FUME	Possible danger to respiratory tract from fumes	ammonia, acetone, nail polish remover, heated sulfur, moth balls	Make sure there is good ventilation. Never smell fumes directly. Wear a mask.	Leave foul area and notify your teacher immediately.
ELECTRICAL	Possible danger from electrical shock or burn	improper grounding, liquid spills, short circuits, exposed wires	Double-check setup with teacher. Check condition of wires and apparatus.	Do not attempt to fix electrical problems. Notify your teacher immediately.
IRRITANT	Substances that can irritate the skin or mucus membranes of the respiratory tract	pollen, moth balls, steel wool, fiberglass, potassium perman-ganate	Wear dust mask and gloves. Practice extra care when handling these materials.	Go to your teacher for first aid.
CHEMICAL	Chemicals that can react with and destroy tissue and other materials	bleaches such as hydrogen peroxide; acids such as sulfuric acid, hydrochloric acid; bases such as ammonia, sodium hydroxide	Wear goggles, gloves, and an apron.	Immediately flush the affected area with water and notify your teacher.
TOXIC	Substance may be poisonous if touched, inhaled, or swallowed	mercury, many metal compounds, iodine, poinsettia plant parts	Follow your teacher's instructions.	Always wash hands thoroughly after use. Go to your teacher for first aid.
OPEN FLAME	Open flame may ignite flammable chemicals, loose clothing, or hair	alcohol, kerosene, potassium perman-ganate, hair, clothing	Tie back hair. Avoid wearing loose clothing. Avoid open flames when using flammable chemicals. Be aware of locations of the fire safety equipment.	Notify your teacher immediately. Use fire safety equipment if applicable.

Eye Safety
Proper eye protection should be worn at all times by anyone performing or observing science activities.

Clothing Protection
This symbol appears when substances could stain or burn clothing.

Animal Safety
This symbol appears when safety of animals and students must be ensured.

Radioactivity
This symbol appears when radioactive materials are used.

DISPOSAL

Special disposal procedures need to be followed for certain chemicals and living organisms.

Do not dispose of these materials in the sink or trash can.

Dispose of wastes as your teacher directs.

BIOLOGICAL

Organisms or other biological materials that might be harmful to humans: bacteria, fungi, blood, unpreserved tissues, plant materials

Avoid skin contact with these materials. Wear mask or gloves.

Notify your teacher if you suspect contact with material. Wash hands thoroughly.

EXTREME TEMPERATURE

Objects that can burn skin by being too cold or too hot: boiling liquids, hot plates, dry ice, liquid nitrogen

Use proper protection when handling.

Go to your teacher for first aid.

SHARP OBJECT

Use of tools or glassware that can easily puncture or slice skin: razor blades, pins, scalpels, pointed tools, dissecting probes, broken glass

Practice common-sense behavior and follow guidelines for use of the tool.

Go to your teacher for first aid.

FUME

Possible danger to respiratory tract from fumes: ammonia, acetone, nail polish remover, heated sulfur, moth balls

Make sure there is good ventilation. Never smell fumes directly. Wear a mask.

Leave foul area and notify your teacher immediately.

ELECTRICAL

Possible danger from electrical shock or burn: improper grounding, liquid spills, short circuits, exposed wires

Double-check setup with teacher. Check condition of wires and apparatus.

Do not attempt to fix electrical problems. Notify your teacher immediately.

IRRITANT

Substances that can irritate the skin or mucus membranes of the respiratory tract: pollen, moth balls, steel wool, fiberglass, potassium permanganate

Wear dust mask and gloves. Practice extra care when handling these materials.

Go to your teacher for first aid.

CHEMICAL

Chemicals that can react with and destroy tissue and other materials: bleaches such as hydrogen peroxide; acids such as sulfuric acid, hydrochloric acid; bases such as ammonia, sodium hydroxide

Wear goggles, gloves, and an apron.

Immediately flush the affected area with water and notify your teacher.

TOXIC

Substance might be poisonous if touched, inhaled, or swallowed: mercury, many metal compounds, iodine, plant parts such as poison ivy

Follow your teacher's instructions.

Always wash hands thoroughly after use. Go to your teacher for first aid.

OPEN FLAME

Open flame can ignite flammable chemicals, loose clothing, or hair: alcohol, kerosene, potassium permanganate, hair, clothing

Tie back hair. Avoid wearing loose clothing. Avoid open flames when using flammable chemicals. Be aware of locations of fire safety equipment.

Notify your teacher immediately. Use fire safety equipment if applicable.

EYE SAFETY

Proper eye protection should be worn at all times by anyone performing or observing science activities.

CLOTHING PROTECTION

This symbol appears when substances could stain or burn clothing.

ANIMAL SAFETY

This symbol appears when safety of animals and students must be ensured.

RADIOACTIVITY

This symbol appears when radioactive materials are used.

SI Conversion Table

To convert from °F to °C, you can:

1. For exact amounts, use the equation at the bottom of this table, or
2. For approximate amounts, find °F on the thermometer at the left of **Figure A.5** and determine °C on the thermometer at the right.

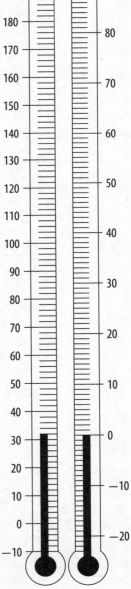

Figure A.5

SI/English Conversions			
	When you have:	**Multiply by:**	**To find:**
Length	inches	2.54	centimeters
	centimeters	0.39	inches
	feet	0.30	meters
	meters	3.28	feet
	yards	0.91	meters
	meters	1.09	yards
	miles	1.61	kilometers
	kilometers	0.62	miles
Mass and Weight*	ounces	28.35	grams
	grams	0.04	ounces
	pounds	0.45	kilograms
	kilograms	2.20	pounds
	tons	0.91	metric tons
	metric tons	1.10	tons
	pounds	4.45	newtons
	newtons	0.23	pounds
Volume	cubic inches	16.39	cubic centimeters
	milliliters	0.06	cubic inches
	cubic feet	0.03	cubic meters
	cubic meters	35.31	cubic feet
	liters	1.06	quarts
	liters	0.26	gallons
	gallons	3.78	liters
Area	square inches	6.45	square centimeters
	square centimeters	0.16	square inches
	square feet	0.09	square meters
	square meters	10.76	square feet
	square miles	2.59	square kilometers
	square kilometers	0.39	square miles
	hectares	2.47	acres
	acres	0.40	hectares
Temperature	Fahrenheit	$\frac{5}{9}(°F - 32)$	Celsius
	Celsius	$\frac{9}{5}°C + 32$	Fahrenheit

* Weight as measured by standard Earth gravity

Differentiated Instruction

Table of Contents

What is it? **121**
Differentiated Instruction 121
What is the value of differentiation? 122

What do I do? **123**
Successful Strategies 123
Flexible Grouping 124
Know Your Students 125
• Student Inventories 125
• Learning Modalities 126
• English-Language Learners 127
• Students with Special Needs 128
• Approaching-Level/On-Level/Beyond-Level Learners 129
• Assess Prior Knowledge 131
• Higher-Order Thinking Strategies 134

Now you try it! **137**
Classroom Scenarios 137
• The Students 137
• Whole-Group Instruction 137
• Small-Group Instruction 138
• In the Lab 140

Differentiated Instruction **141**
In-Class Activities (Frey & Fisher) 142
Projects or Homework (Frey & Fisher) 142
Assessment (Frey & Fisher) 143

References and Resources **143**

Digital Resources for Teachers

Mc Graw Hill **Professional Development** **mhpdonline.com** *These PD modules address both teaching strategies and science content.*

✓ Literacy Strategies: Reading, Writing, Listening, and Speaking
✓ Differentiate Instruction
✓ English-Language Learners
✓ Standards-Based Instruction
✓ Assessment Strategies and Rubrics

✓ Teaching Energy
✓ Teaching Mitosis and Meiosis
✓ Teaching Moon Phases
✓ Teaching Photosynthesis
✓ Teaching Physical and Chemical Change
✓ Teaching Weather Concepts

TEACHING TODAY **teachingtoday.glencoe.com** *A no-fee professional development Web site where you will find resources for:*

✓ Lesson plans with downloads for newsletters, parent conference letters
✓ Teaching tips
✓ How-to articles sorted by discipline, grade level, and instructional type
✓ Math support
✓ Demonstration videos

B

What is it?

Each of your students contributes to the large collection of knowledge, ability, interests, languages, preferences, and viewpoints that makes every classroom unique. As your classroom becomes increasingly diverse, incorporation of differentiated instructional is essential if you are to provide authentic learning experiences for all students. The goal of a differentiated classroom is for you to be responsive to student needs and to create a variety of learning experiences that allow each student to excel.

Differentiated Instruction

A student-centered approach to teaching that strives to provide authentic learning experiences for diverse students in the same class is known as differentiated instruction. It relies on your knowledge of your students and recognizes that students are diverse in the following ways:

- **Knowledge** Your students have different levels of prior knowledge about course content. Differentiated instruction meets each student at his or her level and provides activities that build on prior knowledge.

- **Readiness/Abilities** Promoting differentiated learning enables you to meet each student at his or her level of learning readiness and matches your students' abilities with different teaching strategies. This helps prevent students from feeling overwhelmed by material that is too difficult. Also, different teaching methods can help keep students from becoming bored by work that is not challenging.

- **Learning Preferences/Modalities (Profile)** Some students prefer oral presentations; others would rather write essays. At different times, an individual might like group work or prefer to work independently. When you differentiate, you take into account students' learning styles or modes.

- **Background** Students come from a variety of cultural, socioeconomic, and ethnic backgrounds that influence their ideas about the world around them. By tailoring instruction to students, differentiation allows them to express their unique viewpoints.

- **Language** Differentiated instruction enables students with different levels of proficiency in English to learn at an appropriate pace.

- **Interests** Your students might have interests in music, dance, space, wildlife, motorcycles, or any one of a variety of topics. Differentiation tries to match instruction with students' interests whenever possible.

For more information on Differentiated Instruction visit

 **Professional Development**

at **mhpdonline.com**

B

What is the value of differentiation?

- Differentiated instruction applies an approach to teaching and learning that creates multiple options for students to process information and make sense of ideas. (**http://www.cast.org/ publications/ncac/ncac_diffinstruc.html**) You can differentiate science instruction to enable each student to discover topics of interest, expand his or her research skills, and receive instruction on distinct science and inquiry skills.

Teachers seeking to create differentiated learning experiences need to assess the content, the process, the product, the affect, and the learning environment of instruction for varying levels of students. You can adapt, or differentiate, these classroom elements to increase the possibility that each of your students learns and performs to his or her greatest potential (Tomlinson, 2001).

- **Content** refers to what you expect students to learn. Often a class will study the same content objectives, but at varying degrees of complexity depending on prior knowledge, interests, or abilities.

- **Process** describes how students learn the material. In a science classroom, reading, researching, experimenting, classifying, comparing, and contrasting are all process verbs that describe what you will ask students to do. By differentiating instruction, you enable students to learn according to their unique learning modes, abilities, or skills.

- **Product** is how students will demonstrate what they have learned. This is often an assessment. Again, you can modify the product to account for interests, learning modes, background, or ability.

- **Affect** is how students link thinking and feeling in the classroom.

- **Learning environment** is the way the classroom feels and operates.

What do I do?

Through the use of various strategies, you can provide learning opportunities in the science classroom that meet students' differing levels of readiness, learning profiles, and variety of interests.

Successful Strategies

Strategy	Focus	Example
RAFT: Role, Audience, Format, Topic	Readiness	An adaptable writing strategy, a RAFT can be assigned on a content-related topic, but differentiated for student readiness. Preteach the acronym so students will recognize this technique and learn to construct their own RAFTs. **R**ole—What is the student's role as the writer? The scientist? The inventor? The historian? The reporter? The researcher? **A**udience—Who is the intended reader? Peers? Teachers? Parents? Scientific community? Activists? **F**ormat—What is the best product? Journal? Lab report? Brochure? Song? Critique? News article? **T**opic—What, who, or when is the subject? An issue of personal or public interest or concern? A topic related to a question or problem? A historical time or figure? A prediction for the future?
Think-Pair-Share	Readiness Learning Profiles	Think-Pair-Share is intended to foster higher-quality responses and encourage increased participation during classroom discussions. By asking students to • *think* quietly about their answers; • *pair* with a peer to discuss ideas; • *share* their responses with the entire class, all students are able to participate at their own readiness levels. Meanwhile each step provides a different pathway to meet multiple learning profiles.
Tiered Learning	Readiness	Tiered instruction is a means of teaching one concept and meeting the different learning needs in a group. Ms. Daniels provides some students with direct instruction on the types of simple machines and asks the students to classify examples of each type. She provides other students with the more open-ended task of working in teams to describe types of simple machines, and to then list and explain everyday examples of their own.
Word Wall	Readiness	Mr. Jones posts new vocabulary words in a prominent location in his class and uses them as a student resource. Approaching-level students use the Word Wall to help them recall key words when writing and speaking. Mr. Jones frequently asks advanced students to make connections between words to help them build their science vocabulary.
Vocabulary Builders	Readiness Learning Profiles	Crossword puzzles, word searches, jumbles, and word and picture games all assist students in learning and using new vocabulary. Mr. Thompson arranges vocabulary words into groups based on word families, complexity, or importance to key concepts, then assigns students to groups based on their prior knowledge, readiness, and learning profiles.
Learning Centers	Interests	Ms. Vasquez creates learning centers for the upcoming unit, Space and the Universe. Each center includes books, activities and other print and media resources about related topics, such as space exploration, famous astronauts, constellations, Mars, model-making, the Big Bang, science fiction, and others.

B

Flexible Grouping

Flexible grouping strategies enable a teacher to vary student groups based on his or her knowledge of each student's individual needs, interests, content readiness, or task affinity. Students have opportunities to work with a variety of classmates and to demonstrate learning in many different ways.

Strategy	Focus	Example
Homogenous Groups (Like-Interest and Like-Readiness)	Readiness Interests Learning Profiles	Students are grouped into like-readiness "Expert Groups" to research a different aspect of energy resources, consumption, and policy. The resources and level of structure vary according to the readiness of each group. Later, groups share what they learned with the whole class. Mr. Smith places a different question in each corner of the room. One corner asks, "What's your average 'hallway walking' speed?" Another corner might ask "How long would it take a running cheetah, a walking turtle, and a galloping horse to move around a race track?" Students place themselves into groups by selecting the problem that matches their interests, although all questions relate to the same concept in this example—speed and acceleration.
Heterogeneous Groups Mixed-Interest/ Mixed-Readiness	Readiness	Mrs. Walters organizes students into mixed-readiness groups for a "Word Webbing" exercise. She gives each group a large piece of paper and asks each student to write down words related to the systems of the human body. Every few minutes, the group rotates its paper so the students can add to each other's webs. Mrs. Walters encourages students to discuss the words and web connections they made as a group.
Individualized Work/ Independent Study	Interest Readiness	Janet, a student in Mr. Hansen's class, loves soccer and basketball and wants to know how she can prevent knee injuries. She and Mr. Hansen agree on an independent-study contract in which Janet, through research and personal interviews, diagrams and explains the anatomy and physiology of the leg and joints, specifically in women, and demonstrates three exercises to strengthen the knee joint.
Whole-Class Instruction	Readiness Learning Profiles	When providing instruction to the whole class, Ms. Roberts uses a "Say-Write-Do" strategy to make the lesson more interactive and provide multiple modalities for student responses. *Say*—Ms. Roberts teaches hand signals to indicate that students should think about their answer and then respond in unison. *Write*—Ms. Roberts asks students to write words or statements on paper or individual whiteboards, and then hold up their responses. *Do*—Ms. Roberts has students touch items (parts of a diagram, lab instructions, key facts in the text, and so on) with their index fingers to indicate a response, allowing her to monitor rates of participation and attention.
Peer Partners	Readiness	Partners use a three-step interview process to review what they have learned and to provide the teacher with an informal assessment of students' understanding. First, partner 1 interviews partner 2 about the topic. Then, they reverse roles. Last, partner 1 shares information from partner 2 with the class, and partner 2 shares information from partner 1.

Know Your Students

How is it possible for you to know your students' interests and learning styles? You can use many strategies in order to discover how each student learns best. Just as knowledge of your students' proficiency helps you understand their abilities and learning styles, knowledge of their background and preferences will also help make your instruction more effective. Keep an information card on each student. You might want to sit with each student and fill out information cards together. Ask an ESL instructor or another student to serve as a translator if needed.

Student Inventories

Student inventories can build your students' self-esteem by helping them discover their strengths, learn about areas in which they might need to make greater efforts, and appreciate the differences among themselves.

Student Inventory

My name: _____

Place of birth: _____

Primary language: _____

Language spoken at home: _____

Name(s) of possible translator: _____

My favorite school subject: _____

My favorite books: _____

My hobbies: _____

My favorite food: _____

My favorite song or movie is _____.

The person I most admire is _____.

In the future, I would like to be _____.

What I like most about science: _____

What I find most difficult about science: _____

I learn science best by listening/observing/experimenting _____

My goals for this year are _____

_____.

B

Learning Modalities

Your students' learning profiles describe the ways in which they learn best. Part of a student's learning profile is defined by his or her preferred learning modalities, which highlight common styles in which individuals typically learn. Learning modalities used to identify students commonly distinguish among auditory learners, who learn by listening; visual learners, who learn by seeing; and kinesthetic learners, who learn by doing.

Many students use some combination of the three, but tend to demonstrate a stronger preference for one. When you teach in ways that incorporate the natural learning modalities of students, using strategies to support the ways they learn best, your teaching can become more effective and efficient (Tomlinson, 2003).

Observe student activities. Learn to recognize characteristics of these different learning styles in your students. Although the categories are generalizations, some traits of these learners might be familiar to you.

- **Auditory Learning Preference** Seth easily follows along and participates during lectures. He enjoys listening and often adds valuable insights to class discussions. In lab, he is able to follow complex, multi-step directions with little additional guidance.
- **Visual Learning Preference** Bridget has a "photographic" memory. She easily recalls diagrams and concept maps from class or the textbook. She likes class demonstrations and is a great observer, but she easily loses focus during verbal lectures. In the lab, she does best when first shown what she is supposed to do.
- **Kinesthetic Learning Preference** Josh has a hard time sitting still and frequently needs to get out of his seat and move about. Science is one of his favorite subjects, as long as there are plenty of labs and experiments. He favors a hands-on approach in labs, preferring to figure it out on his own and read the instructions later.

Just as you recognize these traits in your students, your students might also be able to self-identify with Seth, Bridget, or Josh. To obtain additional information about the types of learners in your classroom, ask students how they learn best, or administer the Student Inventory.

Choose effective teaching strategies. Differentiation enables teachers to select strategies based on students' needs and learning styles. The following lists provide ideas for how to meet the needs of auditory, visual, and kinesthetic learners.

Support for Auditory Learners
- Facilitate large- and small-group discussions.
- Have students "talk through" science processes, diagrams, or cycles while partners listen. Then have pairs trade roles.
- Use rhythm, rhyme, and song to help students learn and remember science concepts, or have students make their own verbal memory devices.
- Record verbal lectures.
- Provide recordings of the text read aloud.
- Have students orally complete sentences spoken by the teacher.
- Read problems and equations aloud.

Support for Visual Learners

- Use diagrams, graphic organizers, photographs, and transparencies during class lectures, discussions, and small-group times.
- Provide highlighters, markers, and colored pens to help students organize notes and color code important text.
- Have students draw pictures and create illustrated stories.
- Use visual multi-media to aid instruction (slideshows, microscopes, videos, computers, and so on).
- Allow film or video supplements in place of text.
- Underline or highlight important words or phrases.
- Have students complete written sentences supplied by the teacher.
- Have students sit near the front of the classroom.

Support for Kinesthetic Learners

- Create structured and open-ended inquiry laboratory experiences for hands-on learners.
- Have students make scientific models.
- Use skits, plays, and games to act out and explain science processes, such as cell division, population ecology, or phases of matter.
- Use tactile materials.
- Utilize role-play.
- Substitute projects and laboratory experiments for written assignments and reports.
- Use hands-on activities.

When planning your next lesson or unit, decide how you will engage students who display each learning modality. Using a variety of strategies to meet the needs of all learners can help increase student learning while decreasing frustrations. For example, Ms. Wilson wanted to model a lab procedure involving a chemical reaction for the class. Because of his learning style, she chose Josh to help her demonstrate the lab and safety procedures for the class. Likewise, she asked Bridget to watch the reaction and give a verbal step-by-step analysis of what was happening. She asked Seth to listen to and record Bridget's observations on chart paper.

English-Language Learners

English-language learners, abbreviated as ELLs (or ELs, English Learners) are students who are not proficient at speaking English. These students are learning English as their second, third, or even fourth language. Some have attended schools in other countries and are at the same grade level as other students their age. Others might have had to interrupt their education for one reason or another and might require additional assistance through the use of intervention strategies. Some ELLs do not speak English in school settings or in their home environments, thus limiting their experience and practice with English.

As a teacher, you will evaluate the level of proficiency of your ELLs, just as you would with your English-speaking students. The important thing to remember about English-language learners is that they are trying to master a new language at the same time they are mastering academic content. Remember to be sensitive to your ELLs' primary social and cultural identities.

For more information on English-Language Learners visit

 Professional Development

at **mhpdonline.com**

A group of educational professionals known as the Teachers of English to Speakers of Other Languages (TESOL) has created a set of standards to help ELLs improve their educational achievements. The standards set three goals:

Goal 1: To use English to communicate in social settings

Standard 1: Students will use English to participate in social interaction.

Standard 2: Students will interact in, through, and with spoken and written English for personal expression and enjoyment.

Standard 3: Students will use learning strategies to extend their communicative competence.

Goal 2: To use English to achieve academically in all content areas

Standard 1: Students will use English to interact in the classroom.

Standard 2: Students will use English to obtain, process, construct, and provide subject matter information in spoken and written form.

Standard 3: Students will use appropriate learning strategies to construct and apply academic knowledge.

Goal 3: To use English in socially and culturally appropriate ways

Standard 1: Students will choose appropriate language variety, register, and genre according to audience, purpose, and setting.

Standard 2: Students will use non-verbal communication appropriate to audience, purpose, and setting.

Standard 3: Students will use appropriate learning strategies to extend their sociolinguistic and sociocultural competence.

More information on teaching English-language learners is available in Tab C.

Students with Special Needs

Differentiation strategies can help students with special needs to become active participants in the science classroom, including laboratory and inquiry activities. One significant barrier to successful inclusion of students with special needs is the lowered expectations of teachers and parents (Hassard, 2005). By modifying materials and teaching strategies without lowering content requirements, these students can be fully accepted and encouraged to pursue science in your classroom and as a future career option.

Begin by assessing the type of assistance the student might need. Does the student have mobility needs that require physical modifications to the classroom? Are there any barriers to communication? What types of tasks are difficult for the student? Does the student have difficulty interacting socially with peers? Think creatively about making modifications that promote accessibility, provide structure, and encourage peer interaction. Structure is especially helpful because it allows students to focus on the task and decreases the difficulty of dealing with extraneous classroom stimuli (Hassard, 2005).

It might be useful to think about the following features of your classroom model as you address the needs of students with special needs.

- **Physical Environment** Make sure the classroom environment is orderly and meets the needs of all students. For instance, a student who uses a wheelchair might require a lower table to work on. Students who require assistance keeping organized will benefit from establishing set locations in the classroom for student work, journals, textbooks, and laboratory equipment. This will also help visually impaired students navigate the room. How can you arrange the physical space to better meet the needs of your students?

- **Instructional Methods and Materials** What props, resources, time clues, verbal cues, supports, or other materials will help meet a specific student's particular needs? For example, a personal dry-erase board can help a hearing-impaired student communicate with a lab partner. A visually-impaired student might be able to feel the effects of a precipitate from a chemical reaction, making a lab experience more meaningful. Another student might benefit from an outline of the lesson or step-by-step instructions to the lab in advance. Providing additional resources at the student's reading level might be the only thing a student needs to grasp key concepts.

- **Classroom Routines** Another way of increasing structure for students with special needs is by establishing classroom routines. How will these students hand in their work or sharpen their pencils? How will you communicate goals, upcoming events, and assignments? How will they move from desk work to the lab? Providing clear guidelines and procedures to students can increase the functionality of the classroom, thereby decreasing disruptions and creating more instructional time.

Identify students with special needs in your classroom and list accommodations and modifications that you can implement to support them. If you are having difficulty, contact the student's parent/guardian, advocate, or special education teacher. These individuals might be able to provide additional ideas and review content with students during individual resource time.

Approaching-Level/On-Level/Beyond-Level Learners

Effective differentiation requires that teachers design challenging tasks that are slightly above the students' level of readiness and provide support so that they can succeed (Tomlinson, 2003). It is important to note that readiness levels take into account students' prior knowledge and comprehension of a subject, in addition to their skills and abilities. For this reason, an approaching-level student in English or math might be able to perform beyond-level work in science if it is structured and designed to meet their interests and learning profile. Consider the following readiness levels you might observe in your classroom.

- Approaching-level or struggling learners might be described as easily distracted, inattentive, lacking social skills, fearing failure, or lacking motivation. Do not dismiss these learners so easily. Teachers have historically assigned these students remedial tasks or a "dumbed-down" curriculum. This is a mistake, and you should employ strategies to help these students achieve at a higher level.

- On-level learners still vary greatly in their prior knowledge, abilities, and interests. Assessing what these students know at the beginning of every unit becomes a valuable benchmark of what to teach and how to teach it.
- Beyond-level learners, sometimes called gifted or advanced learners, demonstrate high intellectual ability, high creativity, and high commitment to tasks (Hassard, 2005). Tasks might be too easy for them, and they risk "coasting," often getting good grades without really learning anything new. These students will benefit from an academic challenge in the classroom.

Here are some suggestions of how science teachers can help approaching-level, on-level, and beyond-level learners.

Approaching-Level

Identify students' strengths.	Use a hands-on, relevant approach.	Value cooperative learning.
By discovering students' strengths, teachers can use their learning profiles to teach more difficult material.	Plan activities that enable students to demonstrate knowledge with concrete materials and real-world problems rather than with worksheets.	Students can feel more accepted when included in groups. They also learn valuable skills from their peers, especially those at a different readiness level.

On-Level

Meet learning styles.	Be culturally responsive.	Teach classroom rules and procedures.
Students still need tasks that meet their individual learning modalities.	Create a classroom environment that respects family and community backgrounds of students. Design activities based on ideas that are familiar to students.	By running your classroom efficiently, all students will benefit from knowing what is acceptable and what to expect.

Beyond-Level

Utilize learning contracts.	Compact the lesson.	Value cooperative learning.
Allowing students to study topics of their own choosing can increase their engagement and motivation.	Advanced students with more prior knowledge about a topic can benefit from being excused from part of the curriculum. Instead, work to develop the depth of these students' knowledge.	Help students take a leadership role in the classroom by encouraging them to help others in the class. Being tolerant of others might be something some advanced students need to practice.

Assess Prior Knowledge

Many science educators follow a constructivist philosophy, believing that scientific knowledge is built through personal experience and observation of the natural world. These prior experiences and understanding shape how students view new scientific information (Llewellyn, 2005). Sometimes, this results in students having inaccurate interpretations, referred to as preconceptions or misconceptions, of science concepts. You need to address preconceptions and misconceptions if you are to help students deepen content knowledge, increase their level of comprehension, and construct new scientific beliefs. Before beginning a new unit or topic, try to gain a sense of what students already know about the topic. Here are several ideas for assessing prior knowledge.

Ask Questions Often the most efficient method of learning what a student already knows is to ask, "What do you know about...?" Students might say or write down what they know in the form of a list, a short paragraph, a picture, or a word web. For example, before beginning a lesson on evolution, sedimentary rocks, the periodic table of elements, or speed, you can simply ask each student to write down on a piece of paper what they already know, questions they have, or what they find most interesting about the subject you are about to introduce (Llewellyn, 40).

K-W-L Charts (Donna Ogle) Creating K-W-L charts helps students take control of their learning. "What do I KNOW?" helps to establish prior knowledge of a topic. "What do I WANT to know?" arouses curiosity and helps the student set goals for learning. "What did I LEARN?" allows students to evaluate their own learning at the end of a unit.

K-W-L Chart		
Topic: _____		
K What I know about	**W** What I want to find out about	**L** What I learned and still need to learn

T-Charts T-Charts are good tools for note-taking and organizing information. On a T-Chart, the main ideas are listed in the first column and details or examples are listed in the second column. Partially completed T-Charts might be helpful in determining prior knowledge and later to assess learning and evaluate comprehension.

Main Ideas	Details and Examples
1. Sedimentary rocks form when sediments are pressed or cemented together or when sediments precipitate out of solution.	a. shale, siltstone, sandstone b. sediments: clay, silt, sand, gravel c. compaction, cementation
2.	a. b.
3.	a. b. c.

Graphic Organizers Using graphic organizers can enable your students to present information visually, show patterns and relationships, and help them organize important information. You can use them at several points in the learning process, including the time you spend previewing a topic or chapter with students. Students can share their prior knowledge of a topic as they visually record the concepts you present. They can revisit and add to their graphic organizers, just as they can with their K-W-L Charts, in order to develop their understanding of a topic.

Here are some useful graphic organizers for the science classroom that you can alter for many concepts.

A cycle concept map shows how a series of events interacts to produce a set of results again and again.

Cycle Concept Map

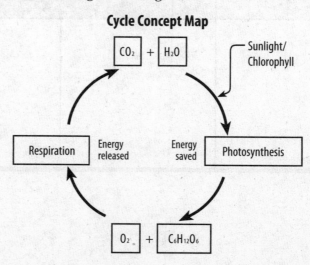

A spider concept map shows how unrelated categories connect to a broad topic. Useful for brainstorming and discussions.

Spider Concept Map

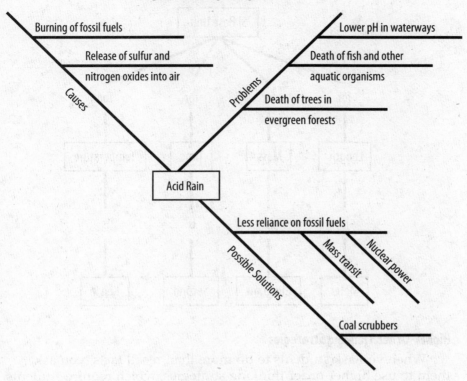

An events chain shows a sequence of events or steps in a process.

Events Chain

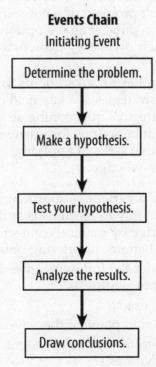

A network tree shows causal information, hierarchical relationships, and branching procedures.

Network Tree

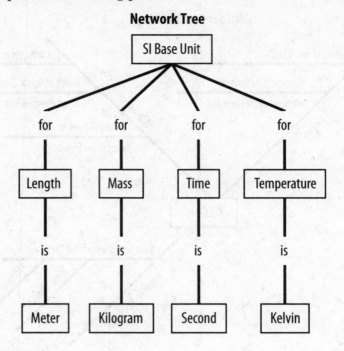

Higher-Order Thinking Strategies

When you ask students to do more than recall facts, you ask them to use higher-order thinking strategies, which require students to go further with their comprehension of content knowledge. These strategies ask students to do something with or create something new from what they have learned. They ask students to apply their knowledge to a different problem or a new situation. When students analyze information and data, evaluate options, or synthesize new ideas or products of their own, they demonstrate higher-order thinking.

Providing opportunities for all students to learn and practice higher-order thinking strategies is a key goal of differentiated instruction. Through effective questioning strategies, varied tasks and activities, and product options for learners, you can promote the higher-order cognitive skills of applying, analyzing, and synthesizing content knowledge.

Vary questions. By using a variety of questioning strategies, you can encourage students not only to recall facts and information, but to assimilate that knowledge by making connections, providing examples, making predictions, or offering opinions.

For example, consider the following questions you might ask your students about photosynthesis.

- What is photosynthesis?
- What would happen to plants if there were no sunlight?
- What are the steps in the light-dependent and light-independent reactions of photosynthesis?
- Can you design an experiment to test which wavelengths of visible light are important for photosynthesis?

To answer the first and third questions, students must recall a definition or a series of facts that they have previously memorized. They might demonstrate comprehension of the process, but these questions don't require students to do anything new with their knowledge. The second and fourth questions require students to apply their knowledge of photosynthesis to a new situation and create a plan to discover something about photosynthesis on their own, respectively. These types of questions do a better job of having students use higher-order thinking skills.

You might find the following question starters useful when composing questions that promote higher-order thinking:

Do you know another instance in which…?

Could this have happened in…?

What factors would you change if…?

Can you apply the method used to some experiences of your own…?

From the information given, can you develop a set of instructions about…?

Which events could have happened…?

If … happened, how might the result have changed?

How was this similar to…?

What are some possible outcomes…?

Can you explain what happened…?

What are some problems of…?

Can you design a … to…?

Can you see a possible solution to…?

Can you devise a way to solve the problem with…?

What would happen if…?

How many ways can you…?

Can you develop a proposal which would …?

Is there a better solution to …?

Judge the value of ….

Can you defend your position about…?

Do you think … is a good or a bad thing?

How would you have handled…?

What changes to … would you recommend?

Do you believe…? Why?

Ask students to do a variety of tasks. It's routine for teachers to ask students to label, identify, write about, or describe someone or something. These verbs are valuable ways of assessing what students know or what they have learned, but they don't ask students to use higher-order thinking skills.

Fortunately, there are many higher-order process skills that are probably incorporated into most science curriculums. These include the following verbs that comprise our science vocabulary: *measure, classify, compare, contrast, infer, predict, estimate, hypothesize, plan, draw conclusions, model, categorize,* and *investigate.* By consciously choosing tasks and activities that require students to use these skills, you are more likely to create lessons that access higher-order thinking.

In addition to these typical science-related words, consider using the following verbs to add variety and interest to tasks.

analyze	construct	originate	organize	refer
examine	distinguish	role-play	invent	recommend
differentiate	research	formulate	compose	summarize
point out	separate	develop	appraise	assess
select	survey	design	critique	solve
subdivide	combine	create	criticize	relate
take apart	produce	add to	judge	evaluate
				consider

B

Provide many pathways to demonstrate learning. Use your knowledge of individual talents, interests, and learning profiles to create options for students. How can they show you, their peers, or a larger community what they have learned in science class? One student might be interested in composing a song about photosynthesis while another might enjoy creating a science-fair poster about an experiment. A student who is computer-savvy might want to create and present a slideshow to the class or to a younger audience. Yet another student might find it more efficient to write an essay on the topic. All of these methods can effectively communicate what students have learned.

This is not to say you need to make all options available at all times. You might identify two or three acceptable activities and allow groups to choose from those. Or, sometimes, based on readiness or learning profiles, it could be more effective to assign a specific assignment to half the class, and something else to the other half. It is neither essential nor even recommended that students be able to freely choose a method all the time.

The following activities all encourage higher-order thinking skills, such as applying, analyzing, creating, and evaluating.

Apply	Analyze	Synthesize	Evaluate
construct a model	survey	invent a machine to do a specific task	conduct a debate
make a diorama	sell an idea		prepare a list of criteria to judge a…
keep a journal	compose music	create a new product	
draw a map	conduct an investigation	write a show, play, song about…	convince others
make a game			form a discussion panel
forecasts	make a flow chart	make up a new language code	
sculpture	construct a graph	devise a way to…	write an editorial or opinion letter
painting	make a diagram showing relationships	group discussion	prepare a case to present your view about…
puzzle		put new words to a melody	
cartoon	prepare a report		comparison of standards
illustration	review a procedure	formulate a hypothesis or question	self-evaluation
slideshow	draw a conclusion		recommendation
a paper following an outline	break down an argument	plan an alternative course of action	
		develop a set of rules	

As you write objectives, plan activities, create test or discussion questions, and assign student projects, review the lists above. How can you incorporate some of these strategies into your lesson plans to encourage student engagement in higher-order thinking?

Now you try it!

Classroom Scenarios

The Students

- James is a new student with special needs. At his previous schools, he was pulled out of class for remedial help in reading and writing. He thinks this is a drag because he enjoys learning with his classmates. James likes to work on machines and is good at figuring out how to put things together. He already knows that he wants to work in a field like construction, where he can use his hands, and he thinks schoolwork is unrelated to his job choice.

- Raphael is very bright. He finds school easy and does just enough to get As. Rarely is he academically challenged, and this is fine with him. He fears failure, so he is reluctant to take academic risks.

- Alicia reads and writes at an advanced level, at least three grade levels above her peers. She learns readily from lectures and textbooks and is an excellent test-taker. Alicia finds science labs tedious and frustrating. She's not used to finding things difficult and is having an increasingly harder time figuring out what to do in the labs.

- Marcus has a keen interest in news, current events, and politics. He excels in social studies classes, but is otherwise an average, on-level learner. Marcus is well-liked by his peers and sometimes tries to use his charm to get others to do the work for him.

- Nancy has special needs that make it difficult for her to participate with classmates without support. Over the course of her schooling, she has been educated in a special education classroom without access to peers. Nancy wishes she could interact more with her classmates.

- Jeremiah is always listening to or making music by tapping, singing, humming. Many teachers and students find this disruptive, and Jeremiah resents that there is no place for his music in school.

These are just a few of the students in Ms. Ray's science class. She finds it challenging but important to meet the varied needs of these and the other 18 students in her class. She is beginning a unit on the conservation of materials and resources and wants students to grasp the importance of reducing, reusing, and recycling waste. In lab, she plans to have students explore the process of decomposition and compare decomposition rates of different materials. Standards addressed in this unit involve the role of organisms (including humans) in an ecosystem, the causes of environmental degradation, and the social perspectives related to resource management.

Whole-Group Instruction

Ms. Ray begins the unit with a whole-group discussion to find out what students know about where resources come from, how they are disposed of, and the importance of recycling. She poses the question,

For Lesson Plans go to

TE**A**CHING
TODAY
at teachingtoday.glencoe.com

B

"What do you do with waste in your home? Is recycling a part of your daily routine, and why is it so important?" She uses a *Think-Pair-Share* method to encourage participation and thoughtful answers from the whole class. She has previously taught this method to students, and they are familiar with the three steps of this method.

As students verbally share their answers, she writes down their comments on a large piece of chart paper at the front of the room, providing a visual for students that they can keep, add to, and revise throughout the unit. Prior to class, she wrote the words *reduce, reuse, recycle, decompose,* and *resources* on her classroom Word Wall. She makes sure to point out these words as she hears students use them in the discussion and draws the familiar recycling symbol next to the first three words on the wall. She frequently reviews the words that are new to students.

Small-Group Instruction

Classroom Procedures Ms. Ray frequently uses cooperative learning strategies in her classroom with great success. She took time at the beginning of the year to explicitly teach the following procedures:

Group Roles Students defined and discussed various group roles, including *leader, taskmaster/timekeeper, recorder, skeptic,* and *materials gatherer.* Her students know what she expects of each position in the group. In smaller groups, she might omit certain roles or combine roles into one. For example, one student might gather materials and also keep time.

Headings Ms. Ray taught students a system for heading papers that includes group roles. This allows her to know each student's role as she walks around the room, monitoring groups. She did this through a posting with examples and non-examples:

Heading Requirements	Example	Non-Example
Recorder	Carrie Johnson	Carrie J.
Skeptic	Marcus Smith	MS
Timekeeper	James Green	Green
Date	3-15-09 or March 15, 2009	March
Subject/Period	Biology/4	bio
Assignment	p. 93, # 1, 3–4	questions

Group Composition Ms. Ray varies the size and composition of groups depending on the activity. Her students are familiar with this, and have learned that while they won't always get to work with their best friends, they will not be with undesirable group members for long. For the first activities in this unit, she assigns students to heterogeneous, mixed-readiness groups. Ms. Ray explains how student readiness, learning profiles, and motivation guide her choices.

- I look at students' needs. If Marcus had his way, he'd be in a group with Raphael every time because he can easily get Raphael to do most of the work. It would not challenge either of them. Instead, I chose to pair Marcus with two students who will speak up and expect him to do his own share of the work. Nancy, on the other hand, could easily get ignored in a group, but does quite well when paired with students who are patient and will make an effort to include her in their work.

- I also take notes about past groups—their difficulties and successes. Sometimes I let students choose groups and then observe what works about them and what doesn't. Over time, I've refined my knowledge about the students so I have a pretty good idea of what works and what doesn't.

Other techniques useful for small-group instruction include:

Walk around the room. As students work on their small-group assignments or activities, Ms. Ray listens to group conversations. Sometimes, she asks questions to direct and guide each student's work. At times, she might change or broaden the group's discussion or direction to draw in another group member. For example, to pull Jeremiah back into his group's discussion on community recycling projects they might implement, she asked the group to think about how they might reach the community through music and songs.

Stop and review. When some groups appear to be confused, it is helpful to stop and ask a group who is on the right track to review the directions or guidelines. As the group retells instructions, Ms. Ray points to the directions on the board or an overhead. Ms. Ray finds that hearing the directions repeated helps students like James and Jeremiah refocus and understand what they are supposed to do.

Stop and share. Ms. Ray also stops to highlight groups that have an interesting idea or discover something new by asking them to share their ideas with the class. This helps other groups by giving them examples of what is an expected or a desired outcome. Because there is little risk in participation, it helps to boost the confidence and motivation of students like Raphael, who might otherwise not volunteer to share a good idea.

Wrap it up. Providing an opportunity for groups to share their finished answers, findings, or projects is essential and should not be left out of any small-group instruction. Ms. Ray uses this as an opportunity to check student comprehension and guide further instruction. Students are able to express interest in each other's work, ask questions, and clarify meanings. At times, Ms. Ray might ask each small group to pitch its best idea to the entire class for a vote. Students might debate and discuss the direction of a lab experiment or a community service project in this way.

In the Lab

Ms. Ray previously introduced and taught the roles of organisms in ecosystems, and now she wants students to investigate how different materials decompose. She plans to relate this experience to the larger problem of waste disposal, including discussion of landfills and recycling centers in the state where they live.

Ms. Ray begins by assigning lab partners. Whenever possible, she prefers students to work in pairs in the lab rather than in larger groups. The benefits of partners in the lab include

- increased participation and engagement of students;
- decreased unsafe or negative behaviors;
- ease of smaller groups to see results and share equipment (microscopes, Bunsen burners, and so on);
- greater variety of student projects, samples, and results;
- compatible matching of students' strengths and weaknesses. For example, James and Alicia are lab partners, pairing James' hands-on abilities and interest in labs with Alicia's intellectual ability and difficulty in lab.

Then, she forms two readiness groups.

The first group is able to work independently, and most of the students in it have experience with computers and the Internet. Ms. Ray gives students references and pre-screened Web sites related to science, biology, and natural resources. She instructs them to find relevant information and design an experiment on the decomposition of natural and manufactured objects using inexpensive and accessible materials around school or their homes. Ms. Ray explains how they are to write and submit their plans.

With the other group, Ms. Ray follows a more structured approach. She provides background information and reviews it with the group. She also instructs them how to set up a decomposition experiment, and they begin the experiment together. She reviews the concept of controlled experiments and asks students to predict what they think will happen in their experiment.

Each group keeps a weekly log of observations and results. They each create a finished product, either a written lab report or an oral presentation, explaining their experiment, the results, and their conclusions.

For sample Assessments and Rubrics go to

TEAching TODAY

at **teachingtoday.glencoe.com**

Differentiated Instruction

All students need to be accountable for what they learn in the classroom. Begin addressing assessment when you first introduce a new concept. Students need to know what type of outcome is expected of them when it comes to activities, homework, tests, reports, or other types of assessment.

If possible, tailor expected outcomes to match individual needs. Differentiated instruction provides your students with a variety of ways to demonstrate their knowledge and continue to meet the class requirements. At times, you can create a more accessible curriculum by making accommodations and modifications.

An accommodation is a change made to the teaching or testing procedures that provides a student with access to information and creates an equal opportunity to demonstrate knowledge and skills. Accommodations do not change the instructional level, content, or performance criteria for meeting the standards. Examples of accommodations include enlarged print, Braille versions, oral versions of tests, and using calculators. A modification is a change in what you expect a student to learn and/or demonstrate. Although a student might be working on modified course content, the subject area remains the same as the rest of the class. Modifications vary according to the situation. Listed below are four modification techniques:

- **Same–Only Less** The assignment remains the same, but you reduce the number of items. The items you select should be representative areas of the curriculum. For example, you could modify a science test that consisted of multiple choice questions with five possible answers each so that the number of possible answers is two.

- **Streamlined Curriculum** You reduce the assignment in size, breadth, or focus to emphasize key points. For example, a student could outline the chapter rather than write a summary of the chapter's contents. Alternatively, a student with special needs could focus on identifying the themes of the chapter and create a display to support his or her writing on those main ideas.

- **Same Activity with Infused Objective** The assignment remains the same, but you incorporate additional components, such as IEP (Individualized Education Plan) objectives or identified skills. Teachers often do this in conjunction with other accommodations and/or modifications to ensure that all IEP objectives are addressed. For example, if a student has an IEP objective to answer factual and inferential questions, you might need to remember to ask these types of questions so that the student can practice this skill in a natural setting.

- **Curriculum Overlapping** The student might complete the assignment in one area during another time. Some students work slowly and need more time to complete assignments, whereas others need to explore the connections between various content areas. For example, if a student participated in a poster project in his or her cooperative learning group, the student could also use the poster during a language arts lesson.

Deciding which technique to use depends on the type of assignment and the student. You might need only to reduce in size one assignment for a student to succeed, whereas for another, you might need to incorporate infused objectives. Keep in mind that you do not always need to modify the curriculum—even when you consider students with more significant special needs. When you provide multi-level instruction, you might not need to change a lesson. (Frey and Fisher).

Following is a list of additional curriculum accommodations and modifications.

In-Class Activities (Frey & Fisher)

- Break down new skills into small steps.
- Simplify instruction by demonstrating and guiding learning one step at a time.
- Role-play historical events.
- Underline or highlight important words and phrases.
- Group students into pairs, threes, fours, and so on for different assignments and activities.
- Pair students who have different and complementary skills.
- Select key words from the book to read on each page.
- Turn pages in the book while others read.
- Rewrite text or use easy-to-read versions.
- Have students complete sentences supplied by the teacher orally or in writing.
- Supply incomplete sentences for students to fill in appropriate words or phrases.
- Engage students in reading and in write-pair-share activities.
- Use hands-on activities.
- Color code important words or phrases.

Projects or Homework (Frey & Fisher)

- Assign smaller quantities of work.
- Relate problems to real-life situations.
- Highlight problems to be completed.
- Read problems and equations aloud.
- Allow more time for completion.
- Provide study questions in advance of the assignment.
- Encourage oral contributions.
- Assign concept maps.
- Provide sample sentences for students to use as a model.
- Dictate a report to a partner who writes it out or types it on the computer.
- Assign homework partners.
- Assign group projects to illustrate a text (collages and dioramas).
- Substitute projects for written assignments and reports.
- Use complementary software or adapted computer hardware.
- Organize pictures instead of words into categories.
- Have students survey other students using targeted questions on the topic.

Assessment (Frey & Fisher)

- Underline or highlight text directions.
- Read instructions or questions aloud.
- Re-word problems or test questions in simpler language.
- Underline key words.
- Space problems farther apart on the page.
- Reduce the number of questions by selecting representative items.
- Permit oral responses.
- Put choices for answers on index cards.
- Use the sentence or paragraph as a unit of composition rather than an essay.
- Allow oral responses to tests using a tape recorder.
- Use photographs in oral presentations to the class.
- Assign final group projects with each student responsible for specific roles.
- Encourage the use of other media for final products (film, video, audio, photos, drawings, performances, and so on).

References and Resources

Fisher, Douglas and Frey, Nancy,(2006) *Science Classrooms That Work: Strategies for Success.* McGraw-Hill Glencoe.

Hassard, Jack. (2005). *The Art of Teaching Science.* Oxford University Press.

Llewellyn, Douglas. (2005). *Teaching High School Science Through Inquiry.* Thousand Oaks, CA: National Science Teachers Association.

Ogle, D. M. (1986). *KWL: K-W-L: A Teaching Model That Develops Active Reading of Expository Text. Reading Teacher*

Roberts, Julia L. (2007). *Strategies for Differentiating Instruction.* Waco, TX: Prufrock Press, Inc.

Tomlinson, C.A. (2003). *Differentiation in Practice.* Alexandria, VA: Association for Supervision and Curriculum Development (ASCD).

Tomlinson, C.A. (2003). *Fulfilling the Promise of the Differentiated Classroom.* Alexandria, VA: Association for Supervision and Curriculum Development (ASDC).

Tracey Hall, *Differentiated Instruction.* www.cast.org/publications/ncac

sí oui
yes

English-Language Learners

Table of Contents

Who are English-language learners?.. 147

  English-Language Learners in the Science Classroom. 147

   • The Supportive Science Classroom...147

   • The Integrated Science Classroom 148

  English as a New Language...149

   • Some Misconceptions About ELLs 149

  Evaluate a Student's Language Proficiency 150

   • Beginning Learners 150

   • Intermediate Learners 150

   • Beginning Learner Instructional Modifications.........................151

   • Beginning Learner Assessment Modifications............................151

   • Intermediate Learner Assessment Modifications........................152

How do I create the best environment for learning?....................153

  One Size Does Not Fit All...153

  Work Within Your State's or District's System 155

Content-Based Language Instruction 156

  Select Content..156

  Develop Academic-Language Skills 157

Strategies That Work 158

  Use Explicit Learning Strategies...158

  The Classroom Scenario 159

   • The Students...159

Digital Resources for Teachers

McGraw Hill **Professional Development**   **mhpdonline.com**
These PD modules address both teaching strategies and science content.

✓ Literacy Strategies: Reading, Writing, Listening, and Speaking
✓ Differentiate Instruction
✓ English-Language Learners
✓ Standards-Based Instruction
✓ Assessment Strategies and Rubrics

✓ Teaching Energy
✓ Teaching Mitosis and Meiosis
✓ Teaching Moon Phases
✓ Teaching Photosynthesis
✓ Teaching Physical and Chemical Change
✓ Teaching Weather Concepts

TEACHING TODAY   **teachingtoday.glencoe.com**
A no-fee professional development Web site where you will find resources for:

✓ Lesson plans with downloads for newsletters, parent conference letters
✓ Teaching tips
✓ How-to articles sorted by discipline, grade level, and instructional type
✓ Math support
✓ Demonstration videos

Who are English-language learners?

English-language learners (ELLs) are students whose native, or primary, language is not English. Approximately 50 million Americans speak a language other than English in their homes. (www.census.gov) The level of English proficiency among students in these households varies greatly—from students who are hearing English for the first time to students who have a good command of the English language. Just as the level of proficiency varies greatly among English-language learners, so do the primary languages and cultures vary. Many students have relocated from Spanish-speaking countries, as well as from Africa, Asia, and the Middle East.

English-Language Learners in the Science Classroom

The rapid increase in culturally and linguistically diverse students presents certain challenges to teachers. While some school districts might offer sheltered instruction for English-language learners, the more typical model includes an hour or two of separate English-language instruction per day with all students mainstreamed into English-speaking classes for science, mathematics, and social studies.

Many teachers of core subjects have limited experience teaching English as a second language (ESL). While helping students learn a new language, you must also focus on teaching a core subject. This can be a difficult challenge when coupled with the demands of state-mandated curricula and tests.

The Supportive Science Classroom

If you have English-language learners in your science classroom, you probably will be asked to provide practical tools and suggest modifications that can help these students master scientific concepts while they develop their English language skills. This support should focus on methods for successful participation of English-language learners in the science classroom. These strategies rely not only on teacher intervention, but also on student intervention to create ownership of the learning process. Your overall approach should be compatible with research that shows that English-language learners are most successful when using a hands-on, inquiry approach with clearly articulated learning strategies. You can structure lessons around major science concepts, focusing on subject depth rather than breadth. Teaching support and strategies should include basic thinking skills, such as fact recall and identifying and defining vocabulary, as well as more complex critical-thinking skills, such as comparison, classification, and prediction.

For more information on English-Language Learners visit

 Professional Development

at **mhpdonline.com**

> A machine reduces the effort force needed
> to counter a resistance force.

Imagine walking into a classroom and reading the sentence above on the board. If you are an English speaker with some science background, you can probably recognize its general meaning. Now, consider how students who are just beginning to learn English might read this sentence. Depending on their proficiency, they might recognize the subject—*machine*—and the verb—*reduces*. Other words in the sentence might be more difficult. Consider the use of *effort* and *resistance*. English speakers commonly use these words as nouns. This sentence uses them both as adjectives to describe *force*—a word that can be a verb or a noun. *Counter* is used as a verb meaning "to go against," but dictionaries list at least five other definitions. This is just one example of an obstacle English-language learners face in the science classroom. As science classrooms become more ethnically and culturally diverse, teachers continue to search for the best way to convey scientific concepts while simultaneously being challenged by teaching a new language.

The Integrated Science Classroom

At one time, English-language learners were in special classes where they only learned language skills. This practice assumed that students had to be proficient in English before learning any content. This not only isolated them from other students but also delayed their learning in content areas. Current research shows that the best approach is an integrated one—using content as a way of developing English-language proficiency. Researchers have learned that many students are more motivated when they are learning about a subject than when they are learning language alone. Science is particularly motivating because of its hands-on approach and students' inherent interests in scientific topics.

English as a New Language

What is it like to learn a new language? While research has shown that it takes most English-language learners about two years to learn enough English to communicate in social situations, it takes between five and seven years for students to master the academic language necessary to succeed in a classroom.

Social language is the language of everyday living. It is easier to learn than academic language because people are immersed in it in their neighborhoods, in stores, on television, and on the Internet. In addition, there are many nonverbal cues that aid English-language learners in social situations, such as facial expressions and body language.

Academic language is the language students need to help them understand and process a subject, such as science. Mastering academic language is more difficult than mastering social language because it includes more than just terminology. For instance, in science, students must learn to think scientifically. This involves using basic thinking skills (such as recalling facts) as well as developing critical-thinking skills, which will help students succeed in the science classroom and laboratory. Observation, creating hypotheses, designing experiments, drawing conclusions, making predictions, and presenting information in a variety of scientific formats are all part of the scientific learning package.

Some Misconceptions About ELLs

One misconception about English-language learners is that if they have a good command of social language, they will do well in the content classroom. This is not always the case and points to the necessity of carefully assessing the language proficiency of ELLs.

It also is important to realize that even if students are unable to articulate their knowledge of content in a particular area, you cannot assume that they do not possess that knowledge. Many ELLs find it difficult to speak in a new language in front of their peers in the classroom. Until they become confident, it is helpful to let them express their knowledge in other ways. For example, ask them to draw a picture or label a diagram to illustrate a particular concept. Alternatively, if a student is more confident speaking in small groups, you can create an activity that focuses on that strength.

Another misconception is that if the content is watered down, students will benefit by being able to understand more. There are problems with this assumption as well. One is that ELLs might have already achieved proficiency of the content in languages other than English. Instead of reducing the level of the material, the best solution is to help students retrieve and convey the knowledge they have already acquired. A second problem with diluting content is that it will isolate ELLs from the rest of the students in your classroom. Rather than providing lower-level content, your time is better spent modifying the content to make it more accessible to all learners.

Evaluate a Student's Language Proficiency

To work effectively with ELLs, you need to know your students' levels of language proficiency. Obviously, the needs of beginning English-learners will differ from those of more linguistically proficient learners. When you recognize and understand each student's proficiency level, you will be armed with the information you need to support learning and modify classroom instruction.

Some sources break down proficiency into four main categories—novice, beginning, intermediate, and advanced. The term "novice" applies to someone who has a minimal ability to communicate and understand English. At the other end of the scale is the advanced learner, whose reading, writing, listening, and speaking skills approximate those of a native English speaker.

Beginning Learners

Beginning learners might be able to understand social language if it is spoken slowly and repeated several times. However, they often are hesitant to speak due to limited vocabulary and difficulty with pronunciation. Beginning learners need structure in the classroom and support from both you and other students.

Intermediate Learners

Intermediate learners have well-developed social language skills but lack the academic language skills required in a content classroom. The fact that they speak well conversationally often leads teachers to believe that they are more proficient than they really are. Intermediate learners are capable of comprehending, reading, and writing in English. They can work well independently but still benefit from teacher support and support from students, especially in cooperative learning groups. With intermediate learners, it is important to define major content areas and overtly suggest learning strategies to help them master content and complex thinking skills.

The checklists that follow can help you modify your instructional and assessment approaches for ELLs who are at the beginning and intermediate levels of language proficiency. ESCORT, a national resource center at the State University of New York, developed these lists as part of a kit designed to help secondary teachers of migrant English-language learners. The project was funded by the U.S. Department of Education.

Beginning Learners

Instructional Modifications

All Students

____ Use visuals/hands-on manipulatives.

____ Use gestures to convey meaning non-verbally.

____ Provide concrete "real" examples and experiences.

____ Build on the known. (e.g., Make connections with students' culture, experiences, interests, and skills.)

____ Simplify vocabulary, or change slang and idioms to simpler language.

____ Highlight, review, and repeat key points and vocabulary frequently.

____ Establish consistent classroom routines. List steps for completing assignments.

____ Use *yes/no, either/or*, and *why/how* questions. (Allow wait time for response.)

____ Check for comprehension on a regular basis. ("Do you understand?" is not detailed enough.)

____ Create story and semantic maps.

____ Use "Language Experience Approach" (through the use of students' own words and writing as teaching material).

____ Plan ways for ELLs to participate in class and in cooperative learning groups.

____ Make outlines or use graphic organizers.

____ Use audiotapes to reinforce learning.

____ Use simplified books and texts that cover content concepts.

____ Translate key concepts into a student's native language.

Students with adequate literacy in their native language (if bilingual person is available)

____ Use textbooks and/or books in the native language that cover key concepts you teach.

____ Encourage the student to use a bilingual dictionary as a learning tool.

____ Have the student write essays/journal entries in the native language.

Assessment Modifications

All Students

____ Have the student point to the picture of a correct answer. (Limit choices.)

____ Have the student circle a correct answer. (Limit choices.)

____ Instruct the student to draw a picture illustrating a concept.

____ Reduce choices on multiple-choice tests.

____ Instruct the student to match items.

____ Have the student complete fill-in-the-blank exercises with the word list provided.

____ Give open-book tests.

_____ Ask the student to retell or restate (orally and in writing).

_____ Instruct the student to define, explain, and/or summarize orally in English or the native language.

_____ Have the student compare and contrast (orally and in writing).

_____ Use cloze procedure with outlines, charts, time lines, and so on. (This procedure is a technique in which words or phrases are deleted from a passage. Students must fill them in as they read.)

Students with adequate literacy in their native language (if bilingual person is available)

_____ Instruct the student to write what he or she has learned in the native language.

Intermediate Learners

Assessment Modifications

All Students

_____ Instruct the student to explain how he/she achieved an answer (orally and in writing).

_____ Have the student complete fill-in-the-blank exercises.

_____ Ask the student to retell or restate (orally and in writing).

_____ Instruct the student to define, explain, or summarize (orally and in writing).

_____ Have the student compare and contrast (orally and in writing).

_____ Use cloze procedure with outlines, charts, time lines, and so on.

_____ Have the student analyze and explain data (orally and in writing).

_____ Instruct the student to express opinions and judgments (orally and in writing).

_____ Have the student write essays.

How do I create the best environment for learning?

There is no magical formula for determining the one best learning strategy, instructional routine, or activity to use in teaching a particular scientific concept. The best results most often come from a combination of approaches and strategies. Whenever possible, you should focus on multisensory approaches using a variety of media. The variety will not only assist your ELLs but also prove to be a benefit for your English-speaking students.

One Size Does Not Fit All

Before discussing specific approaches to teaching science to English-language learners, there are general guidelines that will help you to create a good environment for learning in your science classroom. In general, flexibility and creativity will go a long way when creating a positive and practical classroom environment. Remember, what works for one student might not work for another. Be flexible, and be willing to try new approaches. Continually develop and add to your repertoire as you discover approaches that work.

Focus on depth rather than breadth. Concentrate your efforts and your students' efforts on learning major scientific concepts rather than trying to learn a little about all scientific concepts. A standards-based curriculum can help you narrow the most important themes.

Speak clearly and precisely. Critique your classroom speech habits to pinpoint areas that might be confusing to ELLs. It is not necessary to dilute scientific material or vocabulary, but you do need to present material clearly and precisely for the best results.

Clearly define expectations. When making assignments, be specific about what you expect students to know, to do, and to submit for a passing grade. It is particularly helpful to develop a set of guidelines or a scoring rubric. Use visual samples to model the expected outcome whenever possible. You might want to display a sample of a lab report, diagram, or other assignment using a dry-erase board, an overhead projector, or some electronic device. Review it with ELLs line by line or element by element and model what information should appear.

Foster independence. Empower ELLs by making them self-reliant. Let them make choices about the learning strategies that work best for them. Use scaffolding to provide support when you teach a new concept, and then gradually pull back as a student becomes more self-sufficient. By providing students with options of how they can learn, it enables them to choose what works best for them. This approach also serves as a motivator and reinforces confidence.

For Lesson Plans go to

TEAᵗCHING
TODAY
at **teachingtoday.glencoe.com**

Encourage interaction. Whenever possible, group students in pairs, small groups, or cooperative-learning situations to encourage verbal interaction and allow ELLs to use other students as models for their communication. Use role-playing situations to reinforce concepts as well as to take advantage of students' more developed social language skills. Pair ELLs with English speakers to encourage collaboration and attainment of common goals.

Build confidence. Model correct language but don't constantly correct a student. If a student answers correctly but uses improper language, provide a response that models the correct language. Incorrect verb choice or subject-verb agreement does not mean that a student does not understand the concept. Remember that speaking a new language can be difficult. Provide other forms of communication opportunities when possible.

To build confidence and also help the learning process, expose ELLs to others that speak their native languages as much as possible. Rely on cooperative learning activities, role-playing, and other interactions to provide those opportunities. Acknowledge and respect the cultures of ELLs and encourage all students to do the same. Whenever possible, provide opportunities for your ELLs to succeed.

Provide classroom resources. Textbooks are a valuable resource in and out of the classroom. However, the amount of material might be difficult for some ELLs to comprehend. Set aside time to describe the organization of your science textbook. Point out the lists of terms at the beginning of each chapter. Show students where to locate review questions. Point out the location and use of the glossary and index. Encourage students to use the organization of their textbooks as a model to create a study outline for major science concepts. Try to provide a variety of resources in your classroom. This is helpful to ELLs and also an excellent way to supplement and enrich the learning experience for all of your students.

Helpful classroom resources include

- a science listening center where students can listen to recordings of class discussions and lessons;
- dictionaries in a variety of languages;
- scientific primary sources;
- samples of completed lab reports, tests, and homework assignments to serve as guides;
- a variety of posters, diagrams, graphs, and graphic organizers that present major scientific concepts;
- pictures or samples of lab equipment labeled in English.

Work Within Your State's or District's System

The structure in place for teaching English as a second language (ESL) varies from state to state and district to district, depending on the ethnic population of the area. Some schools have separate classes for ELLs. Other schools heterogeneously group all students. Some schools have both types of classroom structures. Whatever program is in place in your state, you will need to follow its specific curriculum and assessment guidelines in tailoring your classroom approach.

The National Research Council has defined scientific literacy as "the knowledge and understanding of scientific concepts and processes required for personal decision making, participation in civic and cultural affairs, and economic productivity." According to these standards, "Scientific literacy means that a person can ask, find, or determine answers to questions derived from curiosity about everyday experiences. It means that a person has the ability to describe, explain, and predict natural phenomena. Scientific literacy entails being able to read with understanding articles about science in various forms of media and to engage in social conversations about the validity of the conclusions. Scientific literacy implies that a person can identify scientific issues underlying national and local decisions and express positions that are scientifically and technologically informed. A literate citizen should be able to evaluate the quality of scientific information on the basis of its source and the methods used to generate it."

To meet these expectations for both ELLs and English-speaking students, the nation's science classrooms have had to make some changes. Instead of focusing on a set of specific facts and procedures, instruction has broadened to incorporate methods that encourage scientific discovery through a hands-on approach. Observing, formulating questions, hypothesizing, designing experiments, making predictions, and reporting information in a variety of ways are now central to science instruction. A hands-on approach that incorporates a wide range of discovery strategies provides a means for English-language learners to use and reinforce their written and oral language in authentic ways. This provides a helpful bridge for science teachers who are welcoming ELLs into their classrooms.

Content-Based Language Instruction

In recent years, educational specialists have conducted significant research to determine the most effective way to teach content to English-language learners. Many models focus on teaching content and language simultaneously.

One such model is the Cognitive Academic Language Learning Approach (CALLA) developed by Anna Uhl Chamot and J. Michael O'Malley. In the CALLA model, content becomes the means by which language skills are learned, not vice versa. The model assumes that students will master academic language as they need it to understand and process content. Academic language becomes the means by which students communicate major concepts and processes particular to a subject area. CALLA suggests that ELLs need to be prepared with an arsenal of learning strategies to be successful in a content-based classroom.

The CALLA model focuses on three goals.

1. Select major topics from a content area.
2. Develop the academic language skills needed to understand and process the material from that content area.
3. Determine specific learning strategies that can aid in the learning of that content and language.

Select Content

When teaching content to ELLs, it is important to narrow the range of the content. Students are most successful if they focus on only the most important concepts—concepts that will follow them throughout their science education. The complexity of these concepts increases as students progress from grade to grade, but the basic concepts remain the same.

As a general guide, content is fundamental if it

- represents a central event or phenomenon in the natural world;
- represents a central scientific idea and organizing principle;
- has rich explanatory power;
- guides fruitful investigations;
- applies to situations and contexts common to everyday experiences;
- can be linked to meaningful learning experiences;
- is developmentally appropriate for students at the grade level specified.

Develop Academic-Language Skills

The academic language of science is unique and increases in complexity as students move from one grade to the next. In addition to learning scientific terminology, students must learn how to think scientifically using scientific reasoning and critical thinking skills. The hands-on approach to science also requires that students learn to perform scientific processes and know how to communicate scientific theories, results, and predictions in a variety of written and oral forms. This can be especially difficult for a student who must first process the concept from English into his or her primary language and then translate results back into English.

To be successful, ELLs have to acquire specific learning strategies. Learning strategies are activities or processes that help students learn. They must be customized to fit a particular activity or task.

By choosing from a menu of specific strategies before they immerse themselves in a science task, research shows that ELLs can increase their likelihood of success. Some ELLs are able to identify these learning strategies on their own. Others will need assistance. In time, they will begin to understand which strategies work best for them without prompting.

A suggested format for teaching learning strategies is to first name the strategy and then discuss when and why to use the strategy. Next, a teacher should demonstrate the use of the strategy. Following the demonstration, ELLs should practice using the strategy in small groups. They should be encouraged to try a variety of learning strategies to find out what is most effective for them.

C

Strategies That Work

Use Explicit Learning Strategies

Learning Strategies		
Metacognitive Strategies	**Cognitive Strategies**	**Social/Affective Strategies**
Students use as they plan for learning, monitor their learning, and evaluate their learning.	*Students use as they immerse themselves in the material to be learned.*	*Students use when they interact with others or with themselves.*
Selective Attention Student focuses on what the learning task will be and its purpose as set forth by the teacher, other students, or self.	**Rehearsal** Student reviews information needed to complete the task.	**Cooperation** Student works with other students to find solutions to problems, share information, or obtain feedback.
Planning Student makes plans for how learning will be accomplished—organizes materials, schedules time, and so on.	**Transfer** Student identifies and applies prior knowledge to complete the task.	**Question** Student asks teacher or other students for clarification or explanation.
Advance Organizers Student reviews the material to be learned and identifies the major concepts. This may include pre-reading in a textbook or doing research.	**Translation** Student uses first language to aid in understanding the task. **Resourcing** Student finds resources (textbooks, dictionaries, encyclopedias, and so on) that will provide information to help complete the task.	**Self-Talk** Student relies on self to provide assurance that the task can be accomplished successfully. **Self-Reinforcement** Student determines self-rewards to increase motivation for learning or completing a task successfully.
Self-Monitoring Student reviews the work in progress to make sure that comprehension is accurate, directions are being followed, and the final goal can be achieved.	**Grouping** Student classifies information based on its similarities and differences. **Recombination** Student breaks down larger concepts and recombines them to make them more meaningful or easier to understand.	
Self-Evaluation Student checks completed work to see if it fulfills the requirements of the assignment. If it does, what methods led to success? If it does not, what methods could be improved?	**Deduction** Student applies a set of rules to help in understanding and processing the material. **Note Taking** Student summarizes and records key concepts and key vocabulary. **Inferring** Student uses context to help determine meaning. **Imagery** Student uses images, either mental or on paper, to aid in understanding.	

The Classroom Scenario

The Students

Abdul has lived in the United States for four years. He is an outgoing student and has well-developed social language skills. He enjoys being in a heterogeneous class and loves everything about popular teen culture. He had very little formal education in his country of birth, and he struggles with the academic language needed in a content classroom.

Maria has been in the United States for less than two years. In her country of birth, she attended school regularly and was an advanced student. She has a keen interest in math and science and would like to be a college professor. Her teachers, however, are unaware of her abilities because her limited English-speaking skills keep her from participating in content classes.

These are two of the five ELLs in Ms. Ray's science class. The other three ELLs also come from distinct backgrounds and speak languages other than English. Like Abdul and Maria, the amount and type of education they received in their native countries varies. They are beginning to early-intermediate English-language learners. As you can see, these students are no different than any other student in Ms. Ray's class, having unique learning characteristics, interests, and needs.

Ms. Ray planned to teach a unit on the conservation of materials and resources. She wanted students to grasp the importance of reducing, reusing, and recycling waste. In lab, she planned to have students explore the process of decomposition and compare decomposition rates of different materials. When assessing the prior knowledge of students in the class, she noted that many students were familiar with the recycling symbol on paper, glass, and plastic receptacles, but they didn't often make an effort to use these bins.

Although she designed many features of her lesson explicitly for the ELLs in her class, she learned that these techniques also benefited her other students. As you read what she did, consider how you might employ similar strategies to topics in your own classroom. Remember that this is not an exhaustive list, but rather one meant to highlight how the strategies previously discussed in this section could be put into action.

Use props and gestures to teach vocabulary. Ms. Ray frequently uses familiar props whenever possible. For example, she began her recycling lesson by bringing in a large recycling bin, used by the residents in her students' town to collect curbside recycling each week. She placed this next to the trash can in the classroom. Then she asked students what to do with an empty water bottle. She pantomimed and talked through her options as she taught students the word "recycle." In the end, she filled the bottle from the tap, and taught the word "reuse." She repeated the vocabulary, pointing to the words on the class Word Wall as she said them.

Speak appropriately. Ms. Ray focuses on her rate of speech and word choice in class, deliberately slowing down and repeating key words. In addition to content vocabulary, she also introduces science vocabulary and process words that might be difficult for English learners. For example, she demonstrated words like *observe*, *record*, and *interpret* as well as content-related vocabulary.

Use graphic organizers and visuals. Ms. Ray regularly uses graphic organizers in her classroom to help students organize information. When possible, she uses pictures as well as words on the graphic organizer. For example, she had ELL students identify and sort images demonstrating how people reduce, reuse, and recycle in a three-column graphic organizer.

Use hands-on materials and/or step-by-step lab instructions. Ms. Ray often reviews with her ELLs and some others the steps of lab experiments. As she explains the experiment and shows students what to do, they copy her actions with their own set of materials. For a decomposition lab in this unit, she also provided students with a set of pictures showing the lab setup.

Modify assessments. Ms. Ray is aware that her ELLs' difficulty articulating their knowledge of science content does not indicate a lack of knowledge. For this reason, she frequently provides assessment modifications for the ELLs in her class in an attempt to allow them to demonstrate what they have learned. On tests, she reduces the number of multiple-choice answers from four or five to two or three and provides fill-in-the-blank exercises for students. She designs methods for students to demonstrate knowledge physically as well as orally and in writing. For example, she asked students to draw or demonstrate four uses of a glass jelly jar in addition to a more formal assessment.

Language Arts and Literacy

Table of Contents

Introduction **164**

Reading in Science 164

Writing in Science 164

Supporting National Standards **165**

   Scientific Literacy 165

   Inquiry...166

   No Child Left Behind...166

   Read to Learn Science 167

    • Writing Styles 167

    • Vocabulary 167

    • Read Mathematics in Science...............................168

    • Read Illustrations 169

    • Metacognition 169

   Strategies for Reading Science.................................170

    • Elements of Reading—Environment, Reader, Text 170

    • Vocabulary 172

    • Organize Information 175

    • Prepare to Preread 179

    • Read for Information..180

    • Reflect 184

   Write in Science..185

    • Types of Writing In Science 185

    • Organize and Consolidate Thinking 185

    • Benefits for Teachers 186

    • Criteria for Writing in Science 186

   Implement Writing 187

    • General Strategies..187

    • Improve Student Writing 189

    • Science Journal Writing 190

    • Short Writing Activities 192

    • Experiments and Lab Reports 195

    • Writing for Essay Exams 195

    • Longer Writing Projects.......................................195

    • Portfolios 197

How to Assess Writing Assignments **197**

Teacher Assessment 197

Peer Assessment 197

Self-Assessment 197

Assessment Criteria 198

Read and Write About Science in Literature **198**

Literature 198

Creative Writing 199

Read and Write About Science in the Media **200**

Media 200

Strategies for the Use of Media......................................200

Writing and the Media 201

D

Digital Resources for Teachers

 Professional **mhpdonline.com**
Development *These PD modules address both teaching strategies and science content.*

- ✓ Literacy Strategies: Reading, Writing, Listening, and Speaking
- ✓ Differentiate Instruction
- ✓ English-Language Learners
- ✓ Standards-Based Instruction
- ✓ Assessment Strategies and Rubrics

- ✓ Teaching Energy
- ✓ Teaching Mitosis and Meiosis
- ✓ Teaching Moon Phases
- ✓ Teaching Photosynthesis
- ✓ Teaching Physical and Chemical Change
- ✓ Teaching Weather Concepts

TEACHING TODAY **teachingtoday.glencoe.com**
A no-fee professional development Web site where you will find resources for:

- ✓ Lesson plans with downloads for newsletters, parent conference letters
- ✓ Teaching tips
- ✓ How-to articles sorted by discipline, grade level, and instructional type
- ✓ Math support
- ✓ Demonstration videos

D

Introduction

Reading and writing are skills that students need to master in order to understand science. They facilitate communicating, organizing, clarifying, and revising ideas, and they promote the development of higher-level thinking skills to support scientific inquiry.

Reading in Science

Reading, in addition to observation, hands-on activities, lab work, class discussions, and demonstrations, is essential to learning science. The importance and amount of daily reading increases as students progress to higher-level science courses. At the elementary level, science classes emphasize visual, oral, and tactile activities. College-level and AP science teachers expect students to read their textbooks with comprehension and to be able to study independently. Students need to learn strategies for reading many different types of scientific materials; for example, reading for information and comprehension, lab and activity instructions, creative writing and literature, and questions for assignments and standardized tests.

Reading in science

- extends students' knowledge and comprehension of topics introduced through hands-on activities;
- can convey detailed or complex information more quickly and accurately than illustrations or observations;
- enables students to explore objects, concepts, and processes that are too small, too large, too distant, too dangerous, or too abstract to learn through direct interaction;
- requires students to develop critical-thinking skills that will serve them in and out of the classroom.

Writing in Science

Writing scientifically is more than just writing the correct answer on a test. It is more than simply communicating thoughts and ideas. Writing scientifically is the most concrete mechanism by which students organize their knowledge and clarify their understanding. Because it solidifies comprehension, it is a crucial aspect of studying science.

The role of writing grows as students advance. In middle-school classes, students should be able to write sentences to explain concepts, compare objects, and describe processes. College-level instructors expect students to write essays, lab reports, and scientific arguments. From middle-school sentences to college-level essays, writing helps teachers assess both student understanding and the effectiveness of learning activities.

Reading and writing skills are essential for every career. Reading and writing activities in the science classroom parallel those of professional scientists and engineers, as you will see in the table on the next page.

For Literacy Strategies go to

TeAching Today
at **teachingtoday.glencoe.com**

D

Professional Activity	Classroom Activity
read professional journals	read textbook
read papers on the Internet	read science news on the Internet
write detailed logs of experiments	write lab reports and science journals
write papers for journals	write reports and essays
have papers evaluated by colleagues and peers before they are accepted for publication	have papers evaluated by classmates and the teacher
publish papers in journals	share writings with classmates and create portfolios

This resource provides you with background information and practical classroom techniques that will help you teach your students to read and write in science. You can easily create and adapt additional writing activities that match your students' abilities and needs.

This resource

- explains the unique aspects of reading and writing in science;
- presents effective reading strategies;
- describes how to create an environment for reading and writing;
- offers detailed steps for teaching students how to read their science textbooks;
- describes how to implement journal writing;
- suggests motivating writing activities;
- provides tips for taking notes and reviewing;
- describes reading and writing about science in literature;
- discusses reading and writing about science in the media.

If you have not already used journal writing with your students, keep a journal yourself as you read about language arts in the science classroom. Keeping a journal will help you clarify your thinking and remember key points. Journal writing in science classes is discussed more fully beginning on page 190 of this tab.

Supporting National Standards

This resource provides strategies for helping students gain scientific literacy and for developing understanding through scientific inquiry.

Scientific Literacy

The following passage from the National Science Education Standards demonstrates the critical role of reading and writing in scientific literacy, with underlining added for emphasis.

"Scientific Literacy means that a person can <u>ask, find, or determine answers</u> to questions derived from curiosity about everyday experiences. It means that a person has the ability to

D

For Standards-Based Instruction go to

TEACHING TODAY

at **teachingtoday.glencoe.com**

describe, explain, and predict natural phenomena. Scientific literacy entails being able to read with understanding articles about science in the popular press and to engage in social conversation about the validity of the conclusions. Scientific literacy implies that a person can identify scientific issues underlying national and local decisions and express positions that are scientifically and technologically informed. A literate citizen should be able to evaluate the quality of scientific information on the basis of its source and the methods used to generate it. Scientific literacy also implies the capacity to pose and evaluate arguments based on evidence and to apply conclusions from such arguments appropriately."

Source: National Research Council.
National Science Education Standards.
Washington, DC: National
Academy Press, 1996, page 22.

Inquiry

The following description of inquiry by the National Research Council, with underlining added for emphasis, clearly indicates the value of reading and writing in the inquiry process.

"Inquiry is a multifaceted activity that involves making observations; posing questions; examining books and other sources of information to see what is already known; planning investigations; reviewing what is already known in light of experimental evidence; using tools to gather, analyze, and interpret data; proposing answers, explanations, and predictions; and communicating the results. Inquiry requires identification of assumptions, use of critical and logical thinking, and consideration of alternative explanations."

Source: National Research Council.
National Science Education Standards.
Washington, DC: National
Academy Press, 1996, page 23.

No Child Left Behind

A major emphasis in the No Child Left Behind (NCLB) Act of 2002 is the critical role that reading has in learning. It recognizes that "reading is the essential skill."

"Research shows that children who read well in the early grades are far more successful in later years. Putting it another way—reading is a gateway skill to all learning. Young, capable readers can take greater advantage of school opportunities and develop invaluable confidence in their own abilities. Reading success leads directly to success in other subjects such as social studies, math, and science. In the long term, students who cannot read well are much more likely to drop out of school and be limited to lower-paying jobs throughout their lifetimes. Reading is undeniably one of the foundations for success in society."

Source: NCLB web site: www.nclb.gov/next/faqs/reading.html

D

Read to Learn Science

Reading is the process of creating meaning from written text. Learning to read well requires mastering many skills. By middle school, most students have learned the basics of reading—phonics, fluency, and comprehension—but have not developed more advanced reading skills such as active reading, reflective reading, and critical reading.

Teaching reading in the science classroom enhances both language skills and science comprehension. Reading helps students master scientific concepts, while science texts provide motivation for reading.

For Literacy Strategies go to TEACHING TODAY at teachingtoday.glencoe.com

Writing Styles

Written materials in science have various formats and purposes according to their style. Each of the following types of material calls for appropriate reading strategies:

- Information and Comprehension
- Instructions for Activities
- Pleasure and Literary Experience
- News and Information

Reading a science textbook is different from reading a novel. Readers of science textbooks need to understand each paragraph before continuing, rather than hope to figure out the whole story in the last chapter. Illustrations are not merely decorative; they are essential to understanding concepts. Descriptions in science must be written precisely so that the reader has a clear understanding of the material.

The language of science textbooks is often denser than newspaper or magazine articles. It is packed with statements, descriptions, and explanations of objects and processes. It uses and introduces many specialized terms. Often readers must have mastered the content of previous lessons in order to comprehend the current topic.

Most science textbooks incorporate several types of writing. Expository writing describes and explains concepts. Captions for illustrations present information related to the graphics. Labs and activity pages provide instructions for hands-on investigations. Assessment questions test recall and comprehension of information. Each type of writing calls for different reading strategies.

Vocabulary

The Role of Vocabulary

The role of vocabulary in learning science is both crucial and controversial. Consistent and precise scientific terms enable scientists and students to communicate clearly and efficiently. In fact, using precise vocabulary aids comprehension. Naming a concept is central to fully understanding it. However, limiting class focus to learning vocabulary can impede student comprehension if knowing words and definitions becomes the most important goal, rather than understanding word meanings in context of the lesson.

D

The aim for teachers is to help students understand scientific concepts and the nature and methods of scientific inquiry. The role of vocabulary is to support that understanding—to clarify thinking and promote communication.

The first step in teaching vocabulary is to determine which scientific terms students must master in order to comprehend content. A smaller scientific vocabulary in which concepts are well understood is preferable to a large vocabulary list that students memorize. The larger the vocabulary list, the less likely students will understand and correctly use the words in context.

Introduce science terms as needed after students have begun working with the concept. That way, students realize the need for the vocabulary term. This will help them retain the word and its meaning in their long-term memory. Memorizing a definition for a test limits students' ability to retain information over time because it focuses only on short-term goals—to pass the test.

Scientific Vocabulary

Students will be familiar with some scientific terms learned in other science classes and by watching television and movies. However, entertainment media sometimes misuse scientific terms, creating misconceptions. Correct these misconceptions as quickly as possible so your students can understand and build on scientific concepts properly.

Learning science vocabulary can be challenging. Unlike other English vocabulary, some scientific terms are used only in school—not with friends, at home, or on television. In addition, many science words are difficult to pronounce and to spell.

Categorizing science vocabulary terms as they relate to standard English usage makes word meanings clearer. Some scientific words are unique to science, such as the words *mitosis*, *sporophyte stage*, and *heterozygous*. Students need to learn these new words and to demonstrate that they understand them by using the words in context.

Some scientific words have comparable everyday meanings, but scientific terms are more precise, such as *density*, *dominant*, and *basin*. Help students relate the word's scientific meaning to its colloquial counterpart. However, be sure to point out the differences in the words' applications.

Some science terms are the same as everyday words, but have different meanings, such as *fault*, *element*, *frequency*, *niche*, *plate*, and *revolution*. Students should treat all terms as new words in order to correctly learn their scientific meanings. Section 2 describes strategies for learning vocabulary, such as root words, student-made glossaries, and graphic organizers.

Read Mathematics in Science

Mathematics is sometimes called the language of science, and the ability to read mathematical language is a very important aspect of reading science. Since science increasingly incorporates mathematics as students advance from primary levels through middle school and high school, the ability to interpret and use mathematical language becomes more significant.

D

As students progress to higher-level science courses, their need for functional mathematics skills increases. Reading mathematical symbols for variables, operations, and relationships used in scientific formulas becomes crucial.

Interpreting tables and graphs of data is a key skill in science. Reading data graphs involves understanding data collected, what variable is shown on each axis, what relationship or pattern the graph displays, and how that relationship relates to a real-world situation. Reading a data graph also includes evaluating whether the data are appropriate to answer the question under examination, whether data collection methods are sound, and whether the graphic display accurately portrays the data.

Read Illustrations

Illustrations—photographs, drawings, and diagrams—play a significant role in science because they help students understand concepts explained in the text. Illustrations can show objects that are not easy to see—interior views, microscopic organisms, and huge or distant objects. They can show relationships that might be difficult to comprehend in words. Illustrations can clarify a concept, provide additional details, and depict events or processes.

Reading diagrams in textbooks includes not only reading the captions and labels, but also analyzing graphics to discover and understand relationships between an image and the text. Students must learn how to evaluate diagrams found in newspapers and magazines and on Web sites by using their critical-thinking skills to determine if the diagrams accurately portray the concepts or are incomplete and/or misleading.

Metacognition

In order to learn, it is essential that students understand what they read. To better understand what they are reading, students need to constantly monitor their own thinking and decide whether they understand the material. This awareness of one's own thinking is called metacognition. Using metacognition, a student will become more aware of when his or her comprehension of the text is breaking down. Students learn to pause and read more carefully before going further. You will find more details about metacognition on page 171.

D

Strategies for Reading Science

Strategies for reading science include methods to build vocabulary, encourage pre-reading activities, increase comprehension through active reading, and practice reflection.

It is imperative that teachers model effective reading strategies for students, especially at the beginning of the school year. Talking through and demonstrating strategies in pre-reading, reading, and reflection is a useful approach to working with students of all ages and abilities in the science classroom.

Many of the reading strategies described in this section involve writing. Reading and writing are complementary processes—communicating through written language. You can learn more about writing in science starting on page 185.

Elements of Reading–Environment, Reader, Text

All types of reading involve three interactive elements—the environment, the reader, and the text.

The Environment

A teacher creates the classroom learning environment, and he or she is the most important aspect of that environment.

Supportive Classroom Environment

Students need a classroom environment that encourages reading and writing, and it is important for them to be able to speak openly without fear of disapproval or ridicule. For some students, reading aloud, either with the whole class or in small groups, can improve comprehension but also cause stress. Expect your students to make mistakes and encourage them to consider errors as part of the learning process. You should also emphasize to your students that all learners make mistakes. Students should not be afraid of looking silly because they don't already know what they must learn. Providing support for students who are reading aloud will encourage those learners who are shy or apprehensive about taking a risk to speak more often and share their work with others.

Role Model

At the beginning of the school year, discuss the value of reading in science. Model reading a passage aloud to the class, and "think out loud" about what you are reading. Demonstrate the strategies of previewing, monitoring your understanding, focusing on key concepts, and reflecting on what you have read.

During the year, review reading strategies and continue to demonstrate enthusiasm for acquiring new understanding through reading.

Emphasis on Reading

Early in the school year, emphasize the importance of reading your textbook. Encourage students to take responsibility for reading and studying, both in the classroom and at home.

The Reader

Students bring unique combinations of prior experiences, skills, and attitudes to reading science.

Prior Knowledge

Readers construct meaning by connecting new information with prior knowledge. As they read, students should ask themselves, "How does this fit with what I already know?" and "How is this alike or different from something I learned earlier?" Help students make these connections by relating the new topic to previously learned concepts.

Review previously learned vocabulary and concepts that apply to the current lesson. Check that students understand prerequisite concepts.

Metacognition

Metacognition, as introduced on page 169, is "thinking about thinking." Whether or not students understand what they are reading is an important part of the learning process.

Help students develop metacognitive skills by explaining the concept, providing examples, and encouraging students to practice metacognition through speaking and writing. To introduce the concept of metacognition, ask questions such as these:

- *How did you decide what to wear to school today?*
- *How did you decide what to eat for breakfast today?*
- *What will you try to accomplish in science class this year? How will you keep track of these goals?*

Decision-making is a type of thinking. As students respond with the thoughts that influenced their decisions, point out that they are thinking about their thinking. They are using metacognition.

Have students write their own responses to the questions above in their journals or notebooks and end with the statement, "I used metacognition to write this." Later in the course, they can refer to this activity as an example of metacognitive thinking.

Attitude

Students' levels of motivation and interest in reading science vary considerably and can affect their abilities to learn from reading. Encourage students to become aware of their attitudes, and stress that a positive attitude about learning science will help them overcome many difficulties. Remind students that some scientific concepts are not easy to understand and will require discipline to master.

Students should feel proud of themselves when they gain understanding of a topic or concept. Invite students to share successful methods of studying that might help other students learn a challenging concept.

Read Alone, Aloud, and with Others

Reading alone with full comprehension is the goal. Some students require extra help to reach this goal because of their special needs or learning styles.

D

Reading aloud, a strategy commonly used in elementary school, can also be an effective strategy for middle-school students. As you or a student reads aloud, the rest of the class can view the printed text and hear the words pronounced. This will focus student attention on the text. However, reading aloud can put too much stress on students to perform well, distracting them from the content they are reading. Be aware that fast readers often become bored while others read aloud.

Students might feel more comfortable reading aloud in a small-group setting. Within the small group, students can ask questions about passages that they do not fully understand. If the group cannot answer a question together, invite them to present it to the class. This activity will also help you gain understanding of what concepts students find particularly challenging.

In addition to their textbooks, students can read questions and explanations written by other students. Reading their own writing aloud helps students identify which statements need further clarification or re-thinking.

The Text

To make the best use of their study time, students need to recognize and use the features of their textbooks. Take time at the beginning of the school year to go over with students the different sections and resources in their textbooks.

Vocabulary

A major goal in science education is mastery of inquiry skills—formulating questions, using evidence, creating hypotheses, organizing information, and explaining results. Scientific vocabulary and the concepts behind the words provide building blocks for students to use when practicing scientific inquiry.

Teach Vocabulary

In general, build student understanding of concepts before introducing vocabulary terms. For example, demonstrate the movement of materials through a membrane and discuss how a cell membrane works before defining homeostasis.

Rote memorization of words and their definitions is not an effective long-term strategy. Learning new words in context and connecting them to familiar words helps students to internalize new vocabulary. Provide opportunities for students to "talk science" together in pairs or small groups and make the new terms part of their own vocabulary.

Many scientific terms are not colloquial. Some are versatile enough to use either scientifically or colloquially, but are more precise in science. Comparing and contrasting the colloquial and scientific uses of words can help students master the scientific definitions. For example, *mixture* is used loosely in everyday speech to mean "a combination of things," but in science, it is a combination in which the individual substances do not change chemically.

Students learn sets of related science terms by exploring their commonalities and their differences. In middle school, definitions are usually less formal than in high-school science courses.

Example: cytoplasm

Middle-school science: a gel-like mixture surrounded by a cell membrane

High-school biology: clear, gelatinous fluid surrounded by a cell membrane; it is the site of numerous chemical reactions

In each lesson, decide which new vocabulary terms are most important, emphasize them, relate them to previously learned words, and point out root words or prefixes. Don't overlook verbs. Most science vocabulary words are nouns. Many vocabulary lists indirectly include verbs in their noun forms; for example, *evaporation* rather than *evaporate*. Verbs describe important science processes, like *classify*, *analyze*, and *support*, as well as science actions, like *reflect*, *mutate*, and *reproduce*. Help students recognize and correctly use verbs as well as nouns.

Student-Constructed Glossaries

Students can create their own glossaries or word journals. Have students write a vocabulary word, its definition, and an example of how to use it in a sentence or diagram to illustrate its meaning. Writing or drawing the definition helps students learn its meaning better than simply repeating it to themselves. They can also write the definition in their own words and include a note about why the term is important for understanding a certain concept. These glossary pages become part of each student's science journal.

Word Charts

To help students learn science words whose everyday meanings are different from scientific meanings, have them create charts showing both meanings. Students should write everyday meanings in their own words or use dictionaries to find definitions.

Word	Everyday Meaning	Scientific Meaning
population	the whole number of people or inhabitants in a country or region	all organisms in an ecosystem that belong to the same species
community	people with common interests living in a particular area	all the populations of different species that live in an ecosystem
consumer	one that consumes; one that utlizes economic goods	an organism that cannot make energy-rich molecules but obtains them by eating other organisms

Source: Merriam Webster's
Collegiate Dictionary, 11th Edition, 2006.

D

Students should write two sentences, one that demonstrates the word's everyday meaning and another that demonstrates its scientific meaning. Student pairs or small groups can discuss how the scientific meaning relates to the everyday meaning.

Examples of science words that have **different** everyday meanings:

compound	control	focus	frequency
matter	medium	model	tissue

Students can make charts of words whose scientific meanings are comparable to everyday meanings, but whose scientific meaning is more precise.

Examples of scientific words with **comparable** everyday meanings:

calorie	climate	dominant	echo
element	instinct	reflection	

Word Sorting

Sorting vocabulary words can help students recognize relationships among scientific concepts. You can provide categories, or students can create their own. Print each word or phrase on a small piece of paper, so that students can physically arrange and rearrange them.

Example:

earthquake	volcano
epicenter	cinder cone volcano
fault	composite volcano
focus	shield volcano
magnitude	lava
rift	hot spot
seismic wave	
tsunami	

A variation of this activity asks students to choose which of four or five terms does not fit with the others. Students must identify how the words are related and which word is unrelated to the others.

Example:

endothermic

<u>three-chambered heart</u>

hair

mammary glands

Answer: All except *three-chambered heart* are characteristics of mammals.

Root-Word Charts

Learning root words helps students increase their vocabularies. You might want to collaborate with your school's Language Arts or English teachers on these activities. The objective is to learn the strategy of analyzing new words by relating them to familiar words.

Root words are often of Latin or Greek origin. Learning an unfamiliar Latin or Greek root is equivalent to learning a new vocabulary word. Therefore, it is important to connect the root to familiar words that students already know. In this way, students can connect the new word and the root to their current vocabulary. For example, *dormire* (Latin, "to sleep") is part of the familiar words *dormitory* and *dormant*.

Help your students make and complete charts of root words with their everyday meanings and examples. Use a dictionary to identify root words and to verify students' examples of derivations.

Root L = Latin, G = Greek		Meaning	Everyday Example	Science Example
bi	L	two	bicycle	bipedal
bio	G	life	biology	biology
dormire	L	sleep	dormitory	dormant
hydro	G	water	hydroelectric plant	hydrolysis
inter	L	between	interstate highway	internode
intra	L	within	introvert	intravenous
neur	G	nerve	nervous	neuron
photo	G	light	photograph	phototropism

Help students master vocabulary by using some of the following strategies:

- use bold font to highlight new terms within the text
- list vocabulary words at the start of each section
- include word origins
- provide vocabulary review and practice activities at the end of each chapter
- include a glossary of terms, in both English and Spanish
- provide instructions for students on how to record key concepts, definitions, and examples

Organize Information

Concept Maps

Concept maps are diagrams that show how concepts relate to one another. These graphic representations help students organize and clarify information. In addition to strengthening vocabulary skills, concept maps are valuable learning tools that can help students internalize complex concepts and processes.

Concept maps have various formats. In each format, ovals or boxes contain concepts, and line segments or arrows link related concepts together.

To create concept maps, students must think about the concepts and how they relate to each other. The objective for students is not to create an attractive concept map, but to deepen their

D

understanding of the concept while constructing it. To introduce concept maps to your students, complete these steps.

1. Explain the content of the boxes or ovals.
2. Describe how relationships are shown.
3. Complete a concept map with the class, using a well-known concept as an example.
4. Assign students the concept that they will use.
5. Have students work in pairs to complete their concept maps for that concept.

After your students create concept maps, students should discuss their maps in small groups. As they share ideas, they will probably become aware of more examples, characteristics, and relationships.

Network Tree

A network tree shows relationships among concepts. Concepts are enclosed in ovals or squares. Lines connect the concepts to one another based on how the concepts are related. Words written on the lines describe the type of relationship.

Start by choosing the topic and major concepts. Find related concepts and order them from general to specific. Draw an oval around the main concept. Connect the related concepts with lines and label the lines with the type of relationship. Continue until you have mapped all of the concepts. Then, check to see if you should draw additional connecting lines between the concepts to show they are also related.

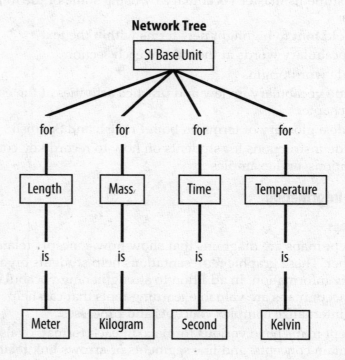

Network Tree

D

Spider Map

A spider concept map shows relationships between the main topic and one or more concepts that might not be related to each other. It can be especially useful when brainstorming.

Start with a central concept. Draw a line from this concept and label it with a description of the relationship. Connect the related concepts to the line. Draw other lines from the central concept representing other relationships and add more concepts.

Spider Concept Map

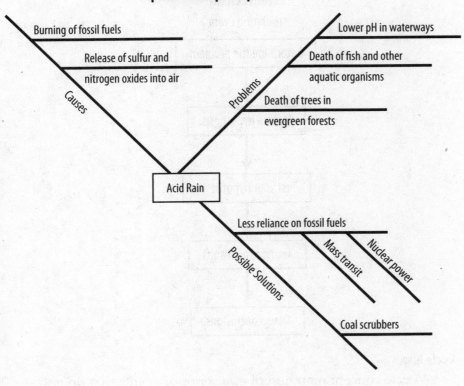

Events Chain

An events-chain concept map, or flow chart, describes a linear sequence of events. For example, the steps in a procedure or the stages of a process might be shown in an events chain.

Start by identifying the event that begins the chain—the initiating event. Connect it to the next event in the sequence. Continue adding events in chronological order until you reach an outcome.

Events Chain

Initiating Event

Determine the problem.

↓

Make a hypothesis.

↓

Test your hypothesis.

↓

Analyze the results.

↓

Draw conclusions.

Cycle Map

A cycle concept map describes a series of events that do not produce a final outcome. It is like an events chain, except that the last event in the chain relates back to the initiating event.

Cycle Concept Map

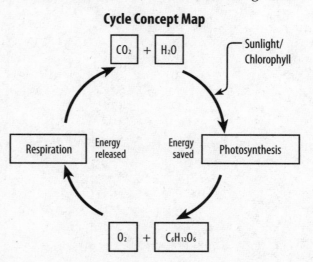

Prepare to Preread

Prereading describes activities students do before they begin to read. These activities have several important functions. Prereading activities

- focus student attention on the topic;
- stimulate interest in the topic;
- help students relate the topic to previously learned concepts;
- connect the topic to students' everyday experiences;
- make students aware of the organizational pattern of the text;
- assess students' prior knowledge.

Prereading includes activities, demonstrations, discussions of students' prior experiences, and making graphic organizers. Try one of these activities with your students.

Predict Questions

To introduce the chapter, have students write a list of questions that they think the chapter will answer. At the end of the chapter, students can check to see which of their questions were answered in the chapter.

Example:

Chapter: Plate Tectonics

Possible Questions:

- How long did it take for the continents to move to their current locations?
- What pulls apart Earth's crust?
- What is a rift valley?
- How do fossils give clues to the movement of continents?

D

Prior Knowledge Chart

List the key concepts in a lesson or chapter. Ask students to rate how familiar they are with these concepts. Use this **Prior Knowledge Chart** as a guide for making your own.

Prior Knowledge Chart

For each term, write 0, 1, or 2.

0. I've never heard of the word (or phrase).

1. I've heard the word but don't know its scientific meaning.

2. I understand the word and can use it.

_____ wave   _____ wavelength

_____ frequency   _____ reflection

_____ refraction   _____ interference

_____ diffraction

Statements Chart

Write Agree/Disagree statements related to the topic. Before reading the textbook, students write either *agree* or *disagree* for each statement related to the material. After students finish reading, they can go back to the list and check those statements that they now know are true.

I Agree/Disagree	Statement
	Light waves can travel faster through air than through water.
	If an object reflects all the light that hits it, its color is black.
	A convex lens can be used to magnify objects.
	A translucent object reflects some light and transmits some light.
	The angle of incidence is greater than the angle of reflection.

The **Statements Chart** and **Prior Knowledge Chart** are particularly useful with topics that students have studied in previous science courses. By analyzing students' responses, you will quickly see which concepts need greater explanation and which students will need to review the material. An additional strategy for the use of these types of charts is to target common misconceptions that students have about the topic. These charts and other types of formative assessments are useful tools for addressing misconceptions.

Read for Information

Reading strategies differ depending on the subject and type of written material. These skills are best taught through explanation, modeling, and practice. Explain each reading strategy to students and explain why it is useful. Model the strategy aloud. Discuss with students when and how to use the strategy to their greatest advantage.

D

Reading is a multi-faceted activity. Educators have developed many different ways to describe its components. The particular system you choose is not as important as communicating the idea to your students that the reading process involves multiple levels of thinking skills.

Components of Reading for Information

The table below shows one way to describe the components of reading for information. Ideally, readers employ each of these actions at appropriate times in their reading, not necessarily in the order shown.

This approach calls for two readings of the text—one to gain a general understanding, and one to more deeply comprehend concepts and relationships. Some readers prefer to read the text just once after scanning to pick out the main topic headings. Readers should adapt this or any other approach to fit their individual learning styles. Each of these reading components require active-reading skills.

Components	Steps	Actions
Recall of Knowledge	1. At the first reading, focus on headings, highlighted terms, and illustration topics.	• identify the main idea • recall major concepts • summarize
Comprehension and Analysis	2. At the second reading, focus on details in the text and illustrations.	• differentiate and classify concepts • compare and contrast • describe relationships and cause and effect
Inference	3. During or after the second reading, relate information to prior knowledge and experience.	• draw conclusions • make predictions
Evaluation	4. After the second reading, assess what you have learned.	• identify evidence to support conclusions and predictions • judge usefulness

Read Actively

In order to fully comprehend scientific concepts, students must mentally engage with the material; that is, they need to read actively. Active reading involves more than just pronouncing each word correctly and knowing its meaning. It requires comprehending entire passages and relating new ideas to previously learned concepts. Active readers continuously monitor their understanding and relate new concepts to their current knowledge and experience.

To help students learn the skills of active reading, model the thinking processes by speaking your thoughts as you read aloud. Students can practice this think-aloud technique in small groups. The first two strategies in the list below employ metacognitive skills. The others involve reflection, which is discussed more fully below and in later sections.

Active Reading Strategies

1. Be aware of whether you understand each statement or question.
2. When you do not understand, stop and reread.
3. Relate what you read to your prior knowledge.
4. Consider how new concepts fit with preceding concepts.
5. Predict what concepts might be presented next.

Model Active Reading Strategies

Bracketed numbers [1] indicate a pause for a spoken thought and are correlated to the italicized section below.

Passive Transport [1]

"…The movement of substances through the cell membrane [2] without the input of energy is called **passive transport.** [3] Three types of passive transport can occur. [4]"

[1] The heading is "Passive Transport," so it must be about transport— transport means something like carrying or moving. I'll look for the definition of this term.

[2] Let's see, what is a cell membrane? Oh yes, that was in the last chapter. The membrane is the outer covering of a cell.

[3] Here's the definition. I'll record that in my notebook or journal.

[4] Okay, I'll be on the lookout for the three types. They will probably be the next three subheadings. Yes, there they are on the next two pages.

Read to Understand Basic English

Students who lack basic reading skills might find it difficult to master both English vocabulary and scientific concepts at the same time.

To ensure that your students understand the everyday words in the reading material, write a list on the board of any words that students don't understand. Have students suggest informal definitions for the words and write them in their science journals so they can be found again easily.

If some students have difficulty reading, ask a proficient reader to read aloud while the others follow along in their textbooks. In small groups, have the stronger readers read aloud to help struggling readers.

Read to Understand Math Terms and Symbols

In chapters that involve mathematical terms, symbols, or graphs, check that your students understand the underlying mathematical concepts, recognize the symbols, and read information from the graphs correctly.

Help students learn to appreciate how symbols can quickly and efficiently express concepts. Emphasize the importance of graphs to organize data and depict relationships.

Work with your school's mathematics department to coordinate the skills students learn in mathematics class with their applications in science class.

Diagrams and Illustrations

Diagrams and drawings or illustrations can present large amounts of information in relatively small spaces. Demonstrate to students how to properly read diagrams in the text.

Properly reading diagrams requires that students be able to recognize and interpret the positions and sizes of objects relative to other objects in the illustration, in addition to reading captions and labels. Students must also be able to infer how a motion or process progresses by using arrows, multiple views, or other graphic devices within the diagram.

Most readers look at drawings or diagrams first, before reading the text. Discuss the role of illustrations in the reading process. Before reading the text, use the diagram to form a general idea of the text's content. During reading, refer to the diagram when you read a description or explanation. After reading the text, use diagrams as a way to review the main concepts.

Scientific diagrams might use specialized terms that refer to the type of view shown. When your students first encounter these terms, take time to explain their meanings. Examples include cross section, longitudinal section, anterior, and posterior.

Student-created diagrams, such as concept maps, are effective learning tools. By creating diagrams themselves, students learn to look carefully at the diagrams they encounter in reading.

How to Read Diagrams and Illustrations

- Look at the whole graphic to get a general idea of its subject.
- Read the caption to learn specifically what is shown.
- Read each label and relate each labeled part to the other parts of the diagram.

Read Instructions

Because labs and activities are an essential part of science, reading instructions to perform tasks is an important skill for the classroom and for everyday life. Reading instructions takes a different strategy than reading explanatory text. However, both strategies involve prereading, reading, and reflecting skills.

Model the process of reading instructions by reading and pausing to think aloud. Emphasize that time spent carefully reading instructions will pay off by minimizing confusion and error. Model these strategies for reading instructions for students.

How to Read Instructions

1. Look at the title or heading to identify the task.
2. Recall what you already know about the topic.
3. Identify the question that the task will answer.
4. Completely read through the instructions to get a general idea of the task. Mark any steps that seem difficult or unclear.
5. Read again, carefully examining any illustrations.

6 Check that the materials listed for the task are available.

7 At each step in the instructions, pause to visualize what action you will take and what the outcome will likely be.

8 Predict the outcome of the lab or activity.

9 If the task involves data collection, visualize what the data will look like.

10 After completing the task, reflect on the task and the instructions. How did your predictions differ from your results? What part of the task was similar to other science activities you have done? Which steps were well-designed for this investigation? What additional information or diagram could improve the instructions or the task? How could someone use the results of this activity?

Strategies to Read Standardized Tests

In addition to general reading strategies, multiple choice and standardized test questions call for special strategies. Read this list for some strategies you can share with your students.

- Read the question carefully. Be certain you understand what each question asks.

- If a problem seems difficult, reread the question slowly and carefully. Ask yourself "What have I been asked to find?" and "What information will help me find the answer?"

- Circle important words if you are allowed to write in your test booklet.

- Read the question, cover the response choices, decide what the answer should be, and then read the choices.

- Read each multiple choice response before you mark your answer.

- As you read the response choices, eliminate any that you know are incorrect. Cross these out if you are allowed to write in the test booklet.

- Read the accompanying diagram or graph before you read the problem.

Reflect

Remind students that good readers occasionally pause and think about what they have read. Students need to learn to pause and express a paragraph's main concept in their own words. They can ask themselves how a new concept relates to prior concepts they have learned, their own experience, and future topics they would like to learn about.

Reflecting on what you have read is not the same as metacognition. Reflection deals with concepts and relationships. Metacognition, as mentioned previously, involves the reader's level of understanding of their thinking process.

Speaking and writing encourage reflective thinking. You can find more information on writing strategies that promote reflection beginning on page 185.

Write in Science

Think of writing as the flip side of reading. Reading involves recognizing each word, recalling its meaning, and connecting words into thoughts. Students begin the writing process by collecting their thoughts and recalling words to express their ideas. Then students organize their thoughts into logically sequenced concepts by creating outlines or making notes. Finally, students use their outlines to compose a piece of writing by communicating their ideas into sentences and paragraphs on paper or the computer. Most people find writing more difficult than reading because it requires creative thinking skills.

Writing is a powerful learning tool. As a teacher, you know firsthand that explaining a concept to someone clarifies it in your own mind. In the same way, writing strengthens students' understanding. Learning to formulate ideas and express them clearly in words is fundamental to learning science.

As students write, they construct meanings around the concepts and make connections to their knowledge base. The value of writing in science is not in the finished product, but in the process itself. Consider writing one way of doing science. Students extend their scientific understanding and give you a window into their thinking process through their writing. This makes writing an effective assessment tool.

Types of Writing in Science

Writing activities are often short tasks that ask students to define, explain, or compare. Science-journal writing involves writing on topics related to the day's lesson. Writing class notes and writing to review a chapter can have a major impact on student learning.

Writing lab reports includes forming hypotheses, analyzing data, and summarizing results. Longer writing projects can involve researching several sources, analyzing data, making summaries of observations, and writing a report on the results.

Organize and Consolidate Thinking

Writing explanations or summaries helps students organize their thinking. Thoughts become explicit through the process of writing. Writing helps students construct meaning from concepts.

Reflect on Learning, Increase Retention, and Communicate Ideas

Writing is an excellent tool for reflecting on reading and learning. Students often gain additional insights to the material by thinking back to concepts they have already learned and connecting them in new ways to the current lesson. Summarizing compels students to reflect on their reading. Even the simple act of copying a definition can improve student retention. By writing a definition in their own words, students take ownership of the concept. Explaining a concept in writing helps students remember it. Writing, along with speaking and drawing, enables students to communicate their ideas. Over time, writing helps students learn to express scientific ideas more precisely.

D

Develop Higher-Level Thinking Skills

Through appropriate writing activities, students can strengthen their higher-level thinking skills, including comparing and contrasting, classifying, determining cause and effect, predicting, and explaining and justifying. Writing, as well as evaluating, arguing, and justifying, helps develop scientific reasoning. Reading and writing scientific material will help your students become good critics of their own and others' scientific arguments.

Benefits for Teachers

Get to Know Your Students

By reading your students' science journal entries, you gain a deeper understanding of your students as individuals. A feasible way to "listen" to each student, reading his or her science journal makes you aware of his or her cognitive and affective strengths and difficulties.

Communication Between Teacher and Students

Students who do not ask questions in class often write in their science journals about what they find confusing. Most teachers cannot talk to each student every day, but they can quickly scan daily writing activities. Science journals are incredibly valuable because they allow students to express themselves without speaking in front of other students. For some students, this might be the only chance you will get to understand the depth to which they comprehend scientific concepts.

Assess Student Comprehension

Daily writing activities help you informally assess student understanding. Students' written responses to open-ended tasks are an effective way to assess learning.

Evaluate Instruction

By reading students' writings, you can evaluate the effectiveness of your instructional strategies. This lets you make adjustments quickly, rather than waiting for chapter test results.

Criteria for Writing in Science

When you first introduce writing to your students, focus on providing worthwhile writing tasks that will motivate your students to write.

After students become comfortable with writing, stress the importance of clear explanations that communicate their thinking processes. Students in middle and early high school often use a less formal writing style, but they should use complete sentences that communicate thoughts clearly.

College-bound high-school students need to learn more formal methods of writing. Good scientific writing is easy to read. Of course, it must contain correctly explained scientific concepts.

Emphasize these characteristics of good writing to your students:

- well-organized
- concise
- uses clear and precise language
- uses science vocabulary correctly
- contains clear statements of purpose and conclusions
- uses appropriate, effective tables, graphs, and illustrations
- demonstrates science methods
- demonstrates higher-level thinking skills

Implement Writing

Writing activities can be short or long, can occur daily or occasionally, be completed in class or as homework, and can be cognitive or affective. They can involve all or just a few of the steps in the writing process—prewriting, drafting, revising, and sharing.

This section provides practical help for implementing meaningful expository writing activities.

General Strategies

Science teachers use various approaches to incorporate writing in their classes. You might want to try some of the following ideas that other teachers find effective.

Find time to write. Writing activities do take time, whether it's class time or homework time. Reading and responding to students' writings takes time too. You might wonder how you can fit more writing into your busy schedule.

You do not need to set aside a large block of time for writing. In many classes, students write for just five minutes. You will discover that the time students spend writing about concepts and procedures saves instruction time later because students need less re-teaching. Writing science is part of doing science.

It does not have to take long to read and respond to your students' writings. By limiting student writing time to five minutes, you can probably read 10–15 papers in about 15 minutes. The benefits gained from reading students' papers far outweigh the investment of time. If you are unsure about the time demands, start by introducing writing in just one class. Choose the class that will benefit the most from writing, such as a large class with a wide range of student abilities.

Use prompts. Although some teachers allow students to write about anything related to the lesson, most provide carefully constructed prompts to focus student thinking. Writing prompts often include verbs like *explain*, *describe*, *compare*, and *summarize*.

- Use writing prompts that reinforce the lesson's concept or skill.
- Write a prompt when you write each lesson plan.
- Be flexible and change the prompt if you think of a better idea in class.

D

Time student writing. Make writing part of the daily routine or commit to have students write at least two or three days each week. Set a fixed, short time for writing. Allow three minutes for students to think and plan their writing, and five minutes for composition. Use a timer, and keep students writing for the full five minutes.

Focus on specific audiences.

- Have students write for the teacher as the audience.
- Have students write for an audience other than the teacher— a friend, a younger student, or someone absent from class.

Understand and utilize your role.

- Participate in the writing activities and share your own writing with the class. Write along with your students. Write a response to the same prompt, but from a teacher's perspective.
- Be patient when looking at results. At the beginning, students' writings might be brief and contain few insights. Provide encouraging feedback and continue the writing activities. It takes some students more time than others to become comfortable with writing.
- Provide regular feedback on writing activities.

Plan when to write. Short writing activities can take place at the beginning, middle, or end of a lesson, depending on the learning objective.

- Write at the beginning of class to make the transition from the previous class, to review, and to "warm up."
- Write during a lesson when students seem confused.
- Write at the end of class to summarize and to assess understanding.

Provide rubrics, assessment lists, evaluation, and feedback. Providing feedback to students on their writing is essential. Give positive and encouraging comments. Provide feedback as soon as possible after the writing session. Your feedback can take several forms. You might make written comments on papers or in science journals, talk to students in private, or talk to the whole class if many students find a concept confusing.

Mark sentences that helped you see what students were thinking. Write positive comments for appropriate use of scientific concepts and for evidence of organized thinking.

Example:

What is the difference between analyzing data and drawing conclusions?

> ⎯ Good description!
>
> To analyze data means <u>to organize it and display it</u> in graphs and tables to find out what information it gives you. To draw conclusions means to decide whether the information from the data <u>does or does not support your hypothesis.</u>
>
> Good—this shows you understand the connection between a conclusion and a hypothesis.

It is not always necessary to grade the writing. It should depend on the type of writing activity. Most teachers do not grade science journals. Some teachers give the same credit for daily writing as they do for class participation or homework. If your students lack writing experience, provide several weeks of writing tasks before you begin to count writing as part of students' grades.

Decide and communicate your policy on English-usage standards. Some science teachers ignore spelling and grammatical errors when grading, while others consider mistakes in usage a contributing element to a student's writing grade. It is beneficial to hold students to high writing standards; students are more likely to be deliberate about what they write if they know your expectations are high. Maintaining high standards also encourages active, thoughtful student involvement.

Introduce your students to writing in science. If your students are not accustomed to writing in science class, start slowly and provide encouragement. Make the first activity affective rather than cognitive. Most students find it easier to write about their feelings and attitudes. This introductory activity will help students become comfortable with writing in science class and give them a sense of accomplishment.

Next, have students write about familiar science ideas. This activity serves to review of key concepts. Since students already understand the concept, they can focus on writing.

Introduce the step of prewriting—thinking about the topic, generating ideas, and organizing them. Allow time for students to think and plan before writing.

After students become comfortable with writing, have them write about concepts and procedures in the lesson they are studying currently.

If students claim that they have nothing more to write about a topic, reassure them that this new activity might seem difficult at first but it is important to write for the whole time allotted. Read what they have written and ask, "What other questions do you have about this topic?" Remind them to keep writing until time is called. Be patient.

Improve Student Writing

After students become comfortable with writing as a way to express science ideas, help them learn to write well. Help students improve their writing ability by comparing anonymous examples of good writing and poor writing from sources outside of the classroom.

Choose a question for which students' writing varied widely—from detailed explanations to "I just knew." Choose writing from another class to avoid embarrassment and help students be more objective. Write the explanations on overhead transparencies. Have students identify which parts of the writing show what the author was thinking. Remind them of metacognition. Ask what else the author might have written to make his or her thoughts clearer. Encourage peer evaluation and self-evaluation of writing. Discuss how following the steps of the writing process—prewriting, drafting, and revising—leads to clear, well-organized writing.

D

Write to organize ideas. Taking notes in class is an important skill for high-school and college students. Emphasize to students that determining what to write and how to organize their notes are skills that develop gradually and with practice.

High-school students should keep portfolios of their work from class and homework assignments. Their science journals can be part of their notebooks or be kept separately. You might want to provide a structure for the notebooks. For each chapter, students can organize notes either chronologically or categorically. Science notebooks should include definitions and theorems, key concepts, examples, lesson summaries, group work, and solutions to homework exercises.

When you give a presentation, help students learn to take notes by mentioning which concepts or procedures are most important. You might need to teach basic note-taking skills, such as starting the notes for each class on a clean sheet of paper, dating the notes, and keeping them in order.

When students work in small groups, assign one student the task of taking notes on the group's activities. However, all group members should summarize the group's results in their notebooks.

Science Journal Writing

Writing in a journal can take different forms and serve a variety of instructional purposes. It always consists of short, frequent, informal writing that is not edited or revised. Many teachers choose not to grade journals.

A journal is a place where students can think aloud and test ideas. It is a draft, not a polished piece of writing. Journal writing helps students clarify, refine, and consolidate their thinking. It contributes to greater self-confidence and increased participation, and encourages students to become active and independent learners. Keeping a science journal will enable students to reflect on what they are learning and strengthen their writing skills through the journal-writing process.

To be most effective, journal writing should occur several times each week. Many teachers use journal writing during class time as a warm-up to the day's lesson. Providing class time demonstrates that you value writing. As with any short writing exercise, journal writing can take place at the beginning, middle, or end of class. Some teachers make it part of the homework assignment.

Types of Journals

Educators have classified journals according to their purpose. You might find that one of the following types, or perhaps a hybrid of a few, fits your students' needs best.

Dialogue journals create dialogues between students and teachers. Students write about a variety of teacher-selected topics that include science content and student attitudes about the current lesson material. Teachers read the entries and provide written responses.

Double-entry journals consist of two columns. In the left column, students summarize their understanding of a science concept.

Opposite this entry in the right column, students record their comments, reactions, or questions after reflecting on the concept. Students should include any reactions that occur to them up to several days after they write their summaries.

Learning logs list or describe students' accomplishments and can include their goals. Students might create learning logs at the end of a unit or semester by reviewing the contents of their science portfolio. Students can pause after an activity, discussion, or presentation to write their reflections. They might also paraphrase a new concept or process.

Science journals are records of students' work in science class. Entries can include notes and lab reports, short research reports, and students' responses to questions or discussions. They might also include short comments, questions, conclusions, or any confusions that students have about class activities.

Practical Tips for Journals

- Decide on the type of notebook students will use for their journals. It can be a three-ring binder, a spiral-bound notebook, or a college "blue book." Some teachers provide students with inexpensive notebooks.

- If your students already use three-ring binders for their class notes and homework, you might want them to add their journal pages to those.

- Keep the students' science journals in the classroom so that students do not lose them or leave them at home. Plan how you will distribute and collect journals each day.

- Number each journal-writing task and have students number their responses, so that students don't have to copy the prompts. Use a timer to help keep students writing for the whole five minutes or any time limit you choose.

- Collect, read, and respond to journals regularly.

- Plan how you will respond to students' journal entries. Your response might be a question, comment, or a note of encouragement. Avoid being judgmental. It is important that students realize that you have taken the time to read their entries and thoughtfully respond. Students should come to view the journal as a one-on-one conversation with you. Most teachers enjoy this form of communication with their students and look forward to reading journal entries.

- Do not grade journals. Students need to be able to write freely in their journals. You might award points for journal writing comparable to homework points. Do not accept responses that show no effort.

- Write in your own journal while students are writing. You might respond to the same prompt, but from a teacher's perspective, or you might write about how you perceive that students have responded to your lesson.

- Have students revisit their journal entries. At the end of a unit or the year, they might choose their best journal entries to include in their portfolios. They can write a table of contents, a short introduction, and a conclusion to their journal.

D

Journal Prompts

Journal prompts help students start writing and focus their attention on key concepts. The suggestions below are adaptable to many science topics and grade levels. Tailor them to fit your lessons and your students' abilities.

Prompts fall into three categories. Content prompts deal with scientific concepts and relationships. Process prompts focus on processes and events. Affective prompts center on students' attitudes and feelings. Some prompts fit more than one of these categories. All can be effective learning tools. Be aware of which type of prompt you assign to students. Varying the type of prompt helps maintain student interest.

Content Prompts

- Write a note to a student who missed yesterday's class. Select one concept to explain to this student.
- Write and answer a question that you would like to see on the chapter test.
- Which homework question was the most challenging? Explain why.
- What is the most important thing you learned in class today?
- What questions do you still have about the lesson?
- Write a statement that is either true or false. Do you agree? Explain why or why not.

Process Prompts

- When I read a question that asks me to compare two things, the first thing I do is . . . , then I. . .
- Describe [a process].
- When I study for a science quiz, I . . .

Affective Prompts

- What confused you about today's topic or activity?
- What challenged you?
- What did you like?

Short Writing Activities

Daily journal writing should not constitute the entirety of your students' in-class writing activities. You can use short writing tasks whenever they fit your lesson plans and your students' needs. Class activities, homework assignments, tests, and quizzes can include short writing tasks. Remind students to write paragraphs that contain a topic sentence and supporting sentences.

Use writing to help students learn critical-thinking skills, such as comparing, predicting, classifying, and explaining. Through writing, students can also learn to summarize topics, create and test hypotheses, support arguments with evidence, and connect new concepts with their prior knowledge.

In contrast to the higher-level thinking skills discussed below, questions that ask students to list or identify information make use of recall and memory skills. These questions call for short answers rather than sentences or paragraphs. They often begin with the following prompts:

- What is _____?
- What are the _____?
- List the _____.
- What kind of _____?
- What happens during _____?
- Give an example of _____.

Extend Prereading Activities

You can extend the prereading activities described on page 179 to include writing tasks.

- After creating a **Prior Knowledge Chart,** have students write a paragraph using vocabulary words that they marked with a 2 (I understand these). Have them write questions about the concepts that they marked with a 1 (I have heard of these). Students should switch questions with a partner and write the answers to test their understanding of the material.
- After creating a **Statement Chart** and completing the chapter, have students choose one statement from their charts and write for five minutes in agreement or disagreement with the statement.

Description

Description is closely connected to observation, a key step in scientific methodology. Describing an object or an event teaches students to look for details and to identify major characteristics. The description must convey enough detail for the reader to understand the event or visualize the object.

- Describe what happens when _____.
- Describe how _____.

Explanation

Explanation can take many forms, such as, "Explain how . . . ," "Explain what happens . . . ," or "Explain the difference between. . . ."

Explanation requires providing reasons for a characteristic, an object, or an event. Explanations of why things occur are similar to cause-and-effect statements.

- How does _____ affect _____?
- Explain the difference between what happened to _____ and to _____.
- Explain the purpose of _____ in doing _____.

Summary

Summarizing readings or the results of an experiment requires comprehension of the material, analysis of the material to determine the main idea, and identification of sufficient details to give the reader a clear picture of the lesson.

D

Comparison and Contrast

Writing to compare and contrast two objects, processes, or events requires describing and analyzing the items in question and then determining their commonalities and differences.

- What are the similarities and differences between _____ and _____?
- Compare and contrast _____ and _____.
- How is _____ different from _____?
- How are _____ and _____ related?

Classification

Classification means separating objects or events into appropriate categories. Classifying objects includes determining important characteristics and then analyzing each object to decide which of these characteristics the object possesses. Sometimes you will provide the categories; other times students should create their own.

Hypothesis

A hypothesis is a testable explanation. Making and testing hypotheses is central to scientific inquiry. Making a hypothesis involves giving a possible explanation based on previous knowledge and observation.

- Make a hypothesis about what will happen when _____.
- Design an experiment that tests the hypothesis that _____.

Prediction

A prediction is a guess about a future event based on observation or experience. When you apply a hypothesis to a specific situation, you predict something about that situation. Predicting an event requires that students understand the underlying hypothesis and apply it to the given situation.

- What would happen if _____?

Argument

A scientific argument is a main statement and a set of supporting statements that provide evidence that the main statement is valid. Writing an argument involves precisely stating the conclusion and providing reasons based on observation or widely accepted statements.

Metacognition

Metacognition, discussed previously is thinking about the thought process. Although all of the writing activities described above contribute to students' metacognitive skills, you occasionally should focus on developing this skill.

- Explain what made the activity hard or easy for you. Give specific examples.
- What I need to work on is _____.
- What I do best is _____.

Small-Group Work

When students work in cooperative groups, have them write about their experience.

- Summarize how your group reached a conclusion.
- Explain how your group accomplished a task.
- Compare two different answers to the same question.

Experiments and Lab Reports

Writing lab reports is an essential science skill. Your textbook probably suggests a data-table format and provides questions to analyze results and draw conclusions.

By practicing the writing and thinking skills described above, students will be better equipped to write clear, comprehensive reports.

Writing for Essay Exams

By practicing writing for exams, students will learn how to structure their thoughts and will become successful at writing good essays. Begin by having students read a sample essay and its prompt. Students should read the prompt carefully to determine whether the essay is supposed to explain, describe, support an opinion, or persuade.

Point out the parts of an essay—the opening paragraph, the body paragraphs, and the conclusion. The opening paragraph should state the topic of the essay and include appropriate, interesting details, such as definitions, anecdotes or examples. The body paragraphs might use any of the strategies described above as short writing activities—comparison, argument, or description. The conclusion must correspond to the purpose of the essay and be a clear, well written statement that summarizes the author's point of view.

Have students practice prewriting techniques, including brainstorming and using graphic organizers such as concept maps. Have students practice writing conclusions to existing essays.

Longer Writing Projects

Projects provide opportunities to research topics, organize and represent data, and summarize results. They often involve time in and out of class.

Students should follow each step in the writing process:

1. prewrite
2. draft
3. review and revise
4. share (or publish/submit)

Set due dates for each stage in the writing process. You might wish to assign dates for students to submit an outline, opening statement and introductory paragraph, first draft, and final report.

Use anonymous, well-written papers from previous years' classes as models for students to study. Give students the rubric you will use when grading, and have them grade the model paper.

D

Prewriting activities might include brainstorming, concept maps, or an activity called cubing. Based on the six sides of a cube, this method challenges students to approach a topic from six different perspectives. Use a sheet of paper with six boxes, each labeled with one of the following verbs—*describe, compare, associate, analyze, apply, argue*—as shown below. Students then write their ideas for each topic in the appropriate boxes.

describe	compare
associate	analyze
apply	argue

In addition to research projects, you might have students write a science autobiography at the beginning of the year. This should include their feelings about science and their accomplishments in science, not simply a list of past courses they have taken. Students might also research and write a report on a specific area of science, a current scientific controversy, or a famous scientist.

Advanced students should write more formal papers. The checklist below can help students focus attention on clear thinking and writing.

Checklist for Writing Projects

___ Clearly state the problem or purpose.

___ State what you will show or conclude.

___ Create an outline of your paper.

___ Organize the paper into paragraphs, each with a topic sentence.

___ Assemble and label your illustrations, data, graphs, and tables.

___ Refer to your data and graphs to support your points.

___ Summarize the main points and end with a conclusion statement.

___ Cite your sources, including books, Web sites, and people.

___ Use correct spelling, grammar, and punctuation.

Portfolios

Portfolios are collections of student work that represent the students' learning over a given period of time. Students should have ownership of their portfolios; that is, they should evaluate their work and decide which pieces they want to include.

You might want to have students edit some of the written work that they choose to include in their portfolios. This not only improves the quality of the portfolio, but it also motivates students to learn to evaluate and edit their writing.

A chart at the front of the portfolio functions as a table of contents, lists the subject matter of each item, and sometimes includes teacher comments.

How to Assess Writing Assignments

Develop a consistent policy on assessing writing assignments. Students should be aware what criteria you will use and how writing assignments will affect their grades. Communicate your policy clearly so that students understand what you expect.

Teacher Assessment

Giving students positive feedback is the most valuable aspect of assessing writing. Write comments that focus on the best parts of the writing to encourage deeper thinking and clearer writing. Comment on just one or two things within the writing, rather than on many things. When you comment on incorrect thinking or poor writing, be specific.

Most teachers do not assign grades for journal writing or short writing tasks assigned as homework. Instead, many teachers give the same credit they give for class participation or homework. Most teachers assign grades for longer writing projects, using a rubric based on a set of criteria.

When you assign grades to written work, you will want to use a rubric. List the characteristics you will assess—content, organization, grammar, and so on—and the criteria for exemplary, good, adequate, and unacceptable work. Explain the rubric to students so that they know what you expect and understand that good writing involves several components.

Peer Assessment

When students assess one another's writing, they learn to evaluate their writing and thinking. This helps them become better writers and thinkers.

Ask volunteers to read their writing aloud in class or within small groups. Or have students silently read and edit one another's writing in small groups and then discuss their reactions, pointing out strengths and weaknesses. Encourage students to be specific in their comments to their peers and to offer constructive criticism.

Self-Assessment

Revision and editing are important steps in the writing process. Over time, students need to learn to evaluate and edit their own

D

writing. They should read their written work and decide whether it correctly represents their thinking. This is another application of metacognition. You can assist by pointing out students' writing strengths and asking questions about poorly written sentences.

Assessment Criteria

Regardless of who is assessing the writing, criteria like those listed below can provide a useful framework. You might want to have your students create their own list of criteria.

Suggested Assessment Criteria for Writing in Science

- Content . . . . accurate, complete, and appropriate content
- Vocabulary . . . . correct use of vocabulary
- Organization . . orderly, logical writing
- Originality . . . . evidence of independent thinking
- Mechanics . . . . . correct grammar and spelling; complete sentences

Read and Write About Science in Literature

Literature

In addition to textbooks, non-fiction trade books can play a valuable role in science classes. Students who are actively engaged in reading tend to learn factual information presented in the text more easily than their peers who are not. Reading high-quality trade books can heighten student interest and motivate inquiry.

Many fine trade books present readers with story-like accounts of topics and events in science—from the composition of a drop of water to hurricanes, from the animal kingdom to the solar system. Some focus on scientific inquiry and methods of discovery, while others investigate the lives and work of famous scientists. Trade books provide students with a base of knowledge on which to build new understandings. They motivate students to explore new topics and help them master new vocabulary.

You might wish to read excerpts from a book—or two related books—in class to lead discussion of a new topic. Students can then read the whole book outside of class either for credit or for pleasure. Try to locate books on the same topic but at different reading levels to accommodate your students' abilities. If the reading is an assignment, have students write or draw something about what the book meant to them.

Help students understand the role of science writers in society. Authors such as Rachel Carson, John Muir, Henry David Thoreau, and Charles Darwin have influenced public opinion and government policy, particularly with regard to environmental issues.

Fiction writing can motivate students and connect science to other aspects of their lives. Reading poems, legends, and stories gives students different perspectives on science content. Even science fiction classics, like Jules Verne's *Twenty Thousand Leagues Under the Sea*, can shed light on science topics like air pressure and volume in the context of how submarines submerge. Connecting science and literature can help create lasting images in students' minds.

Creative Writing

While expository writing is essential to science, creative writing also plays an important role in student learning. Writing that uses creative, expressive language is another way to communicate scientific concepts. Through creative writing, students relate scientific concepts to their own feelings, thoughts, and life experiences.

The following suggestions for creative writing activities can be adapted to various science topics:

Personification Write a poem or short story that uses human emotions or human traits to describe an animal or inanimate object.

Point of View Write a story of a nonliving thing from the first-person point of view.

Imagery Write a paragraph that evokes a picture of a place that is familiar to you.

Legends and Oral Tradition Create an idea for a story about how something came to be. Write an outline of your story. Tell your story to your classmates using the outline.

Nonfiction Writing Write a one-page nonfiction account of a favorite outdoor place. After you have written it, mark the sentences that are facts. Use another method to mark the sentences or phrases that are opinions.

Poetry Write a poem or a riddle using vocabulary words from a chapter.

Dialogue Write a dialogue in which one person has a misconception about a science concept and the other person understands the concept.

D

Read and Write About Science in the Media

News, educational, and entertainment media can provide many sources of reading and writing activities that motivate students to learn science. This section looks at ways to incorporate newspapers, magazines, Web sites, and even movies into worthwhile science activities. The Internet has not diminished the need for reading or writing. Instead, it provides a new medium for these skills.

Media

Newspapers, magazines, and the Internet are all forms of media that involve reading. Using media in science classes can

- demonstrate that science is relevant and useful to students' daily lives;
- motivate students;
- actively involve students in science;
- help students learn to read critically.

Widely accessible and inexpensive, newspapers are a valuable source of everyday science. Science articles in newspapers often focus on medicine and drugs, environmental issues, and natural disasters. Occasionally discoveries in astronomy and breakthroughs in chemistry and physics also make the news. Science magazines often offer more in-depth coverage than newspapers and have enticing color photographs and diagrams. The Internet provides up-to-the-minute science news and photographs, but also contains sites of questionable scientific accuracy. This aspect of the Internet calls for active reading skills to evaluate written material. Students should be taught to judge the quality of an internet site as an informational resource.

Finding examples of science in news media is not difficult, but incorporating them into your curriculum can be. It takes time and effort to find appropriate examples and develop activities around them.

Strategies for the Use of Media

It is helpful to view skill development for reading science in the media as a three-stage process. The first step develops an awareness of science writing in media. The next step uses active reading to analyze science writing. The third step involves critically thinking about what is being read.

Awareness

Ask students to find examples of science writing in a newspaper (or a news Web site or news magazine). Students discover that in addition to news articles, science writing can be found in weather reports, sports injury stories, entertainment news, business news, consumer news, and occasionally even comics.

Have students read a newspaper (or one section of a newspaper) and take notes on the science topics. Have students create a list of the type of science articles that appear most often. Graph the data collected over several days or weeks. Use the data to answer the question, "What topics in science are most frequently in the news?"

Active Reading

As students read media, they should ask themselves questions about the facts and opinions, the author's point of view, the source of the data, the type of experiment, and the results. Here are examples of questions to ask:

Active Reading in Media

1 What is the title? What topics are included?

2 Who is the author? What are the author's qualifications? What is the author's point of view?

3 Who is the intended audience? How much science does the audience know?

4 Which statements are facts and which are opinions?

5 What sources does this article cite for factual statements?

6 Did this article use a poll or survey?

7 Did someone conduct an investigation for this article? Was it a valid, scientific experiment?

8 Was an experiment done on animals or on people?

9 Where did the data come from? How and when was it collected?

10 What are the results of the experiment?

11 Were the data interpreted correctly?

Critical Reading

Taking active reading a step further, students need to develop skills in critical reading to evaluate science writing.

News media do not always present explicit, correct science. Readers need to learn to question whether the experimental results justify the conclusions presented in the article.

A good method for teaching critical reading is to discuss examples of misleading, incomplete, or incorrect science in articles you find. You and your students might want to start a collection of these examples.

Writing and the Media

Science articles and programs in the media can prompt student writing. Students might evaluate the item in terms of science content and goal—informative or persuasive. They might analyze the organization of an article or program, identifying the theme and supporting ideas. They could write an essay following the program's outline. They might practice writing in the style of media articles, using persuasion, anecdotes, or opinions. Some additional examples are provided here.

- After students read articles and analyze them by identifying sentences that are either facts or opinions, have them write on a topic that includes both fact and opinion.

- After they read an article that uses persuasion—convincing someone through a reasoned argument—have students write their own persuasive articles. Ask them to identify their main point from statements they write to support their argument.

- Analyze a news article in terms of whether it describes a cause and effect relationship or whether the events are simply correlated. Have students write a cause-and-effect article on a topic they have studied.

- Analyze a news article in terms of its use of anecdotal evidence or personal testimony, and its use of experimental results. Have students write a short article using an anecdote from their own lives. For example, a persuasive article on recycling might include an anecdote of how separating materials for recycling at a student's home led to a lower fee for trash pickup, but an additional fee for recycling.

- After reading a science article that includes survey results, discuss the wording of survey questions and have students write a short survey of opinions on a topic they are studying. Have them give their survey to several classmates or family members and decide how they might revise the questions to make the survey easier to understand. Students might write about which situations are appropriate for collecting data by a survey and which situations call for collecting data from an experiment. Students could also research ways in which medical trials combine survey information and experimental data.

Science in Entertainment Media

Entertainment media, such as film and television, offer connections to science that can provide motivating opportunities for students to engage with science lessons outside the classroom. Though the science depicted in films is often unrealistic or incorrect, it can prompt interesting class discussions and writing activities. Have students write about the use of science in a film, describing which aspects are correct and which are misleading or incorrect.

Mathematics Support

Table of Contents

Introduction **206**

Structure of Skill Reviews **207**

Numbers and Operations...208
- Negative and Positive Integers................................... 208
- Fractions (Multiplicative Identity, Inverse, Multiply, Divide, Add, Subtract) 210
- Ratios 212
- Proportions 213
- Decimals (Multiply, Divide).. 214
- Percents 215
- Significant Digits 217
- Powers 217
- Scientific Notation 219
- Logarithms... 220

Algebra...**222**
- Solve for Unknowns.. 222
- Quadratic Equations 222
- The Quadratic Formula 224
- Linear Equations... 225
- Solve Systems of Linear Equations (Substitution, Elimination).......... 226

Geometry **228**
- Angles... 228
- Area Formulas.. 230
- Circumference 232
- Volume Formulas 233

Measurement **235**
- Volume, Mass, and Density 235
- Dimensional Analysis 236

Data Analysis..**237**
- Averages: Mean, Median, and Mode.............................. 237
- Probability.. 238
- Laboratory Calculations 240

Problem Solve...**242**

Reasoning and Proof **244**

Communication..**245**

Representation...**247**
- Create and Analyze Graphs.. 247
- Use a Graphing Calculator 249
- Use Graphing Calculators in Cooperative Learning 251

Graph Paper...**252**

E

Digital Resources for Teachers

 Professional Development **mhpdonline.com**
These PD modules address both teaching strategies and science content.

✓ Literacy Strategies: Reading, Writing, Listening, and Speaking
✓ Differentiate Instruction
✓ English-Language Learners
✓ Standards-Based Instruction
✓ Assessment Strategies and Rubrics

✓ Teaching Energy
✓ Teaching Mitosis and Meiosis
✓ Teaching Moon Phases
✓ Teaching Photosynthesis
✓ Teaching Physical and Chemical Change
✓ Teaching Weather Concepts

TeAching Today **teachingtoday.glencoe.com**
A no-fee professional development Web site where you will find resources for:

✓ Lesson plans with downloads for newsletters, parent conference letters
✓ Teaching tips
✓ How-to articles sorted by discipline, grade level, and instructional type
✓ Math support
✓ Demonstration videos

E

Introduction

"The Universe is a grand book which cannot be read until one first learns to comprehend the language and become familiar with the characters in which it is composed. It is written in the language of mathematics..." —Galileo Galilei

Mathematics is the language of science. It enables scientists to easily communicate numerical ideas using universally understood symbols. However, many students have trouble applying what they learn in their math classes to their studies in science. This section presents strategies that will prepare teachers to help their students solve math problems in the science classroom.

Mathematics and science are interwoven. Scientists and mathematicians constantly interact and share research, and this interaction results in many of the products we use today. Fiber-optic networks, computers, weather radar, hybrid automobiles, and medical imaging are just a few examples of what results when mathematical analysis and scientific discovery come together.

Mathematics is a way of describing relationships among numbers and other measurable quantities. You can use mathematics to express the equation of a straight line, but you can also use it to help describe the interactions that occur among the universe's smallest particles.

Yet mathematics largely remains behind the scenes. The inner workings of complex technology are taken for granted by many, but every graphing calculator holds sets of ones and zeroes: the basic units of a computer's intelligence. Understanding what goes on "behind the scenes" can help students better understand the world around them.

This section will help middle- and high-school teachers prepare students for the mathematics they will use during science exams. The contents correlate to the national content standards for school mathematics. The National Council of Teachers of Mathematics (NCTM) developed this list of standards. For a detailed list of the national standards and a discussion of their application, consult the online version, the E-Standards, located on the NCTM's Web site at http://standards.nctm.org.

E

For Standards-Based
Instruction go to

TE**A**⁺CHING
TODAY

at **teachingtoday.glencoe.com**

Structure of Skill Reviews

Most of the reviews in this section will have four steps:

1 a question to assess your students' prior knowledge

2 a review of the skill or topic

3 a "real-world" example with its step-by-step solution

4 if applicable, a mentioning of common misconceptions students have

You can use prior knowledge questions to determine what mathematical skills your students must review and how. Ask the appropriate prior-knowledge question, and then review the skill. Be sure to review the skill and ask questions before examining the "example" portion. Encourage students to check their answers and double-check their calculations. It is advisable to pre-assess your students' mathematical skills before they are a hindrance to learning science.

For more information on English-Language Learners visit

 Professional Development

at **mhpdonline.com**

E

Numbers and Operations

Negative and Positive Integers

Assess Prior Knowledge What does $-72 - (-41) = ?$ [-31]

An integer is any number from the set $\{\ldots-3, -2, -1, 0, 1, 2, 3\ldots\}$. A number line is a good visual representation of negative and positive integers:

Point out that $+1$ is to the right of zero on the number line while -1 is to the left of zero. Stress that $0 > -1 > -2$ and so on. This can be explained with the concept of owing. Would you prefer to owe someone one dollar (-1) or two dollars (-2)? In other words, would you rather have -1 dollars or -2 dollars?

Adding Integers

Adding a negative number is equivalent to subtracting the *positive* of that number.

$$3 + (-2) = 3 - 2 = 1 \qquad \text{Move 2 places left.}$$

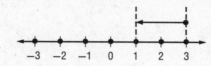

Adding a negative number to another negative number results in a *smaller* negative number.

$$-1 + (-2) = -1 - 2 = -3 \qquad \text{Move 2 places left.}$$

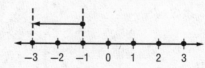

Subtracting Integers

Subtracting a negative number is the same as adding the positive of that number.

$$-1 - (-2) = -1 + 2 = 1 \qquad \text{Move 2 places right.}$$

E

Multiplying Integers

Multiplying a negative number by a positive number yields a negative product.

$$3 \times (-4) = -12 \qquad\qquad (-3) \times 4 = -12$$

However, just like multiplying two positive numbers, multiplying two negative numbers yields a positive product.

$$3 \times 4 = 12 \qquad\qquad (-3) \times (-4) = 12$$

Dividing Integers

Dividing integers involves the same rules as multiplying integers. When dividing a negative number by a positive number, or vice versa, a negative quotient will result.

$$12 \div (-4) = -3 \qquad\qquad (-12) \div 4 = -3$$

And just like dividing two positive numbers, dividing two negative numbers will yield a positive quotient.

$$12 \div 4 = 3 \qquad\qquad (-12) \div (-4) = 3$$

The two-dimensional number grid below can help students visualize equations involving multiplying and dividing with positive and negative integers. Point out that quotients and products that lie in the first and third quadrants are positive and those that lie in the second and fourth quadrants are negative.

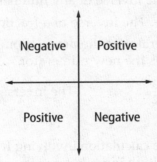

Example A tank of liquid nitrogen begins with a temperature of −209°C. It warms to a temperature of −197°C. What is the tank's change in temperature?

Step 1 Subtract the starting temperature from the ending temperature to find the change.

$$-197°C - (-209°C) = -197°C + 209°C =$$
$$209°C + (-197°C) = 209°C - 197°C = 12°C$$

Misconceptions Students might have difficulty recognizing that the lack of a sign before a number indicates that it is positive.

E

Fractions

Assess Prior Knowledge What does $\frac{1}{4} \times \frac{6}{8} - \frac{7}{64} = ?$ $\left[\frac{5}{64}\right]$

The Multiplicative Identity and Inverse Relationship

One way to represent the numbers between whole integers is with fractions. Each fraction has two main parts. The numerator, or the top number, is the number of parts that you have. The denominator, or the bottom number, is the number of parts in the whole.

There are a number of mathematical manipulations that can help you calculate fractions. An important concept in multiplication is the multiplicative identity, or a way of representing the number 1. It is special because any number times the multiplicative identity is that same number.

$$4 \times 1 = 4$$

There are many ways to write the multiplicative identity. You can write it as 1, $\frac{1}{1}$, $\frac{2}{2}$, $\frac{3}{3}$, and so on. This is because any number divided by itself equals 1. This leads mathematicians to ask, "What could you multiply a number by to get the multiplicative identity?"

$$4 \times x = 1$$

In this case, $x = \frac{1}{4}$. $\frac{1}{4}$ is the multiplicative inverse of 4. Multiply any number by its inverse, and it equals one, the multiplicative identity. You can find the inverse of any number by dividing it into 1. So, the inverse of x is $\frac{1}{x}$. The inverse of a fraction is a new fraction with the original numerator as the new denominator and the original denominator as the new numerator.

The inverse of $\frac{2}{3}$ is $\frac{3}{2}$.   The inverse of $\frac{1}{4}$ is $\frac{4}{1}$, or just 4.

Multiply Fractions

Multiplication is the calculation involving fractions with the fewest steps. When multiplying two fractions, you multiply the numerators together and the denominators together.

$$\frac{1}{2} \times \frac{3}{4} = \frac{(1 \times 3)}{(2 \times 4)} = \frac{3}{8}$$

What if one of your multipliers is an integer, such as 4? As you saw above, $4 = \frac{4}{1}$. We can write 4 as $\frac{4}{1}$ and carry out the same procedure.

$$\frac{2}{9} \times 4 = \frac{2}{9} \times \frac{4}{1} = \frac{(2 \times 4)}{(9 \times 1)} = \frac{8}{9}$$

Divide Fractions

Dividing fractions is similar to multiplying them.

How would you divide $\frac{1}{2}$ by $\frac{2}{3}$? Dividing by a number is the same as multiplying by that number's multiplicative inverse.

E

Let's look at an example with integers.

$$8 \div 4 = 2$$

You know that the inverse of 4 is $\frac{1}{4}$. By multiplying 8 by the inverse of 4, you get the answer, 2.

$$8 \times \frac{1}{4} = \frac{8}{1} \times \frac{1}{4} = \frac{(8 \times 1)}{(1 \times 4)} = \frac{8}{4} = 8 \div 4 = 2$$

In $\frac{1}{2} \div \frac{2}{3}$, the inverse of $\frac{2}{3}$ is $\frac{3}{2}$. So, multiply $\frac{1}{2}$ by $\frac{3}{2}$.

$$\frac{1}{2} \div \frac{2}{3} = \frac{1}{2} \times \frac{3}{2} = \frac{(1 \times 3)}{(2 \times 2)} = \frac{3}{4}$$

You can also divide a whole number by a fraction.

$$7 \div \frac{3}{4} = 7 \times \frac{4}{3} = \frac{7}{1} \times \frac{4}{3} = \frac{(7 \times 4)}{(1 \times 3)} = \frac{28}{3}$$

Mathematicians call $\frac{28}{3}$ an improper fraction because its numerator is greater than its denominator. You can also write this fraction as a mixed number, which is a whole number and a fraction. This is because any fraction can be thought of as a division problem in which the numerator is divided by the denominator. Therefore, the improper fraction $\frac{28}{3}$ can be expressed as $28 \div 3$. In this case, it is equal to the mixed number $9\frac{1}{3}$.

Add and Subtract Fractions

To add or subtract fractions that have the same denominator, add or subtract the numerators.

$$\frac{1}{3} + \frac{1}{3} = \frac{2}{3} \qquad\qquad \frac{3}{4} - \frac{1}{4} = \frac{2}{4} = \frac{1}{2}$$

The fraction $\frac{2}{4}$ can be simplified to $\frac{1}{2}$. You know this because the numbers 2 and 4 both can be divided evenly by the number 2 and you get $\frac{1}{2}$. This does not change the value of the fraction because you divided the fraction by a multiplicative identity, $\frac{2}{2}$, or 1. You can use this same process in reverse to add or subtract fractions with different denominators.

What is $\frac{1}{3} + \frac{1}{4}$? In order to answer this, you must find fractions that are equivalent to the ones in the problem and have the same denominator. To do this, find the smallest number that has both 3 and 4 (the original denominators) as factors. The smallest number that 3 and 4 both can be divided evenly into is 12. You could also use 24, 36, 60, or 372, but 12 is the smallest.

E

Now use the information from the previous page. You know that $\frac{1}{3} \times 1 = \frac{1}{3}$, and you can write the number 1 as $\frac{4}{4}$. Use the rules for multiplying fractions.

$$\frac{1}{3} \times \frac{4}{4} = \frac{(1 \times 4)}{(4 \times 3)} = \frac{4}{12}$$

Of course, you can see this is true because $\frac{4}{12}$ simplifies to $\frac{1}{3}$. So, you can substitute $\frac{4}{12}$ for $\frac{1}{3}$ in the original problem. You can use a similar process, multiplying $\frac{1}{4}$ by $\frac{3}{3}$, to show that $\frac{3}{12} = \frac{1}{4}$. Substituting these equivalent fractions, you get an addition equation in which the fractions have the same denominator.

$$\frac{1}{3} + \frac{1}{4} = \left(\frac{1}{3} \times \frac{4}{4}\right) + \left(\frac{1}{4} \times \frac{3}{3}\right) = \frac{4}{12} + \frac{3}{12} = \frac{7}{12}$$

Example Female tortoises lay their eggs on a beach and then swim back out to sea. Suppose that on land, a tortoise moves about $\frac{1}{15}$ m/s. Then, when swimming out into the ocean, she swims at a speed of about $\frac{3}{5}$ m/s. If the tortoise lays her eggs $\frac{3}{4}$ m away from the ocean, how long will it take her to travel 10 m out to sea?

Step 1   Divide the distance to the ocean by the speed of the tortoise on land to find the time it takes to travel to the ocean. (Note: When you invert a number, you also invert the units.)

$$\frac{3}{4}\,\text{m} \div \frac{1}{15}\,\text{m/s} = \frac{3}{4}\,\text{m} \times \frac{15}{1}\,\text{s/m} = \frac{45}{4}\,\text{s}$$

Step 2   Divide the distance she must swim by the tortoise's swimming speed to calculate for how long she must swim.

$$10\,\text{m} \div \frac{3}{5}\,\text{m/s} = 10\,\text{m} \times \frac{5}{3}\,\text{s/m} = \frac{10}{1}\,\text{m} \times \frac{5}{3}\,\text{s/m} = \frac{50}{3}\,\text{s}$$

Step 3   Add the time that the tortoise moves across land to the time the tortoise swims in the ocean to find the total time. (Note: The multiplicative identity has no units.)

$$\frac{45}{4}\,\text{s} + \frac{50}{3}\,\text{s} = \left(\frac{45}{4}\,\text{s} \times \frac{3}{3}\right) + \left(\frac{50}{3}\,\text{s} \times \frac{4}{4}\right) = \frac{135}{12}\,\text{s} + \frac{200}{12}\,\text{s} = \frac{335}{12}\,\text{s}$$

So, it will take the tortoise $\frac{335}{12}$ s, or $27\frac{11}{12}$ s, to travel 10 m out to sea.

Misconceptions Students might have difficulty remembering whether or not to operate on the denominator in a calculation with fractions. They might simply add or subtract both numerators and both denominators when adding or subtracting fractions. When multiplying, they might multiply one number or fraction by both the numerator and denominator of the other fraction.

Ratios

Assess Prior Knowledge An experiment calls for a solution of 1 L of water and 2 mL of HCl. what is the ratio of HCl to water in the solution? [1:500]

A ratio compares things that are part of a whole or parts to parts. A ratio is written as two or more numbers in a series with a colon between each two numbers or as a fraction. To write a ratio, write the number of times an event happens or a quantity is used, write a colon, and then write the number of times another event happens or another quantity is used. If writing a ratio of parts, write a colon between each two numbers that represent the parts.

Example Mendel allowed pea plants that were heterozygous for a trait, such as seed color, to self-fertilize. This means that the parents for each seed were hybrids (*Aa*). Calculate the ratio of the genotypes in the offspring of this plant.

Step 1   Find the number of possible genotypes in the offspring.
There are three: AA, Aa, and aa.

Step 2   Complete a Punnett square and then count the number of times that each genotype appears in the cross.
AA would appear once, Aa twice, and aa once.

Step 3   Write the comparison as a ratio.
1:2:1

Misconceptions Students might think that ratios are equivalent to fractions, but sometimes they are not. $1{:}8 \neq \frac{1}{8}$. To express probabilities as a fraction instead of a ratio, you first add up the parts to determine the whole. In the case of the ratio 1:8, the whole would be $8 + 1 = 9$. Then you divide the number of times an event occurs in the ratio by the whole. So, the probability would be $\frac{1}{9}$.

Proportions

Assess Prior Knowledge Solve for x: $\frac{x}{5} = \frac{24}{15}$. [$x = 8$]

A proportion is an equation that relates two ratios or two fractions. Some examples of proportions are:

$$\frac{1}{2} = \frac{2}{4} \qquad\qquad 3{:}5 = 15{:}25$$

The cross-products of any proportion are equal. This means that two fractions are proportional if $\frac{a}{b} = \frac{c}{d}$ and $a \times d = b \times c$. Proportions allow you to find equivalent fractions and ratios.

Example In a dihybrid cross, approximately 9 out of 16 offspring show both dominant traits. If an organism has 800 offspring, how many would expect to show both dominant characteristics?

Step 1   Let x be the number of offspring that show both dominant characteristics. The fraction of offspring that show both dominant traits is $\frac{x}{800}$.

Step 2   Set up a proportion that equates the fractions of offspring.

$$\frac{x}{800} = \frac{9}{16}$$

Step 3 Calculate the cross products.

$$\frac{x}{800} \diagup\!\!\!\!\diagdown \frac{9}{16}$$

$$16x = 9 \cdot 800$$

$$16x = 7200$$

Step 4 Divide both sides by 16 to find x.

$$x = 450$$

We would expect 450 of the offspring show both dominant characteristics.

Decimals

A decimal is a number that contains a decimal point and numbers to the right of that decimal point. The table below shows various place values for the number 3,736,205.864119.

millions	hundred thousands	ten thousands	thousands	hundreds	tens	ones		tenths	hundredths	thousandths	ten thousandths	hundred thousandths	millionths
3	7	3	6	2	0	5	.	8	6	4	1	1	9

The place value names can help you convert fractions into decimals. The key is looking at the last (right-most) non-zero, non-repeating decimal place. Let's start with the decimal 0.4. This is equal to $\frac{4}{10}$ or $\frac{2}{5}$. It is also equivalent to 0.40, 0.400, 0.4000 and so on. To convert a fraction into a decimal, divide the numerator (dividend) by the denominator (divisor).

$$\frac{1}{4} \text{ becomes } 4\overline{)1.00}$$
$$\underline{-\ 8\downarrow}$$
$$20$$
$$\underline{-\ 20}$$
$$0$$

Multiply Decimals

When multiplying decimals, one method is to ignore decimals until the end of the calculation. Multiply the numbers 1.4 and 0.23.

First multiply the numbers as if they had no decimals, 14 and 23.

$$14 \times 23 = 322$$

Now, count the total number of decimal places to the right of the decimal point in each of the original numbers. 1.4 has one decimal place and 0.23 has two decimal places. That makes a total of three decimal places. In the product, count from the right that many places. Counting three places from the right, we find that

$$1.4 \times 0.23 = 0.322$$

Divide Decimals

Now divide 2.6 by 0.25. To divide two decimal numbers, look first at the divisor, in this case, 0.25. Determine the power of ten that you must multiply the divisor by to make it a whole number. In this case, the power of ten is 100. You then multiply the dividend by the same number. Thus, instead of dividing 2.6 by 0.25, you can calculate $260 \div 25$.

$$2.6 \div 0.25 = \frac{2.6}{0.25} = \left(\frac{2.6}{0.25}\right) \times \left(\frac{100}{100}\right) = \frac{(2.6 \times 100)}{(0.25 \times 100)} = \frac{260}{25}$$

You can solve this expression with long division. You find that

$$260 \div 25 = 10.4; \ 2.6 \div 0.25 = 10.4$$

Example Suppose a snail moves along the ground at a speed of 0.0025 m/s. How far would it travel in one minute? How long would it take the snail to travel 1.5 meters?

Step 1 Multiply the rate by the time to find the distance traveled. Remember, 60 s = 1 minute.

$$0.0025 \text{ m/s} \times 60 \text{ s}$$

Step 2 Multiply the two numbers without the decimal.

$$25 \times 60 = 1,500$$

Step 3 Count the decimal places in the two numbers (4), and count from the right that many places in the solution.

The snail would travel 0.15 meters in one minute.

Step 4 Divide the distance to travel by the rate to find the time necessary.

$$1.5 \text{ m} \div 0.0025 \text{ m/s}$$

Step 5 Multiply the expression by the multiplicative identity $\frac{10,000}{10,000}$ so that 0.0025 is a whole number.

$$\left(\frac{1.5 \text{ m}}{0.0025 \text{ m/s}}\right) \times \left(\frac{10,000}{10,000}\right)$$

$$\frac{15,000 \text{ m}}{25 \text{ m/s}} = 600 \text{ s}$$

So it would take the snail 600 seconds, or 10 minutes, to travel 1.5 meters.

Misconceptions Students might think that while dividing decimals they can use the same rule of counting the decimal places that they use in multiplication.

Percents

Assess Prior Knowledge In a flock of 53 geese, 30 are female and 23 are male. About what percent of this flock is male? [about 43%]

Copyright © Glencoe/McGraw-Hill, a division of The McGraw-Hill Companies, Inc.

All percentages relate to parts of a whole. The whole, 1, is equal to 100%. If a number is less than 1, it equals less than 100%. If it is greater than 1, it equals more than 100%. If you want to change a fraction into a percentage, set up a proportion in which the fraction $\left(\dfrac{\text{part}}{\text{whole}}\right)$ is equal to $\dfrac{\text{part percentage }(x)}{100\%}$.

Example You conduct a survey of people's blood types. Your results are in the table below. Calculate the percentage of people in your survey that have each blood type.

A	B	O	AB
273	68	307	34

Step 1 Add the numbers to find the total number of people surveyed—the whole.

$$273 + 68 + 307 + 34 = 682$$

Step 2 Express each group as a fraction of the whole.

A $\dfrac{273}{682}$

B $\dfrac{68}{682}$

O $\dfrac{307}{682}$

AB $\dfrac{34}{682}$

Step 3 The number 682 is 100% of the whole. Set up a proportion to find the part percentage for each blood type.

A $\dfrac{273}{682} = \dfrac{x}{100}$

B $\dfrac{68}{682} = \dfrac{x}{100}$

O $\dfrac{307}{682} = \dfrac{x}{100}$

AB $\dfrac{34}{682} = \dfrac{x}{100}$

Step 4 Solve each proportion and round to the nearest whole percentage.

A $682x = 27{,}300$ $x = \dfrac{27{,}300}{682}$ $x \approx 40\%$

B $682x = 6{,}800$ $x = \dfrac{6{,}800}{682}$ $x \approx 10\%$

O $682x = 30{,}700$ $x = \dfrac{30{,}700}{682}$ $x \approx 45\%$

AB $682x = 3{,}400$ $x = \dfrac{3{,}400}{682}$ $x \approx 5\%$

E

Significant Digits

Assess Prior Knowledge Express 2,538.7 to three significant digits. [2,540] Clarify that significant digits are often referred to as significant figures.

The precision of a measurement depends on the precision of your measuring tool. A pencil might be exactly 10.4876 cm long. However, if you measure it with a ruler that is marked with tenths of a centimeter (millimeters), the most accurate measurement you can make is 10.5 cm. This is similar to rounding to the tenths place. The number in the tenths place, 5, is the last significant digit in the measurement.

When counting significant digits in a number, all non-zero numbers are significant. All zeroes, no matter how many, between two non-zero numbers are significant. Therefore, 12,089.005 has eight significant digits. If there is no decimal point, zeroes to the right of all non-zero numbers are not significant. However, if the number has a decimal point, all zeroes are significant. Thus, 120 has two significant digits, but 120.050 has six significant digits.

When adding or subtracting numbers with different precisions, add or subtract the numbers and then round the answer to the decimal place of least precision (farthest to the left of the decimal). When multiplying or dividing numbers, determine which number has fewer significant digits. Round the answer to that number of significant digits.

Example Water is flowing into a pool from two hoses. The rate of flow for one hose is about 10.04 mL/s and the other is about 0.008 mL/s. At what rate is water flowing into the pool? Write the solution in the correct number of significant digits.

Step 1 Write out the expression.

$$10.04 \text{ mL/s} + 0.008 \text{ mL/s}$$

Step 2 Add together the rate of flow for each hose.

$$10.048 \text{ mL/s}$$

Step 3 The addend 10.04 is precise to the hundredths. The addend 0.008 is precise to the thousandths. Round the sum to the hundredths place.

$$10.05 \text{ mL/s}$$

Water is flowing into the pool at a rate of 10.05 mL/s

Misconceptions The last (right-most) significant digit might be marked by a bar above or below the number. This is especially important when a zero is significant. Thus, 12,0$\underline{0}$0 has four significant digits. If the number ends with a decimal point, zeroes between the decimal point and a non-zero number are significant. Thus, 4,500. has four significant digits.

Powers

Assess Prior Knowledge How could you simplify the expression $(x \cdot x^3)^2$? [x^8]

Powers are a shorthand way of expressing repeated multiplication of the same number. You could write $4 \times 4 \times 4$, or you could write 4^3. They both mean the same thing. The first number is called the base. It is the number that is being multiplied. The second number, which is written slightly above the base, is called the exponent. The exponent is also called the power. It tells you how many times to use the base as a factor.

Rules for Combining Bases

If you multiply two powers that have the same base, the base of the product does not change, but the exponent of the product is the sum of the exponents.

$$x^a \times x^b = x^{a+b}$$

This rule is the basis for all exponent expressions. Look in the example below. A number by itself can be thought of as that number to the power of 1.

$$4 = 4^1$$
$$4 \cdot 4 \cdot 4 = 4^1 \cdot 4^1 \cdot 4^1 = 4^2 \cdot 4^1 = 4^3$$

When you divide two powers with the same base, the base of the quotient does not change. The exponent of the quotient is the difference of the exponents.

$$x^a \div x^b = x^{a-b}$$

For example,

$$2^5 \div 2^2 = 2^{(5-2)} = 2^3$$

Knowing this helps you understand another rule: a number raised to the 0 power equals 1.

$$x^0 = 1$$

If you raise an exponent expression to another power, the base does not change, and you multiply the exponents.

$$(x^a)^b = x^{(a \times b)}$$
$$(5^2)^3 = 5^2 \times 5^2 \times 5^2 = 5^{(2+2+2)} = 5^{(2 \times 3)} = 5^6$$

A fractional exponent can be written as a root of the base.

$$x^{\left(\frac{1}{a}\right)} = \sqrt[a]{x}$$

A number raised to the power of $\frac{1}{2}$ is the positive square root of that number; a number raised to the power of $\frac{1}{3}$ is the cube root of that number, and so on.

$$16^{\left(\frac{1}{4}\right)} = \sqrt[4]{16} = 2$$

Finally, a number raised to a negative exponent equals the inverse of the number raised to the positive exponent.

$$x^{-a} = \frac{1}{x^a}$$

Example Light travels at approximately 3×10^8 m/s. The star Polaris is approximately 4×10^{18} meters from Earth. How long does it take for light from Polaris to travel to Earth?

Step 1 Divide the distance by the rate to find the time traveled.

$$(4 \times 10^{18} \text{ m}) \div (3 \times 10^8 \text{ m/s})$$

Step 2 Regroup the terms.

$$\frac{(4 \times 10^{18} \text{ m})}{(3 \times 10^8 \text{ m/s})} = \left(\frac{4 \text{ m}}{3 \text{ m/s}}\right) \times \left(\frac{10^{18}}{10^8}\right)$$

Step 3 We can use the rules of exponents to simplify the second grouping. (We estimate the answer to the first grouping.)

$$(1.33 \text{ s}) \times (10^{18 - 8}) = 1.33 \times 10^{10} \text{ s}$$

Misconceptions A common misconception is that powers can be distributed over addition: $(x^2 + y^2)^3 \neq x^6 + y^6$. Also, the addition of exponent expressions cannot be simplified using the rules above: $x^2 + x^3 \neq x^5$ or x^6.

Scientific Notation

Assess Prior Knowledge The mass of Earth is approximately 5,974,200,000,000,000,000,000,000 kilograms. How could you write this number in a more compact form? [5.9742×10^{24} kg]

Scientific measurements often involve extremely large or extremely small numbers. Such numbers are cumbersome to write out or type into a calculator, especially if you must do it more than once. Writing these numbers in scientific notation makes them easier to manipulate.

A number expressed in scientific notation consists of a decimal number between 1 and 10 multiplied by a power of 10. For example, the average distance between Mars and the Sun is 227,800,000,000 meters. This distance written in scientific notation is 2.278×10^{11} m. To write a number in scientific notation, move the decimal point until only one non-zero digit is to its left. Then count the number of places you moved the decimal point. This number is the power of 10. For large numbers (or any number larger than 1), this exponent will be positive.

For numbers smaller than 1, the exponent will be negative. For example, the mass of an electron is approximately 0.00000000000000000000000000000911 kg. Written in scientific notation, it is 9.11×10^{-31} kg. Because the decimal point moved to the right, the power of ten is a negative number.

Example The average distance from Earth to the Sun is 149,600,000 km. Express this in scientific notation.

Step 1 Move the decimal point until only one non-zero digit sits on the left of it to form a new decimal number.

$$1.49600000$$

Step 2 Count the number of places you moved the decimal point. In this example, you moved it eight places.

Step 3 Place this number as the exponent of the number 10. If the original number is between 0 and 1, the exponent is negative.

$$10^8$$

Step 4 Write an expression showing the decimal multiplied by the power of 10. This is the original number in scientific notation.

$$1.496 \times 10^8$$

Earth is 1.496×10^8 km from the Sun.

Misconceptions For numbers less than one, the original 0 to the left of the decimal place is not counted.

Logarithms

Assess Prior Knowledge How could you express the exact value of x in the equation $10^x = 44$? [$x = \log 44$]. A logarithm is an exponent.

Some problems involving exponents are difficult to solve through usual mathematical operations, so instead you would use logarithms. Logarithms are related to exponential equations. If $a^b = x$, then $\log_a x = b$. In both equations, a is the base. For example, $\log_3 9 = 2$ because $3^2 = 9$.

When no base is written with a log, the implied base is 10. This is sometimes called the common log. For example, $\log 10,000 = 4$ because $10^4 = 10,000$. Another type of logarithm is the natural log, which is written ln. The base of the natural log is a special non-terminating, non-repeating real number called e, which approximately equals 2.718.

$$ln\ x = \log_e x \qquad \qquad ln\ e = 1 \text{ because } e^1 = e$$

Logarithm Rules

The sum of logs of two numbers with the same base is equal to the log of the product of those numbers with that base.

$$\log_x a + \log_x b = \log_x (a \times b)$$

$$\log_2 4 + \log_2 8 = \log_2(4 \times 8) = \log_2(32)$$

$$2\quad +\quad 3 \qquad\qquad\qquad\qquad = \quad 5$$

The difference of logs of numbers is the log of their quotient.

$$\log_x a - \log_x b = \log_x(a \div b)$$

The log of a number raised to a power is equal to that power times the log of the number.

$$\log_a (x^r) = r \times \log_a x$$

$$\log_3 9^2 = \log_3 81 = 4 \text{ and } \log_3 9^2 = 2 \times \log_3 9 = 2 \times 2 = 4$$

E

The log of 1 with any base is equal to 0, since any number to the power of 0 equals 1.

$$\log_a 1 = 0 \text{ for any number } a$$

From this you can show a rule about the logarithm of fractions.

$$\log_a\left(\frac{1}{x}\right) = -\log_a x$$

$$\log\left(\frac{1}{5}\right) = \log 1 - \log 5 = 0 - \log 5 = -\log 5$$

There is another rule that you can use to convert logs between different bases.

$$\log_b a = \log a \div \log b$$

Example A machine called a seismograph gathers information about earthquakes. The Richter scale measures the magnitude of an earthquake. The equation for determining the magnitude of an earthquake is

$$M = \log A + 3 \times \log (8 \times t) - 2.92$$

where M is the magnitude, A is the highest amplitude in millimeters of the waves on a seismograph, and t is the time in seconds between when the p-waves and the s-waves reach the seismograph. Suppose a seismograph records a p-wave at 5:46:30 and then an s-wave at 5:46:39. The maximum amplitude recorded on the seismograph is 29 millimeters. What was the magnitude of the earthquake that caused these readings?

Step 1 Find the time between the s-wave and p-wave at this location.

$$5:46:39 - 5:46:30 = 9 \text{ seconds}$$

Step 2 Substitute into the equation.

$$M = \log (29) + 3 \times \log (8 \times 9) - 2.92$$

Step 3 Solve for M. You will need a calculator or a log table to calculate the approximate logarithms.

$$M = \log (29) + 3 \times \log (72) - 2.92 \approx 4.11$$

Algebra

Solve for Unknowns

Assess Prior Knowledge What is the value of x in the following equation?

$$\frac{x}{5} + 33 = 10 \quad [x = -115]$$

Algebra involves the use of variables that stand for various numbers or quantities. Finding the value of these variables is one of the most basic goals in algebra. These variables are usually represented by a letter, such as x, y, or z. Solving for a variable means isolating it on one side of an equals sign. You do this by performing operations on both sides of the equation. For most operations, as long as you perform the same operation on both sides of an equation, the equation remains true. For example, if $a = b$, then

$$a + 4 = b + 4 \qquad 3 \times a = 3 \times b \qquad \log a = \log b$$

Example If the temperature of a room is 77°F, the equation to find the temperature in Celsius (C) looks like this:

$$77 = \left(\frac{9}{5}\right) \times C + 32$$

Solve to find C.

Step 1 Subtract 32 from each side of the equation.

$$77 - 32 = \left(\frac{9}{5}\right) \times C + 32 - 32$$
$$45 = \left(\frac{9}{5}\right) \times C$$

Step 2 Multiply both sides by 5.

$$5 \times 45 = 5 \times \left(\frac{9}{5}\right) \times C$$
$$225 = 9 \times C$$

Step 3 Divide both sides by 9.

$$225 \div 9 = 9 \times C \div 9$$
$$25 = C$$

Misconceptions There are some functions that can cause confusion when applied to equations. For example, if $x^2 = 9$, then you can solve for x by taking the square root of both sides. Most people would say that this tells us that $x = 3$, but -3 is also a possible answer.

Also, when dividing or multiplying by a negative number in an inequality, the inequality sign must be reversed.

Quadratic Equations

Assess Prior Knowledge What are the possible values for x in the equation $x^2 + 2x - 15 = 0$? [3 and −5]

It is often impossible to isolate the variable in an equation which contains multiple powers of the variable. For some of these equations, you can factor the expression, which means expressing it

E

as the product of simpler expressions. For example, the expression $3x^2 - 7x + 2$ can be written as $(3x - 1) \times (x - 2)$. Expand the second expression to show they are equal. This expansion is also called FOIL (<u>f</u>irst, <u>o</u>uter, <u>i</u>nner, <u>l</u>ast) because you multiply the terms according to their location in the expression.

*Multiply **first** terms.*
$$3x \times x = 3x^2$$

*Multiply **outer** terms.*
$$3x \times -2 = -6x$$

*Multiply **inner** terms.*
$$-1 \times x = -x$$

*Multiply **last** terms.*
$$-1 \times -2 = 2$$

Add these terms together and compare them to the first expression.

$$3x^2 + -6x + -x + 2 = 3x^2 - 7x + 2$$

To perform the reverse, factor the expression $3x^2 - 7x + 2$. First, assume that for the equation that is in the form $Ax^2 + Bx + C = 0$, $(Mx + Y)(Nx + Z) = 0$. Start by finding the factors of A. A = 3, and the only positive factors of 3 are 1 and 3. So, M and N must be 1 and 3. (You can neglect negative factors for the purposes of this example.) Next, find the factors of A × C. A × C = 6 in the example, and the factors of 6 are 1, 2, 3, and 6. So, Y and Z must be either 1 and 6, −1 and −6, 2 and 3, or −2 and −3. You need to find which two numbers, when added together, give us B. −1 + −6 = −7. Put these numbers in a grid to find the factored equation.

$3x^2$	
	2

Place the first and third terms of the equation in the corners of the grid.

$3x^2$	$-1x$
$-6x$	2

Place the factors you found, multiplied by x, in the other boxes. It doesn't matter which factor goes in which box.

	$3x$	-1
x	$3x^2$	$-1x$
-2	$-6x$	2

Find the largest factor of each row and column. The factor will have the sign of the left-most box in a column or the top box in a row.

These factors give the answer: $(3x - 1)(x - 2)$. For some equations, you might be able to do these manipulations in your head. For example, when A = 1, you just need to find two numbers whose product is C and whose sum is B.

Example To find distance that an object travels, use the equation

$$d = \left(\frac{1}{2}\right)a^2 + vt$$

where a is the acceleration of the object and v is the original speed of the object. Suppose an object is constantly accelerating at 10 m/s^2. If it begins at a speed of 20 m/s, how long will it take for the object to travel 160 meters?

E

Step 1 Substitute the known values into the equation.

$$160 \text{ m} = \left(\frac{1}{2}\right)(10 \text{ m/s}^2)\, t^2 + (20 \text{ m/s})t$$

Step 2 Subtract 160 from each side of the equation in order to have the expression equal 0. You can simplify the expression by dividing both sides of the equation by 5.

$$0 = (5 \text{ m/s}^2)t^2 + (20 \text{ m/s})t - 160 \text{ m}$$

$$\left(\frac{0}{5}\right) = \frac{[(5 \text{ m/s}^2)t^2 + (20 \text{ m/s})t - 160 \text{ m}]}{5}$$

$$0 = (1 \text{ m/s}^2)\, t^2 + (4 \text{ m/s})t - 32 \text{ m}$$

Step 3 Find the factors of A × C = −32. Since the product is negative, one factor must be negative and the other positive. The possible factor pairs are 1 and −32, −1 and 32, 2 and −16, −2 and 16, 4 and −8, and −4 and 8.

Step 4 Choose the factor pair whose sum is B = 4. 8 and −4 add to 4.

Step 5 Create a grid and solve for the factors.

	t	-4
t	t^2	$-4t$
8	$8t$	-32

Step 6 Substitute the factored form. $0 = (t - 4)(t + 8)$ Since the only way the product of two numbers can be zero is if at least one of those numbers is zero, we know that either $t - 4 = 0$ or $t + 8 = 0$. Solving each of these for t tells that the time is either 4 seconds or −8 seconds. Since negative time makes no sense in this problem, we know that the answer is 4 seconds.

The Quadratic Formula

Assess Prior Knowledge What are the possible values for x in the equation $x^2 + 4x + 1 = 0$? $[-2 + \sqrt{3}, -2 - \sqrt{3}]$

An equation in which the highest power of a variable is 2 is called a quadratic equation. In a quadratic equation with one variable, that variable can have two possible values. Some quadratic equations can be solved by factoring, but not all equations are easily factored. To find the solutions for x in these equations, you can use the quadratic formula:

If $ax^2 + bx + c = 0,$ then $x = \dfrac{[-b \pm \sqrt{(b^2 - 4ac)}]}{(2a)}$

Example The distance that an object travels is given by the equation

$$d = \left(\frac{1}{2}\right) a t^2 + vt$$

where a is the acceleration of the object and v is the original speed of the object. Gravitational acceleration on the surface of the moon is about 1.6 m/s². If a meteoroid is 1.0 kilometer above the surface of

E

the Moon and dropping at a speed of 512.0 m/s, how long will it take to hit the Moon's surface?

Step 1 Substitute the known values into the equation.

$$1{,}000 \text{ m} = \left(\frac{1}{2}\right)(1.6 \text{ m/s}^2)t^2 + (512.0 \text{ m/s})t$$

Step 2 Subtract 1,000 from each side of the equation in order to have the expression equal 0.

$$0 = (0.8 \text{ m/s}^2)t^2 + (512.0 \text{ m/s})t - 1{,}000 \text{ m}$$

Step 3 Plug the corresponding values into the quadratic equation to solve for t.

$$t = \frac{[-512.0 \pm \sqrt{(512^2 - 4 \times 0.8 \times -1{,}000)}]}{(2 \times 0.8)}$$

$$t = \frac{(-512.0 \pm \sqrt{265344})}{1.6}$$

$$t \approx 1.9 \text{ and } t \approx -641.9 \text{ or } 640 \text{ s}$$

Step 4 Choose the answer which makes sense in the equation (in this case, the positive solution). So, the meteoroid will hit the Moon's surface in approximately 1.9 seconds.

Linear Equations

Assess Prior Knowledge What does the graph of $2x + 6y = 12$ look like? [It is a line that passes through the x-axis at 6 and through the y-axis at 2.]

A linear equation is one in which the highest power of any variable is 1. Some examples of linear equations are

$$x = 3 \qquad x + 7y = 12 \qquad y = 4x + 10$$

The first equation has one solution. The other two equations have unlimited solutions.

You can graph a two-variable linear equation by putting it in the form $y = mx + b$. In this form, b is the y-intercept. It is the point at which the line strikes the y-axis. The number m is the slope of the line. For every 1 unit of increase along the x-axis, the line will move m units up the y-axis. Some educators refer to slope as rise over run.

Example Suppose you are measuring the growth of a kudzu vine. Your first measurement shows that the vine is 4 m long. After subsequent measurement, you find that it grows about 30 cm every day. Graph the growth of the plant, assuming it grows at a constant rate, and tell how long it will take for it to be 100 meters long.

Step 1 Because the rate is constant, growth is represented by a linear equation. In this case, the variables are time (t) and length (y). At $t = 0$, $y = 4$, so

$$y = mt + 4$$

Step 2 For every day (increase of t by 1), y increases by 0.3 m, so the slope, m, is $\frac{.3}{1}$, or just .3.

$$y = 0.3t + 4$$

E

Step 3 The slope, m, is .3 or $\frac{3}{10}$, and the y-intercept, b, is 4. We can use this information to graph the equation.

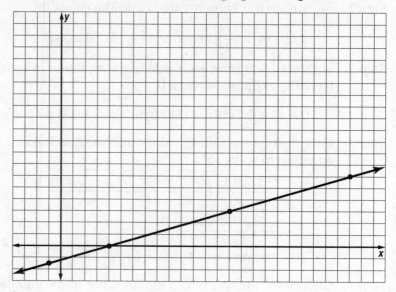

Step 4 To find how long it will take to grow to 100 m, we let $y = 100$ and solve for t.

$$100 = 0.3t + 4$$

$$t = 320 \text{ days}$$

Solve Systems of Linear Equations

Assess Prior Knowledge What values of x and y solve the equations $2x - y = 1$ and $x + 3y = 11$? [$x = 2$ and $y = 3$]

Both of the equations in the question above describe lines. These two lines have one point in common, the point at which they intersect. This point, described by an x- and a y-coordinate, is the common solution of the two equations. One way to find this solution is to graph each equation and measure the point where they intersect. However, in some cases it can be difficult to find the exact coordinates of this point.

Substitution

Another method of solving simultaneous equations is substitution. Let's use substitution to solve the Assess Prior Knowledge problem.

First, isolate one of the variables in one of the equations.

$$x + 3y = 11$$
$$x = 11 - 3y$$

Next, substitute the equivalent expression for that variable in the other equation.

$$2x - y = 1$$
$$2(11 - 3y) - y = 1$$

Then, solve this new equation to find the value of the other variable.

$$22 - 6y - y = 1$$
$$22 - 7y = 1$$
$$7y = 21$$
$$y = 3$$

Finally, substitute this numerical value into either equation to find the value of the other variable.

$$x + 3(3) = 11$$
$$x + 9 = 11$$
$$x = 2$$

E

Elimination

Another method for solving simultaneous equations is by eliminating one of the terms. You know that if you multiply both sides of an equation by the same number, the equation remains true. Also, if you subtract equivalent quantities from both sides of an equation, the equation remains true. You can use these rules to solve the simultaneous equations.

First, multiply the equations by values in order to make the coefficients of one variable identical in each equation.

$$2 \times (x + 3y = 11) \qquad\qquad 1 \times (2x - y = 1)$$
$$2x + 6y = 22 \qquad\qquad\qquad 2x - y = 1$$

Second, subtract each side of one equation from each side of the other equation to eliminate one variable.

$$\begin{array}{r} 2x - y = 1 \\ - (2x + 6y = 22) \\ \hline 0x - 7y = -21 \end{array}$$

Then, solve for the remaining variable.

$$-7y = -21$$
$$y = 3$$

Finally, substitute this numerical value into either equation to find the value of the other variable.

$$2x - 3 = 1$$
$$2x = 4$$
$$x = 2$$

Example A rabbit sees a wolf approaching from 6 meters away and starts running at 13 m/s. The wolf chases at a speed of 15 m/s. How long will it take the wolf to catch the rabbit, and how far will the rabbit run before the wolf catches it?

Step 1 Write equations for each animal. Let r = the rabbit's position, w = the wolf's position, and t = the time from when they start running.

rabbit: $r = 13t$ \qquad wolf: $w = 15t - 6$

Step 2 When the wolf catches the rabbit, the animals' positions will be the same, so r will be equal to w. Now you can use substitution to solve for the time (t).

$$13t = 15t - 6$$
$$-2t = -6$$
$$t = 3 \text{ seconds}$$

Step 3 Substitute the value of t into the rabbit equation to see how far the rabbit ran.

$$x = 13(3) = 39 \text{ meters}$$

Geometry

Angles

Assess Prior Knowledge If a right triangle has one acute angle that measures 30 degrees, what is the measure of the other acute angle? [60 degrees]

Angles can be important for calculating many quantities in science, including the area or volume of some shapes and the length of paths that an object travels. There are different classifications of angles and several rules that can help you determine the value of unknown angles.

A 180° angle forms a straight line. An angle that measures half of that, 90°, is called a right angle. This is the kind of angle you would find at the corner of a rectangle. An angle that is larger than 90° is called an obtuse angle. An angle that is smaller than 90° is called an acute angle.

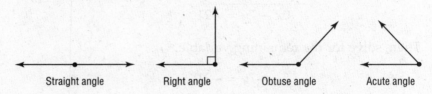

Straight angle   Right angle   Obtuse angle   Acute angle

If one line intersects another line at a right angle (all four angles will be right angles), then the lines are perpendicular. If one line is perpendicular to another, the first line's slope (m) will be the opposite inverse $\left(\frac{-1}{m}\right)$ of the other line's slope.

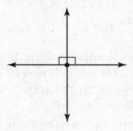

There are many relationships that can help you find the value of unknown angles. For example, if you know all but one angle in a polygon, you can calculate the missing angle. The sum of the three interior angles of any triangle is always 180°. A parallelogram (such as a rectangle or a square) has a total angle measure of 360°. For a polygon with n sides, the sum of all n angles can be calculated by $180° \times (n - 2)$. So, a pentagon has $180° \times (5 - 2) = 540°$ of interior angles. For a regular pentagon, we divide this number by 5 and find that each angle in a regular pentagon measures 108°.

E

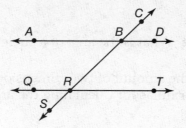

Look at the figure. The two horizontal lines are parallel to each other. Two angles that are next to each other are called adjacent angles. ∠ABC and ∠CBD form a straight line. Since straight lines form 180° angles, the measures of ∠ABC and ∠CBD add up to 180°. These are called supplementary angles. ∠DBR and ∠CBD are also supplementary angles.

$$m\angle ABC + m\angle CBD = 180°$$

$$m\angle CBD + m\angle DBR = 180°$$

$$m\angle ABC = m\angle DBR$$

∠ABC and ∠DBR are called vertical angles or opposite angles. Vertical angles form from the same pair of lines but are not adjacent. Vertical angles are equal to each other. ∠CBD and ∠ABR are also vertical angles.

Since the two horizontal lines are parallel, the intersecting line forms the same angles. ∠ABC and ∠QRB are equal to one another because similar lines form them. This means that ∠QRB equals ∠RBD. ∠QRB and ∠RBD are alternate interior angles. Alternate interior angles are equal to each other.

∠QRB and ∠QRS are supplementary, just like ∠CBD and ∠RBD. From this, we see that ∠QRS equals ∠CBD. ∠QRS and ∠CBD are alternate exterior angles. Alternate exterior angles are equal to each other.

Example A beam of light ricochets down a hall of mirrors. When light strikes a mirror, the angle of incidence equals the angle of reflection. If the diagram below shows the path of the light, what is the measure of angle C?

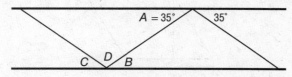

Step 1 Since A and B are alternate interior angles, angle B = 35°.

Step 2 According to the laws governing reflection of light, B = C = 35°.

Step 3 Since angles B, D, and C form a straight line, B + D + C = 180°, so angle D = 110°.

Area Formulas

Assess Prior Knowledge What is the area of a circle with a diameter of 8? [16π]

Area describes the amount of two-dimensional space a shape covers. There are formulas for calculating the area of common two-dimensional shapes.

The area of a circle is $A = \pi r^2$, where r is the circle's radius.

The area of a triangle is $A = \frac{1}{2}bh$, where b is a base, or one side, of that triangle and h is the height of the triangle from that base. Height is the perpendicular distance to the base from the angle opposite the base.

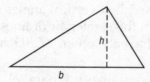

You can divide a trapezoid into two triangles of equal height. Thus, the area of a trapezoid is the sum of the area of these two triangles: $A = \frac{1}{2}(b_1 + b_2)h$ where b_1 and b_2 are the lengths of the parallel sides.

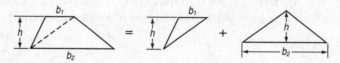

A parallelogram is a similar shape in which $b_1 = b_2$, so the area is simply $b \times h$.

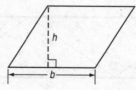

A rectangle is a parallelogram with four right angles. In a rectangle, if one side is the base, or length (ℓ), then an adjacent side is equal to the width (w). The area of a rectangle is the length multiplied by the width, $A = \ell w$.

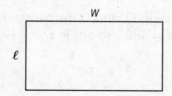

E

A square is a special rectangle in which all sides are equal ($\ell = w$). Thus, the area of a square is $A = s^2$.

You can divide any polygon into triangles. Adding the areas of these triangles gives the area of the polygon. A regular polygon is one in which all sides are the same length, such as a square. The area of any regular polygon is $\frac{1}{2}nsr$, where n is the number of sides, s is the length of a side, and r is the apothem (the length from the center to a closest point on the polygon, along a perpendicular line).

Three-dimensional shapes have surface area, or the amount of two-dimensional space that covers the outside of the shape. The surface area of a three-dimensional shape is the sum of the areas of its faces. The surface area of a rectangular prism is $2(\ell w + wh + \ell h)$. The surface area of a sphere is $4\pi r^2$. You can separate a cylinder's surface area into two circles, each having an area of πr^2, and a rectangle that has an area of $h(2\pi r)$, so the surface area is equal to $2\pi r^2 + 2\pi rh$. You can separate the surface area of a cone into a circle, with an area of πr^2, and a triangle with base $2\pi r$ and height s (the slant height of the cone), so its surface area is equal to $\pi r^2 + \pi rs$.

Example The surface area of exposed water affects how quickly water evaporates. A larger surface area allows water to evaporate more quickly. In which container would a quantity of water evaporate most quickly: a cylinder with diameter 20 cm or a square prism of side 20 cm?

Step 1 Calculate the exposed area of water in the cylinder.

$$A = \pi \times r^2 = \pi \times (10 \text{ cm})^2 = 100\pi \text{ cm}^2 \approx 314 \text{ cm}^2$$

Step 2 Calculate the exposed area of water in the square prism.

$$A = s^2 = (20 \text{ cm})^2 = 400 \text{ cm}^2$$

So, the water would evaporate fastest from the square prism.

Circumference

Assess Prior Knowledge What is the circumference of a circle with a diameter of 8? [8π]

The circumference of a circle is the perimeter of a circle. Since a circle has no sides, you must calculate its perimeter differently than that of polygons. The circumference of a circle is πd, where d is the diameter, which is twice the radius of the circle.

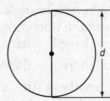

Example Suppose that a satellite moves in a circular orbit around Earth along the equator. The diameter of Earth is about 13,000 km. If the satellite is at an altitude of 36,000 km, how far does it travel in one revolution?

Step 1   Calculate the diameter of the satellite's orbit. This is the diameter of Earth plus twice the satellite's altitude.

$$d = 13{,}000 \text{ km} + 2 \times 36{,}000 \text{ km} = 85{,}000 \text{ km}$$

Step 2   The length of the satellite's path of revolution is equal to the circumference of the circle it makes around Earth.

$$c = \pi d = 3.14 \times 85{,}000 \text{ km} \approx 267{,}000 \text{ km}$$

E

Volume Formulas

Assess Prior Knowledge Which has a larger volume, a sphere of diameter 2 cm or a cube of side 2 cm? [the sphere]

Volume is the measure of the amount of three-dimensional space an object occupies. There are formulas for calculating the volumes of three-dimensional shapes.

The volume of a sphere is $\frac{4}{3}\pi r^3$.

You can find the volume of any prism by multiplying the area of one of the bases by the height of the prism. The height is measured perpendicular to the base, even if the prism is slanted. A box is a rectangular prism that contains only right angles. To find the volume of a box, multiply its length by its width by its height.

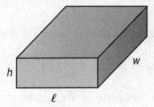

A cube is a special prism in which all edges are the same length. The volume of a cube is s^3, where s is the length of one edge.

A cylinder is similar to a prism, except its base is a circle. A cylinder's volume is $\pi r^2 h$, where r is the radius of the base and h is the height of the cylinder.

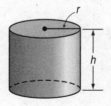

The volume of a pyramid is $\left(\frac{1}{3}\right)A_B h$, where A_B is the area of the base and h is the height of the pyramid (measured perpendicular to the base). A cone is similar to a pyramid, except it has a circular base. Its volume formula is $\left(\frac{1}{3}\right)A_B$, or $\left(\frac{1}{3}\right)\pi r^2 h$.

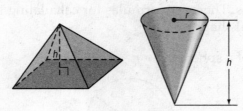

Any polyhedron can be divided into pyramids. Each face of the polyhedron would form a base of a pyramid. The height of each pyramid would be the shortest distance from the center of the polyhedron to the face that forms the base of the pyramid. Thus, you can find the volume of any polyhedron by adding the volumes of the pyramids that make it.

Example Light projected through a pinhole onto a black surface forms a cone of light. If the pinhole is 6 m from the surface, and the light illuminates a section 2 m across, what is the volume of the lighted space?

Step 1 Calculate the area of the base of the cone.

$$A_B = \pi r^2 = \pi\left(\frac{2\text{ m}}{2}\right)^2 = \pi\text{ m}^2$$

Step 2 Calculate the volume of the cone.

$$V = \left(\frac{1}{3}\right)A_B h = \left(\frac{1}{3}\right)\pi\text{m}^2(6\text{ m}) = 2\pi\text{ m}^3$$

Misconceptions Students often mistake common shapes because they are not upright or are shown in a way that is unfamiliar to students.

E

Measurement

Volume, Mass, and Density

Assess Prior Knowledge What is the density of a metal cube with an edge of length 3 cm that has a mass of 521 g? [about 19.3 g/cm^3]

Density is the amount of matter in a given unit of space. You can calculate the average density of an object by dividing its total mass by its total volume.

Normally, you determine an object's mass by comparing it to known masses using a balance. This is based on the fact that gravity exerts equal force on equal masses. You can use a scale to find the weight of the object. Since the exact pull of gravity varies with altitude, a balance is a better tool for measuring mass. However, if necessary you can determine the mass from the weight if you know the pull of gravity.

You can calculate the volume of regular shapes using certain formulas. However, many objects have irregular shapes. One method for finding the mass of an irregularly shaped object is to place it in a liquid and measure the volume of liquid that it displaces.

Example You find a gold-colored rock and want to determine its density in order to identify its composition. You use a pan balance to measure its mass. The pans balance each other when one pan holds the rock and the other holds two 100-gram masses, one 50-gram mass, and one 1-gram mass. You pour some water into a beaker that has a diameter of 8 cm. When you drop the rock into the water, the water level rises 1 cm. What is the density of the rock?

Step 1 Calculate the mass of the rock by adding the known masses that balance it.

$$m = 2 \times 100 \text{ g} + 1 \times 50 \text{ g} + 1 \times 1 \text{ g} = 251 \text{ g}$$

Step 2 Calculate the volume of the cylinder that makes up the displaced water in the beaker when the rock is added. This is the area of a cross-section times the increase in height of the water.

$$V = Ah = \pi r^2 h = \pi \times \left(\frac{8 \text{ cm}}{2}\right)^2 \times 1 \text{ cm} = 16\pi \text{ cm}^3$$

Step 3 Calculate the density by dividing the mass by the volume.

$$\rho \text{ (density)} = \frac{m}{V} = \frac{251 \text{ g}}{16\pi \text{ cm}^3} \approx \frac{5.0 \text{ g}}{\text{cm}^3}$$

E

Dimensional Analysis

Assess Prior Knowledge How many inches are there in 2 yards? [72 in.]

There are many different units used in measurement. Distance measurements include inches, feet, yards, miles, meters, kilometers, and astronomical units. Most students will be more familiar with the U.S. Equivalent system of measurement (yards, gallons, ounces); however, scientists almost always use the SI system (meters, liters, grams) when performing investigations. To add, subtract, or compare two measurements, those measurements need to be in the same units. To find an equivalent measurement in a different unit of measure, you can convert using dimensional analysis. Dimensional analysis involves multiplying a quantity by one or more conversion factors. A conversion factor is a ratio of two equivalent measurements with different units. All conversion factors are, thus, equal to 1, and multiplying a measurement by 1 does not change the value of the measurement. For example,

$$1{,}000 \text{ mL} = 1 \text{ L}$$

$$\frac{1{,}000 \text{ mL}}{1 \text{ L}} = \frac{1 \text{ L}}{1{,}000 \text{ mL}} = 1$$

You can use conversion factors to convert between units within one system of measurement or between different systems.

Example If you know that there are 2.54 cm in an inch, how can you find how many meters are in 3 feet?

Step 1 Multiply the measurement by the conversion factor from feet to inches.

$$3 \text{ ft} \times 12 \text{ in.}/1 \text{ ft}$$

Step 2 Multiply by the conversion factor from inches to centimeters.

$$3 \text{ ft} \times \frac{12 \text{ in.}}{1 \text{ ft}} \times \frac{2.54 \text{ cm}}{1 \text{ in.}}$$

Step 3 Multiply by the conversion factor from centimeters to meters.

$$3 \text{ ft} \times \frac{12 \text{ in.}}{1 \text{ ft}} \times \frac{2.54 \text{ cm}}{1 \text{ in.}} \times \frac{1 \text{ m}}{100 \text{ cm}}$$

Step 4 Carry out the multiplication and division making sure the final answer is in meters.

$$0.9144 \text{ meters}$$

$$3 \text{ feet} = 0.9144 \text{ meters}$$

Misconceptions You cannot convert temperature readings using conversion factors because different temperature scales do not measure 0 from the same point. In mathematical terms, 0 gal = 0 L, but $0°F \neq 0°C \neq 0 \text{ K}$.

E

Data Analysis

Averages: Mean, Median, and Mode

Assess Prior Knowledge Calculate the mean, the median, and the mode of the numbers 3, 3, 6, 7, and 11. [The mean is 6, the median is 6, and the mode is 3.]

When researching a topic, scientists often measure more than once or conduct multiple identical experiments. Finding the average of the data can be useful in drawing conclusions. However, there is more than one kind of average.

Mean

The most commonly used type of average is the mean average. The mean of a set of numbers is the sum of all numbers in the set divided by the number of items in the set.

Median

If there is an odd number of items in the set, then the median is the middle number in the set when the numbers are arranged in numerical order. If there is an even number of items in the set, then the median is the mean of the two middle numbers.

Mode

The mode of a set of numbers is the number that appears most often. If no number appears more often than another number, then the set has no mode. If more than one number occurs the same number of times, and these numbers occur most often, then the set has more than one mode.

Example Lisa measures the running speed of six different cheetahs. See the chart below for her data. What are the mean, the median, and the mode of the data?

Cheetah	1	2	3	4	5	6
Speed	113 km/hr	107 km/hr	118 km/hr	116 km/hr	113 km/hr	117 km/hr

To find the mean:

Step 1   Add the items in the set together.

$$113 \text{ km/hr} + 107 \text{ km/hr} + 118 \text{ km/hr} + 116 \text{ km/hr} +$$
$$113 \text{ km/hr} + 117 \text{ km/hr} = 684 \text{ km/hr}$$

Step 2   Count the number of items in the set.

In this example there are 6.

Step 3   Divide the sum of the items by the number of items.

$$684 \text{ km/hr} \div 6 = 114 \text{ km/hr}$$

E

To find the median:

Step 1   Arrange the items in the set in numerical order.

> 107 km/hr, 113 km/hr, 113 km/hr,
> 116 km/hr, 117 km/hr, 118 km/hr

Step 2   Find the number or numbers in the middle of the set.

In this example the numbers are 113 km/hr and 116 km/hr.

Step 3   Calculatethe mean of these two numbers.

> (113 km/hr + 116 km/hr) ÷ 2 = 114.5 km/hr

To find the mode:

Step 1   List each unique item in the set.

> 107 km/hr, 113 km/hr, 116 km/hr,
> 117 km/hr, 118 km/hr

Step 2   Count the number of times each item appears in the set.

107 km/hr	113 km/hr	116 km/hr	117 km/hr	118 km/hr
1	2	1	1	1

Step 3   The item that occurs most often (in this example, 113) is the mode.

The mean of the set is 114 km/hr, the median is 114.5 km/hr, and the mode is 113.

Misconceptions Students might assume that the mean average is always the most accurate average. However, different averages are useful in different situations. For example, economists are usually more concerned with median incomes than with mean incomes.

Probability

Assess Prior Knowledge What is the probability that a thrown die will land on an even number? $\left[\frac{1}{2}\right]$

Probability theory predicts the likelihood of an event in a certain situation. An outcome is the result of an experiment. For example, possible outcomes of rolling a standard six-sided die are the numbers 1, 2, 3, 4, 5, and 6. An event is a set of possible outcomes, such as rolling an even number.

The probability of an event is represented by a number, usually written as a fraction. A probability of 0 means that the event absolutely cannot happen. For example, rolling a 7 with a standard six-sided die has a probability of 0. A probability of 1 means that the event is a certainty. For example, the probability of rolling a number 1–6 is 1.

How could you calculate the probability that two events will happen at the same time? To be possible, the events must be independent. For example, if you flip one coin, the probability that the result is both heads and tails is 0. It is impossible because these events are not independent. Such events are called mutually exclusive. However, suppose you flip two coins. The outcome of one coin does not affect the outcome of the other. They are independent. The probability that both coins come up heads is the product of the probability that each coin comes up heads. Let's define the probability of an event A as $P(A)$. Then, when flipping two coins:

$$P(\text{heads AND heads}) = P(\text{heads} \cap \text{heads}) =$$
$$P(\text{heads}) \times P(\text{heads}) = \frac{1}{2} \times \frac{1}{2} = \frac{1}{4}$$

You can also calculate the possibility that either one event or another event happens. The formula for this probability is

$$P(A \text{ OR } B) = P(A \cup B) = P(A) + P(B) - P(A \cap B)$$

Calculate the probability of drawing either an ace or a heart from a deck of 52 cards. There are four aces and 13 heart cards in a deck. One card is both a heart and an ace.

$$P(\text{ace OR heart}) = P(\text{ace}) + P(\text{heart}) - P(\text{ace} \cap \text{heart}) =$$
$$\frac{4}{52} + \frac{13}{52} - \frac{1}{52}$$

$$P(\text{ace} \cup \text{heart}) = \frac{16}{52} = \frac{4}{13}$$

The probability that an event will not happen is calculated by subtracting its probability from the certainty. The probability that you will not roll a 4 with a six-sided die is

$$P(\text{NOT } 4) = 1 - P(4) = 1 - \frac{1}{6} = \frac{5}{6}$$

A grid called a Punnett square can be used to aid in finding possible outcomes of two or more independent experiments, such as flipping two coins. Each possible outcome of each experiment is placed outside the grid, aligned with a row or column. By putting together the outcomes in the grid, you can see all of the possible outcomes of the pair of experiments. Geneticists use Punnett squares to determine the likelihood of certain gene combinations.

If H is heads and T is tails, then a Punnett square can show the results of two flipped coins.

	H	T
H	HH	HT
T	TH	TT

Example According to Mendel's law of independent assortment, a pea seed's color and appearance (wrinkled or smooth) are on separate chromosomes. Yellow seeds are dominant over green seeds. Smooth seeds are dominant over wrinkled seeds. What is the probability that a seed produced by two plants will be green and wrinkled?

E

Step 1 Draw a Punnett square to find the probability of green seeds.

Y = yellow allele, y = green allele

	Y	y
Y	YY	Yy
y	Yy	yy

Step 2 Draw a Punnett square to find the probability of wrinkled seeds.

S = smooth allele, s = wrinkled allele

	S	s
S	SS	Ss
s	Ss	ss

Step 3 Calculate the probability that the two plants will produce a green and wrinkled seed. Remember that for the recessive trait to be expressed, both alleles must be recessive.

$$P(yy \cap ss) = P(yy) \times P(ss) = \frac{1}{4} \times \frac{1}{4} = \frac{1}{16}$$

Laboratory Calculations

Assess Prior Knowledge If an object weighs exactly 10 grams, and a researcher measures it to be 9.5 grams, what is the relative error of the measurement? [0.05]

An old adage says, "Measure twice and cut once." Human measurements are often inaccurate. Scientists usually measure the same quantity many, many times. All of these measurements are averaged together to approximate most accurately the exact value. The differences between this average, or exact value, and the individual measurements are known as errors.

Absolute Error

One way to express the error in a measurement is to determine the absolute error. The absolute error describes the magnitude of the error. It is calculated by finding the positive difference between the exact (or averaged) value and the measurement:

$$E_A = |T - A|;$$
where T is the exact value and A is the measurement.

The absolute error has the same units as the measurement itself. You have probably heard an expression of absolute error before, though you may not have realized it. Whenever someone says something like, "200 miles $\pm$ 1 mile," the "$\pm$ 1 mile" is the absolute error.

Relative Error

Another way to express error in a measurement is to give the relative error. The relative error describes how accurate a measurement is by comparing the magnitude of the error to the magnitude of a measurement. For example, if an object is 10 cm long, an error of 1 cm is relatively large. However, if an object is 1 km long, an error of 1 cm is very small. Calculate the relative error by dividing the absolute error by the exact (or averaged) measurement:

$$E_R = \left| \frac{(T - A)}{T} \right|$$

Note that the relative error has no units.

Example You take several measurements of the width of a human red blood cell. Those measurements are 6.8 μm, 7.1 μm, 7.0 μm, 6.9 μm, and 7.2 μm. Calculate the absolute and relative errors of each measurement.

Step 1 Calculate the average value of all five measurements. Take the mean average.

$$\frac{(6.8 \ \mu m + 7.1 \ \mu m + 7.0 \ \mu m + 6.9 \ \mu m + 7.2 \ \mu m)}{5} = 7.0 \ \mu m$$

Step 2 Calculate the absolute error for each measurement.

$$E_A = |\, T - A \,|$$
$$E_{A1} = |\, 7.0 \ \mu m - 6.8 \ \mu m \,| = |\, 0.2 \ \mu m \,| = 0.2 \ \mu m$$
$$E_{A2} = |\, 7.0 \ \mu m - 7.1 \ \mu m \,| = |\, -0.1 \ \mu m \,| = 0.1 \ \mu m$$
$$E_{A3} = |\, 7.0 \ \mu m - 7.0 \ \mu m \,| = |\, 0.0 \ \mu m \,| = 0.0 \ \mu m$$
$$E_{A4} = |\, 7.0 \ \mu m - 6.9 \ \mu m \,| = |\, 0.1 \ \mu m \,| = 0.1 \ \mu m$$
$$E_{A5} = |\, 7.0 \ \mu m - 7.2 \ \mu m \,| = |\, -0.2 \ \mu m \,| = 0.2 \ \mu m$$

Step 3 Calculate the relative error for each measurement.

$$E_R = \left| \frac{(T - A)}{T} \right|$$

$$E_{R1} = \left| \frac{(7.0 \ \mu m - 6.8 \ \mu m)}{7.0 \ \mu m} \right| = \left| \frac{0.2 \ \mu m}{7.0 \ \mu m} \right| = 0.029$$

$$E_{R2} = \left| \frac{(7.0 \ \mu m - 7.1 \ \mu m)}{7.0 \ \mu m} \right| = \left| \frac{-0.1 \ \mu m}{7.0 \ \mu m} \right| = 0.014$$

$$E_{R3} = \left| \frac{(7.0 \ \mu m - 7.0 \ \mu m)}{7.0 \ \mu m} \right| = \left| \frac{0.0 \ \mu m}{7.0 \ \mu m} \right| = 0.0$$

$$E_{R4} = \left| \frac{(7.0 \ \mu m - 6.9 \ \mu m)}{7.0 \ \mu m} \right| = \left| \frac{0.1 \ \mu m}{7.0 \ \mu m} \right| = 0.014$$

$$E_{R5} = \left| \frac{(7.0 \ \mu m - 7.2 \ \mu m)}{7.0 \ \mu m} \right| = \left| \frac{-0.2 \ \mu m}{7.0 \ \mu m} \right| = 0.029$$

E

Problem Solve

Assess Prior Knowledge Danny and Molly can bake 72 cookies in an hour. Each cookie is about 5 cm in diameter and has an average of 8 chocolate chips. If they continue baking at the same rate, how long will it take them to make 300 cookies? [4 hours and 10 minutes]

Some problems are straightforward. They tell how to find the answer, perhaps by directing you to add or multiply certain quantities or numbers. An expression, such as 2 + 3, is the most direct problem. You need only to carry out the operations in the proper order to find the answer. An algebra equation, which contains numbers and variables, is more difficult to solve. In order to isolate the variable, you must decide which operations to perform.

Word problems can require the most work. You must correctly write out the expressions or equations you need to solve word problems. A word problem can require one equation or a sequence of equations. The following is a series of steps you can follow that can help in solving problems.

First, explore the information in the problem. Take notes and outline this information. After reading the whole problem, read through the end of the word problem again and decide exactly what the problem is asking you to solve. This will help when deciding what information in the problem is important and what might be extraneous. Write down and identify the known quantities, such as "length = 5 m." It might help to assign a variable to any unknown quantities, such as d = distance traveled or t = time spent.

Second, make a plan for solving the problem. There are many strategies that can help organize the information: make a table, make a list, act out the problem, work backward, fill in a Venn diagram, look for reasonable answers, look for a pattern, solve a simpler problem, make or draw a model, draw a graph or diagram, guess and check, or eliminate possibilities. If one strategy doesn't solve the problem, try another. Sometimes a combination of two or more strategies works best.

Keep in mind that you might need some information that is not given in the problem. The use of conversion factors, formulas, or mathematical rules might have to be inferred.

It can often be helpful to translate the word problem into math equations or expressions. Mathematics has a language of numbers and symbols. Some sentences in a word problem might translate directly into an equation. The nouns of a sentence might equate to the quantities and variables in an equation. Some of the verbs might correspond to operations. When translating sentences into equations, it is important to be familiar with the vocabulary of mathematics. Words like *sum*, *total*, *add*, and *combine* usually refer to addition. Words like *take* and *take away* often refer to subtraction. Words such as *times*, *per*, and *each* can connote multiplication or division.

Third, carry out the operations to solve the problem. There might be more than one method for solving a given problem.

Finally, examine the answer to see if it makes sense. Is the result a reasonable length of time, distance, or number of objects? If asked

E

to solve an algebra problem, substitute the solution back into the original equation to check it. While solving science problems, keeping track of units can help check the answer. If you expect a speed in meters per second (m/s) and the solution is in meters times seconds (m · s), you made a mistake. Some calculations, especially ones with quadratic equations, can result in more than one solution. In these cases, use common sense to figure out which solution is correct. For example, a negative number is unlikely to be the answer to a problem that asks for mass or a length of time.

Example The Environmental Protection Agency conducts studies to compare the fuel efficiency of commercial vehicles. They often find data telling how far an automobile will travel on one gallon of gas. Driving through a city often involves more starting and stopping, which uses gasoline more quickly than traveling continuously on a highway. Suppose that a typical automobile can travel continuously for 28 miles on a gallon of gasoline and that a similar hybrid automobile can travel continuously for 34 miles on a gallon of gasoline. A full tank has 18.5 gallons of gasoline. Researchers put a hybrid automobile on a circular driving track 5,000 feet in diameter. How many full laps would the hybrid complete on a full tank of gas?

Step 1 Identify the important information.

x = distance a hybrid could travel on a full tank

n = number of laps completed

C = length of lap

18.5 gallons = volume of a full tank of gasoline

34 miles/gallon = hybrid rate of gas consumption

5,000 feet = diameter of track

Step 2 Analyze the problem for missing information.

conversion factor: $\dfrac{1 \text{ mile}}{5{,}280 \text{ feet}}$

formula for the circumference of a circle: $C = \pi d$

Step 3 Develop a plan to solve the problem:

❶ Find the distance (x) the hybrid can travel on a full tank.

❷ Find the length (C) of a lap around the track.

❸ Divide the distance (x) by the length (C) to find the number of laps.

Step 4 Perform the calculations.

$5000 \text{ ft} \times \dfrac{1 \text{ mi}}{5280 \text{ ft}} = 0.9470 \text{ mi}$

$C = \pi d = \pi(0.9470 \text{ mi}) = 2.974 \text{ mi}$

$x = 34 \text{ mi/gal} \times 18.5 \text{ gal} = 629 \text{ mi}$

$n = \dfrac{x}{C} = \dfrac{629 \text{ mi}}{2.947 \text{ mi}} = 213.4$

Step 5 Use logic to find the answer. Since the question asked for the number of full laps, the answer is the largest whole integer less than or equal to n. The answer is 213 laps.

E

Reasoning and Proof

Assess Prior Knowledge A researcher is studying the decay of a certain element. She counts the number of atoms of the element in a sample every two hours. The chart below shows the results of several counts. How many atoms of the element would you expect to find at 4:00 PM? [250]

Time	8:00 AM	10:00 AM	12:00 PM	2:00 PM
# of Atoms	4,000	2,000	1,000	500

Scientists and mathematicians use logic and reasoning to find patterns and discover relationships that govern things in nature. One kind of reasoning is inductive reasoning. Inductive reasoning involves observing a pattern and forming a rule that describes that pattern. These rules begin as generalizations based on observations. The accuracy of inductive reasoning depends on the amount of data collected. For example, since Earth has one moon, one might reason that all planets have one moon. However, since only one planet was observed, this is not a good use of inductive reasoning.

Scientists usually gather large amounts of data. This makes it easier to find patterns and relationships and also makes it more likely that the conclusions they draw will be accurate. Sometimes graphing the data from an experiment can help in finding a pattern. If the points in a graph are all in a line, then the dependent and independent variables are directly related, meaning that they can be expressed with a linear equation. If the points are connected by a curve, the relationship between the variables could be expressed through a quadratic or higher-order exponential equation.

Another kind of reasoning is deductive reasoning. Deductive reasoning begins with certain statements that are known, or at least believed, to be true. These statements are called premises. By combining these premises, you can deduce some other piece of information and show that it must be true based on the accepted premises. Deductive reasoning is often useful in theoretical fields in which large amounts of data are difficult or impossible to gather. This type of reasoning depends on the truth of the premises. If one premise is found to be incorrect, it is likely that the deduced conclusion is also incorrect.

Math and science often incorporate deductive reasoning in writing proofs. People use accepted laws to reach conclusions. However, it is extremely difficult, if not impossible, to truly prove anything in science. Reasoning leads to the development of a hypothesis. Once that hypothesis has been repeatedly tested and supported, it can become a theory. For years, investigators will continue to test that theory by looking for evidence that will or will not support it. Disproving a theory can be easy compared to proving it. If evidence from research supports the theory, then it garners respect among scientists. As a result, they might use that theory as a premise to develop other theories through deductive reasoning. If the theory continues to hold up, in time scientists will consider it a law.

Example Use deductive reasoning to prove that all right angles are congruent.

    Step 1   Identify the necessary premises.

A right angle measures 90°.

    Step 2   Define any variables or given information.

Given: Angle 1 and Angle 2 are right angles.

    Step 3   Write a proof, beginning with the givens and premises.

      1 Given: Angle 1 and Angle 2 are right angles.

      2 The measure of Angle 1 is 90°, by the definition of right angles.

      3 The measure of Angle 2 is 90°, by the definition of right angles.

      4 The measure of Angle 1 equals the measure of Angle 2, by the substitution property.

      5 Angle 1 is congruent to Angle 2 by the definition of congruency.

Communication

Assess Prior Knowledge Suppose you place a sample of carbon dioxide with a temperature of 34°C in a refrigeration unit and slowly cool it. Every minute, the temperature of the sample decreases by 3°. Write an equation that gives the temperature (C) of the sample after a certain time (t). [$C = 34°C - (3°C/min)t$]

    Proper calculations are of little use if a researcher is unable to accurately and effectively communicate his or her results. It is vital that a scientist learns to communicate in order to expose his or her theories to the scrutiny of other people.

    Mathematics can sometimes look like jumbled arrangements of numbers, letters, and symbols, but these make math's language. Equations are useful in expressing numerical relationships that are difficult to explain in ordinary words. Math is precise shorthand that can quickly express certain ideas.

    Communication can be a tool for solving math and science problems. Most real-world problems are not presented as mathematical equations. Scientists often examine problems by first defining what they want to know and then gathering data or examining what they already know about related phenomena. Even the word problems students encounter in school usually require at least some translation to make them into mathematical equations.

    Before Isaac Newton, people had an intuitive knowledge that things fell when someone dropped them and moved when someone pushed them, but most people didn't take the time to wonder why. Newton investigated and uncovered the relationship among the force of a push, an object's mass, and rate of acceleration. He wrote this relationship as a simple mathematical equation: $a = F/m$; acceleration is equal to the force applied to the object divided by the object's mass. Since then, the relationships that Newton discovered and communicated have led to numerous applications in science, from simple machines to space-exploring shuttles and probes.

Another advantage of communication is collaboration. Solving problems with a group can be much easier than solving them alone. By pooling the knowledge of a group and comparing strategies and methods, you can find solutions more quickly and easily. Good communication is necessary in order to share ideas with the group.

There is another important part of science that relies on communication. Scientists and researchers are human, and they can make mistakes just like anyone else. They might make false assumptions, perhaps without realizing it, or they might overlook an important factor. Communicating the methods and results of studies enables other people to examine them and point out flaws or mistakes. This peer-review process is one of the most important parts of the scientific process. Listening to and reviewing other people's ideas is a part of communication. It is just as important to be able to listen to and analyze other people's ideas as it is to communicate one's own.

Example Sarah gathered data about a certain gene in people living on different continents. She recorded in a table what percentage of people on each continent has that gene. Her table is reproduced below.

Continent	Africa	Asia	Australia	Europe	North America	South America
Percent of the Population with the Gene	9.2%	7.7%	18.3%	20.3%	16.1%	12.9%

Sarah explained that by adding these percentages and dividing by 6, she found that approximately 14.1% of the human population has the gene she was studying. What did Sarah overlook in her calculations? How could she calculate more accurate results for her study?

Answer: Sarah overlooked the fact that the 6 continents have different total populations. Her calculation assumed that each continent had the same number of people. To get more accurate results, Sarah needs to find out the approximate population of each continent. Then, she could multiply the percentage of people with the gene on each continent times the total population of that continent in order to estimate the number of people who have the gene on that continent. Then, she could add the results and divide that number by the total population of all six continents. By multiplying this number by 100, Sarah would find the percentage of people worldwide (or at least on the six continents) that has the gene she is studying.

E

Representation

Create and Analyze Graphs

Assess Prior Knowledge Graph the equation $y = 2x - 3$. [The graph is a line intercepting the y-axis at -3 and sloping upward through the x-axis at 1.5.]

Graphs are another method of communicating information effectively. A visual representation can sometimes have a much greater impact on a person than a written equation. In fact, scientists are learning that some animals can understand concepts like *more, less, adding,* and *taking away*, even if they don't understand numbers.

There are many different kinds of graphs, such as bar graphs, circle graphs, scatter plots, and line graphs. Different graphs are useful when displaying different kinds of information. A circle graph shows parts of a whole, such as how a sum of money is spent or the different groups of people that make a total population. You can use a bar graph to compare values, such as the number of animals that live in several different areas. A line graph is useful in showing changes in data, such as the change in a quantity over time.

Scientists might plot the data that they collect on a simple two-dimensional graph. This can help illustrate patterns in the data, revealing significant scientific relationships. There are two basic types of variables in an experiment, independent variables and dependent variables. An independent variable is something the researcher manipulates, such as the amount of water given to a plant. The values of the independent variable are written along the x-axis on a graph. A dependent variable is something the researcher measures, such as the height to which the plant will grow. The values of the dependent variable plot along the y-axis on a graph.

The simplest way to make a graph is to plot individual points. You might graph your data as individual points, such as the temperature of an object every minute. In this case, temperature is the y-coordinate and time is the x-coordinate. By plotting this data over many minutes, you can draw conclusions about how the temperature changes over time. This is useful because you often have individual data points before you have an equation that describes an event. You can use the data and the graphs in order to find an equation that relates the variables.

Certain kinds of equations have similar graphs. For example, all equations of the form $y = mx + b$ are linear. Quadratic equations, ones in which a variable is squared, form curves, such as a parabola. Equations in which both of the variables are squared can form elliptical or circular shapes. Equations in which one of the variables is cubed form sideways S-shaped curves. By being familiar with how different equations look, scientists are better able to write mathematical equations from the data they collect.

For Math Support go to

TEACHING TODAY

at **teachingtoday.glencoe.com**

E

Example Miguel bats a ball into the air. Gravity slows its ascent and eventually begins to pull it back to the ground. The ball moves horizontally 10 m/s. After 1 s, the ball is 24.5 m above the ground. After 3 s, it reaches its maximum height of 44.1 m and starts to fall to the ground. After 5 s, it is again 24.5 m off the ground. Draw a graph that shows the path of the ball. How far will the ball be from Miguel when it lands on the ground?

Step 1 Find several points to plot by finding where the ball is at various times. Let's say that at $t = 0$, when Miguel hits the ball, it is at the origin (0,0). For every second that passes, the ball moves 10 m along the x-axis. So, we can make a chart or plot points using the information in the problem.

Time – t (seconds)	Distance – x (meters)	Height – y (meters)	Plot Point (x, y)
0	0	0	(0,0)
1	10	24.5	(10, 24.5)
3	30	44.1	(30, 44.1)
5	50	24.5	(50, 24.5)

Step 2 When you plot these points on a graph and connect the points with a curve, you draw a parabola that opens down.

Step 3 The ball lands at the point where the curve contacts the x-axis for the second time. If the parabola is drawn accurately, you should find that the curve intersects the axis at 0 and 60 m. The ball will be 60 m away from Miguel when it lands.

Use a Graphing Calculator

Assess Prior Knowledge What does the graph of $y = x^3 - 3x^2 - 24x + 7$ look like? [The graph looks like a sideways, backward "S" with a local maximum at $(-2, 35)$ and a local minimum at $(4, -73)$.]

Calculators are tools, just like hammers and screwdrivers, though obviously more complicated. They are devices that make human tasks easier, but they still need an adept human to make them useful tools. This is especially true of graphing calculators. With the proper instruction, students can use graphing calculators to plot higher-order functions.

Graphing calculators can help students become familiar with mathematical and graphical patterns. For example, a linear equation will always form a line when graphed. If its slope is positive, the line will go from lower left to upper right, while if the slope is negative, the line will go from upper left to the lower right. Lines are not so difficult to graph by paper and pencil. However, higher-order equations can take a lot of time and effort to graph by hand. This is where a graphing calculator can be a useful tool. You can graph several different kinds of equations, including quadratic, cubic, high-order exponential, and logarithmic equations. You can easily analyze the various graphs and see what similar equations have in common and how they differ.

Graphing calculators also enable students to quickly and easily find maxima and minima, x-axis intersections, and so on. It is important to understand that it is okay (and many times necessary) to solve problems with a calculator. The calculator does not "find the answer" but merely helps to find appropriate solutions to problems. Students must be able to interpret information that the calculator provides. The calculator saves time and effort and allows for more time to be committed to more advanced mathematical concepts.

Graphing calculators do have limitations, though. Often, an equation must have the form $y = f(x)$, where y is alone on one side of an equation and all x terms are on the other side. Isolating y is not an easy task with every equation, and thus, students might have difficulty graphing such equations with a calculator. Yet knowing when and how to use a graphing calculator to solve problems will help students become better problem solvers.

E

Example You discover that the population of a certain bacteria doubles every 2 hours. If you begin with 4 bacteria, the equation that gives the total number of bacteria (y), based on the time (t) in hours, is

$$y = 4 \times 2^{\left(\frac{t}{2}\right)}$$

What does the graph of this equation look like? How many bacteria would there be after 5 hours?

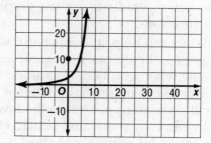

Answer: This is an exponential graph that passes through the y-axis at 4 and continues to increase. By tracing the graph (or substituting 5 into the equation for t), we find that we can expect there to be about 23 bacteria after 5 hours.

E

Use Graphing Calculators in Cooperative Learning

Assess Prior Knowledge What kind of graph do quadratic equations ($y = ax^2 + bx + c$) make? [Quadratic equations form curved graphs, called parabolas.]

A graphing calculator is a powerful tool for students working individually, but groups can also use it. Research has shown that cooperative learning enables students to more deeply understand and internalize concepts than when working alone.

The cooperative group enables questioning and exploring. You might hear students ask, "Are the lines parallel? How do you know? Do the lines have anything in common? Are there maxima or minima we're not seeing? What would the graph look like if we changed the range values for the viewing window?" Working in a group places emphasis on the discovery method. The technical aspect of plotting and sketching the graph is set aside so that students can explore scientific concepts. You can teach more science by removing the mechanics of paper and pencil.

Working in a group, students can graph more equations and share ideas about how certain types of equations relate to certain types of graphs. For example, the graphs of equations in the form $y = a\sqrt{(bx - c)}$ change when you substitute various numbers for a, b, and c. The graphs will have similar curves, but they stretch or move around on the graph. With a graphing calculator and a little guidance, students can use their collective resources to discover the same excitement about mathematics and science that motivated the mathematicians and scientists of the past to bring us the concepts we study today.

Example Graph several linear, quadratic, and cubic equations using the graphing calculator. The basic forms of these types of equations are shown below. How do these kinds of graphs compare to one another?

Linear: $y = ax + b$
Quadratic: $y = a x^2 + bx + c$
Cubic: $y = a x^3 + bx^2 + cx + d$

Possible Answer: Linear equations are straight lines that have no curve and no maximum or minimum values. Quadratic equations are parabolas, curves that have either one maximum or one minimum value of y. Cubic equations are generally sideways S-shaped curves that have one local maximum and one local minimum value of y but no overall maximum or minimum.

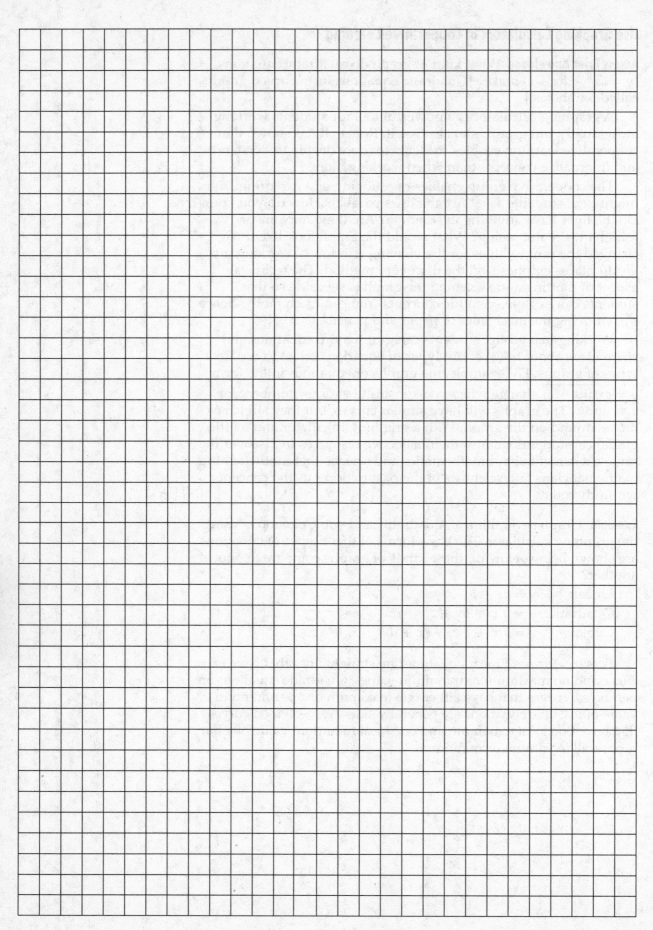

E

School-to-Home Connection

Table of Contents

"Artists, lawyers, psychologists, college faculty and students, business people, neighbors and family members come to support and bolster what schools are working hard to accomplish—ensuring young people's academic, interpersonal, and career success." (*Community Schools: Partnerships for Excellence,* Coalition for Community Schools, 2000)

Effective Communication from School to Home **256**
   Why do we need to study science?...**257**
   Involve Learning Partners...**258**
      • Science Is for Everyone..258
      • Help Learning Partners Help Students......................................258
      • The Learning Partner-Teacher Relationship...............................259
      • Ideas that Encourage Learning-Partner Involvement...................259
      • Commitment Contracts 259
      • Learning-Partner Workshops..260
      • Conferences 260
      • Science Fairs 260
   Create a Classroom Web Site...**261**
   Letters **262**
      • Sample Letter of Introduction 263
      • Plan for This Week 264
      • Track Your Student's Progress..265
      • Assess Your Impact 266

Effective Communication from Home to School **267**
   Prepare for and Take Notes on Teacher Meetings...........................**268**
   Effective In-Home Time Management **269**
      • Rituals...269
      • Routines 269
      • Redirections 270
   Contracts and Written Agreements v. Plans and Schedules....................**271**
      • Time Planner 272
      • Student and Learning Partner Contract....................................273
      • Sample Letters from Learning Partner to Teacher 274
      • Request for Extra-Curricular Enhancement Opportunities.............274
      • Request to Meet with Teacher 275
      • Planned Student-Absence Notification 275
      • Student Performance Communication..276

Effective Communication with the Community **277**
      • The Value of Community Involvement 277
      • What You Can Do...277

Community Involvement **278**
      • A Resource for Learning..278
      • Careers in Science...278
      • Field Experiences/Facility Tours 279
      • Special Presentations...279
      • Science Career Projects..279

F

Other Ideas that Foster Community Relationships......................................280
Sample Science Career Day Letter 281
The Community Partnership...282
  • Examples of Community Benefits/Community Partners......................282

Digital Resources for Teachers

 Professional Development mhpdonline.com
These PD modules address both teaching strategies and science content.

✓ Literacy Strategies: Reading, Writing, Listening, and Speaking
✓ Differentiate Instruction
✓ English-Language Learners
✓ Standards-Based Instruction
✓ Assessment Strategies and Rubrics

✓ Teaching Energy
✓ Teaching Mitosis and Meiosis
✓ Teaching Moon Phases
✓ Teaching Photosynthesis
✓ Teaching Physical and Chemical Change
✓ Teaching Weather Concepts

TEACHING TODAY teachingtoday.glencoe.com
A no-fee professional development Web site where you will find resources for:

✓ Lesson plans with downloads for newsletters, parent conference letters
✓ Teaching tips
✓ How-to articles sorted by discipline, grade level, and instructional type
✓ Math support
✓ Demonstration videos

F

Effective Communication from School to Home

As a teacher, you know that you can achieve better results with your students if you stay in contact with your students' parents, caregivers, and tutors—their learning partners. Effective school-to-home communication begins by establishing a system that is simple and direct. The following pages are intended to help you do just that.

The first step is to write a letter of introduction to your students' learning partners. Consider handwriting a letter rather than composing it on a word processor. You need to establish a personal relationship with learning partners just as you do with students. How you describe yourself and the work you hope to accomplish over the year must capture their attention. Include something about your background, particular educational interests, the subject(s) you teach, some statement of your educational philosophy and approach, and information regarding how they can contact you by phone, e-mail, and through postal mail. Do not make e-mail the only form of contact you provide because some people do not have Internet access.

In your letter of introduction, be sure to discuss the importance of good school-to-home communication. Photocopy the following page—titled "Why do we need to study science?"—and send it with your letter to learning partners. Describe the ways through which you will provide information and feedback about content, assignments, and due dates, and refer to the forms provided here and/or any others you plan to use. Finally, ask learning partners to contact you if they have questions or concerns, and state that you look forward to meeting them in person at your school's Back-to-School Night or Curriculum Night.

A thoughtful and personal letter of introduction will set a tone that makes school-to-home communication natural and effective. Follow-up letters, such as the samples in this section, will reinforce the communication throughout the year.

On Curriculum Night, after discussing your goals for the year, provide learning partners with copies of the **Track Your Student's Progress** chart on page 265. In addition, provide copies of pages 267–269: "Effective Communication from Home to School" and "Effective In-Home Time Management."

F

Why do we need to study science?

Imagine a typical morning in the life of Rafael. He wakes up to the blare of an alarm clock, rolls out of bed, and walks to the kitchen to eat breakfast—orange juice and breakfast cereal. He looks outside only to see that the sky is overcast. He touches the window pane and feels the chill in the air through the glass. He finishes his breakfast, and then brushes his teeth, washes his face, and gets dressed. Before he leaves the house, he makes one final assessment of his appearance in the mirror: jeans, sneakers, and a warm sweater—that should be all right. He heads out the door and waits for the bus. He takes a deep breath as he shakes off the last bit of drowsiness before boarding the bus heading to school. Rafael's entire morning has been touched by science.

Physics is the science of matter. It describes how gravity holds us to Earth's surface, but it also explains much more. Electrical devices, like Rafael's alarm clock, use electricity and circuits to keep time. An alarm clock produces sound waves that we hear as the alarm, and it might display the time using LED—light-emitting diodes. Mirrors are flat, smooth surfaces that reflect light rays that can enter your eyes.

Earth science delves into everything from prehistoric rocks to how climate change could affect our future weather. Morning is a result of Earth rotating on its axis. The side of Earth facing away from the Sun experiences night, while the side of Earth facing the Sun experiences day. Toothpaste contains compounds that help keep the primary mineral in your teeth—hydroxylapatite—strong. Weather occurs in the thin layer of air close to Earth's surface. Changes in pressure, temperature, and humidity produce changes in weather, such as a chilly, overcast day.

Chemistry impacts our daily lives as well. We look out windows made of the compound silicon dioxide, which consists of the elements silicon and oxygen. Orange juice has a pH of 3.0, which means that it is an acid. Parts of our clothes are made of synthetic fibers—long polymer strands developed by chemists in a laboratory.

Biology is everywhere. A breakfast of orange juice and cereal comes from plants that people grew and harvested for our consumption. Our bodies break down plant products that we eat, which releases energy that we need to start the day. When we breathe in, we supply our bodies with one of the components we need to maintain life, oxygen (O_2). Humans walk upright, which enables us to support relatively large heads that contain extraordinary brains. And what species are humans? We belong to kingdom *Animalia*, class *Mammalia*, genus *Homo*, and species *Homo sapiens*.

Science is a part of all our lives. In science class, students will discover countless examples of how science impacts their daily lives, and they will acquire the tools needed to explore and analyze the world in which they live.

F

Involve Learning Partners

Science Is for Everyone

Science involves asking "Why?" and then searching for "Because...." Today, a typical homework assignment has a variety of problems that directly relate to situations outside the classroom. Long-range assignments might include projects and reports, and assignments might be connected to other curricular areas. Students are encouraged to ask questions at every turn, to develop their own hypotheses, and to design fair tests to explore those hypotheses. They use the Internet to complete research, then create documents, charts, and graphs to report their findings.

Help Learning Partners Help Students

Learning partners need to understand that science is a "doing" process; that is, it demands active learning. Science is all about asking questions, looking for answers, and drawing conclusions.

When learning partners meet with teachers, they usually ask, "What can I do to help?" Learning partners can promote a positive attitude about science for students while they are away from school. Specifically, learning partners can

- share life experiences and problem-solving strategies;
- demonstrate the value of science by having students solve problems that are real and relevant to their lives, such as designing, building, and using a compost system; finding ways to decrease household energy use; and trying a new recipe;
- provide time, space, and tools that are necessary for science homework;
- encourage students to join science clubs/organizations;
- do science projects at home that could be developed into projects for science fairs;
- purchase puzzles, games, books, and models and explore science-related computer software;
- ask questions that have more than one answer;
- show students that there are many ways to solve a problem;
- have students draw pictures and diagrams or make lists to represent problem situations;
- monitor students' work while stressing the importance of checking homework;
- value education and reward accomplishment.

Also, learning partners can do two other very important things—when possible, limit recreational television viewing and support the completion of homework assignments.

F

The Learning Partner-Teacher Relationship

Research shows that home life exerts a strong influence on students' attitudes toward science and their decisions to take additional coursework. Keep learning partners informed through periodic telephone conversations, e-mails, and other correspondence. Letters and phone conversations should be informational, not disciplinary. It usually pleases learning partners when teachers take time to write or inform them of students' positive academic progress.

Helping learning partners feel valued and comfortable is a big step in engaging them in a learning partner-teacher relationship. Studies show that learning partners perceive a teacher as a "good" teacher if he or she is committed to increasing learning-partner involvement. Barriers to learning-partner involvement include

- previous negative experiences with the school;
- lack of education and language skills;
- mistrust on both sides;
- cultural and socioeconomic issues;
- time limitations;
- school climate;
- problematic communication.

Build a bridge between learning partners and the school. Create an atmosphere that values their involvement.

Ideas that Encourage Learning-Partner Involvement

While most studies agree that learning-partner involvement in a student's education is important, there's no one way to go about accomplishing it. Many teachers are having great success with such ideas as

- home visits to learning partners who face time limitations or otherwise cannot come to the school;
- workshops in which learning partners create take-home projects, such as flash cards and board games, to use at home with students;
- newsletters and handbooks that keep learning partners informed about what's happening in the classroom;
- volunteer opportunities that invite learning-partner participation.

Following are some additional ideas that others have used to increase learning-partner involvement.

Commitment Contracts

Suggest to learning partners that they sign a commitment contract that encourages at-home learning. The contract should

- designate a place within the home to do schoolwork;
- set a time to discuss what's happening in the classroom;
- give opportunities for extra attention and praise for progress.

F

Learning-Partner Workshops

Hold workshops throughout the school year and focus on learning-partner involvement. Teach learning partners about learning at home. Make them aware of volunteer opportunities both within and outside the classroom.

Conferences

Learning partner-teacher conferences are a great way for learning partners and teachers to share ideas. If learning partners know what is being studied, they're more likely to help students with schoolwork at home. You might even want to involve students in conferences.

Here are some issues for discussion:

- What are your expectations for the student?
- Is the student meeting those expectations?
- If not, what can we do to help improve the situation?
- Are mentoring or tutoring programs available?
- What are the student's strengths and weaknesses?
- Does the student complete his or her homework?

Science Fairs

Middle- or high-school teachers often encourage their students to enter science projects in school, local, and state competitions. These projects provide an outlet for creativity, promote higher-order thinking and problem-solving skills, present an opportunity to develop knowledge in an area of interest to the student, and encourage pride and self-confidence in the student's achievement. A further benefit is that students and learning partners have challenging learning experiences that they can share.

As a teacher, your role is to encourage learning partners to assist and support students in the science fair project. You should provide workshops that demonstrate modeling techniques, such as presenting scientific methods, and monitor each student's progress. Solving problems generally involves the following steps:

1. define the problem
2. formulate a strategy to solve the problem
3. observe and experiment
4. analyze, interpret, and record the data
5. draw conclusions

Using this process, students can select areas of science to study; conduct extensive research; and design, test, and report their findings. It is important to stress to students that they should not follow recipe-type instructions when completing projects. Students should use their own experiences to think of problems they are interested in solving, then use available resources and their own ideas to design tests that could possibly lead to a solution. Emphasize that scientific methods are cyclical, and it is acceptable (and even laudable) if their investigations lead them not to solutions, but to more questions or problems.

There are many resources available to students and parents to help them plan science fair projects. You might want to search for some Web sites that will provide appropriate information for your students and provide a list of Web addresses for them to use.

F

Create a Classroom Web Site

A classroom Web site can be a real asset to your program. Many Internet service providers and web log (or blog) publishing sites offer easy-to-use programs that make it possible for people with very modest computer skills to set up useful Web sites. If your students are already drawn to the Web, they will greatly benefit from support in a format they know well. It is advisable to check with your school administration before establishing a classroom Web site.

The positive aspects of a classroom Web site are obvious. Students can refer to it for up-to-the-minute assignment details and rubrics, information about due dates, supplementary articles about topics of study, and perhaps even audio or video material related to themes they're currently studying. Like most things, though, Web sites are only as good as the effort that is put into them. It is important to be realistic about what you can actually produce and maintain over time.

Because some students do not have Internet access at home, you must provide all materials and resources that you make available on a classroom Web site in another format for those who cannot reach them via computer. Even if your local public library offers free Internet access, there are often long lines of users waiting for a limited number of terminals. If, however, your school is well-equipped with reliable computers that are connected to the Internet, and students can access them easily, *and* you have time to update and maintain the site, then a classroom Web site can be an effective place to invest some time and effort.

If you look at the various Web sites that teachers have set up for their classes, you will discover ideas for what works well and what does not. In addition to posting assignments and due dates, popular features of Web sites include

- news articles about current research and discoveries;
- links to other Web sites where in-depth information concerning a concept can be found.

After reviewing other teachers' sites, outline the various pages, content, and links that you wish to provide on your own Web site. Use flowcharts or storyboards to help organize the navigation of your site. You might wish to consider involving students, parents, or colleagues in this planning stage to ensure your audience will find the site helpful and easy to use.

F

Letters

Letter of Introduction See the sample letter on page 263. Use this letter as a guide for the letter that you send to learning partners at the beginning of the school year. Modify the letter to suit your needs. Personalize the letter rather than making photocopies of it.

Plan for This Week See the sample letter on page 264. Send this letter to learning partners at the start of each week. Photocopy the page, fill in the blanks, and then make multiple copies of the completed letter for distribution or use it as a template for your own letter.

Track Your Student's Progress Read the sample letter on page 265. Send it to learning partners to indicate if students are missing work and, if so, what specific work they need to complete. Ideally, this letter should be sent to learning partners before the final due date for a given chapter's work, while there is still time for students to make up missing work. Photocopy the page, fill in the blanks with the names of assignments you are recording in your grade book, and then make multiple copies of the completed letter. You could also use it as a template for a letter you type on a word processor. Provide each student with a copy of the letter with the appropriate circle checked. If the student has outstanding assignments, be sure to highlight or put an asterisk next to the specific assignment(s) that the student needs to complete. Keep this sample letter in your lesson planning book, and fill it in as you write your lesson plans.

For Lesson Plans go to

TE**A**CHING
TODAY

at **teachingtoday.glencoe.com**

F

Sample Letter of Introduction

In an effort to make learning partners feel comfortable helping students with science activities, you might wish to send a short letter home with the first activity. A sample letter is provided below.

Dear [learning partner name],

I would like to introduce myself to you. I am [your name], [student's name]'s science teacher. [Add some biographical information.]

I also would like to tell you a little bit about the science activities I have planned for this school year. Preparing students for achieving success in the workplace and the world is extremely important. Students need to learn how to become effective problem solvers in situations outside the classroom. Therefore, in this class, as we learn science we will identify how it applies to our lives. In addition to reading and discussing science content, we will design and carry out meaningful activities and draw conclusions based on our experiences.

You can encourage [student's name] by asking questions about the science we are doing in school. You might help [him/her] understand the importance of science in everyday life by showing how science is found in almost everything we do, from cooking with a recipe to fixing the family car.

[student's name]'s success in science is important to me, as is our communication about [his/her] progress. I encourage you to visit our classroom. Feel free to call or e-mail me whenever you have questions or concerns. My school number is ###-#### and my e-mail address is _____ @ _____ .

I look forward to working with you to help [student's name] learn the skills necessary to be successful in science.

Sincerely,
[your signature and name]

F

Plan for This Week

Copyright © Glencoe/McGraw-Hill, a division of The McGraw-Hill Companies, Inc.

_____ , 20 _____

Dear Learning Partner,

This week, we are studying the following science chapter:

Chapter Number	Chapter Title

Our plan for this chapter is as follows:

Reading	
Date	**Pages**

Homework	
Due Date	**Assignment**

Tests and/or Projects	
Date	**Test Material**

Please sign on the line below to indicate that you are aware of this week's assignments.
If you have questions or concerns regarding the work, please feel free to call, e-mail,
or write me a note.

I am aware of this week's assignments: X _____

Learning Partner's signature

Sincerely,

F

Track Your Student's Progress

Name of Student _____ _____ , 20 _____

Dear Learning Partner,
I made the following assignments for chapter _____ , _____ :
                                            chapter number   chapter title

Date Assigned	Due Date	Assignment	Is your student ready to move on?	If not, review these lessons in the textbook:

Your student currently
  ◯ is up-to-date on all assignments.
  ◯ needs to complete assignments that are highlighted or marked with an asterisk.

Please sign on the line below to indicate that you are aware of your student's current status concerning assigned work.

I am aware of this week's assignments: X _____
                                                                    Learning Partner's signature

Sincerely,

F

Assess Your Impact

As with any program, evaluating your efforts can help you fine tune the connection you're making with learning partners. Ask learning partners the following questions to measure the value and effectiveness of your programs.

What have you observed about your student's ability for inquiry? Is he or she asking "why" more often? Please elaborate on your answer.

_____

_____

_____

_____

Can your student generate explanations and develop hypotheses? If yes, please provide at least one example. If no, please suggest one way I can help your student accomplish this.

_____

_____

_____

_____

Please provide an example of an instance when your student investigated, on his or her own, an answer to a question.

_____

_____

_____

_____

Can your student use evidence to support or disprove a hypothesis? (Circle one.)

Yes or **No**

List the area of science in which your student is excelling—asking why, forming hypotheses, looking for answers, or drawing conclusions.

_____

_____

List the area of science in which your student needs to develop more skills. Why do you believe this to be true?

_____

_____

F

Effective Communication from Home to School

This section contains instructions for helping the learning partner effectively communicate with the teacher. There are a number of tools and suggestions for how the learning partner—whether a student's parent, older sibling, foster parent, extended family member, or tutor—can begin to see himself or herself more fully as a teacher and grow in confidence and effectiveness in this role. You can photocopy the pages in this section and send them home to the learning partner for his or her use.

One of the greatest teachers in human history was a Greek philosopher named Socrates. He said that it is not a teacher's role to know and describe things; rather, it is the teacher's role to ask the right questions. Acquiring, retaining, and applying knowledge follow naturally for people who ask good questions. "How can I find . . ." starts a more productive question than does "What is . . .," and it comes from someone who has a sense of confidence in his or her abilities. The first priority of all teachers, especially learning partners, is to convey a sincere commitment to a student's capacity for learning. Attention to this fundamental matter makes any question of "Who's doing the homework?" moot. Students need to hear and see, in words and actions, that no one doubts their capacity to learn.

If a learning partner shows interest in the areas his or her student is studying, he or she will go a long way toward ensuring that the student understands and appreciates science. Be certain that the learning partner understands that you can easily be contacted and that he or she should feel free to do so.

The following pages contain information and sample letters that learning partners can use to ask you questions regarding work that is being done, progress that is being made, and other concerns he or she might have. Also, there is a worksheet on which he or she can prepare for and then keep notes of meetings with you. Completing these forms will make communication, planning, and record-keeping easier and more effective.

For teaching tips go to

TEACHING TODAY

at **teachingtoday.glencoe.com**

F

Prepare for and Take Notes on Teacher Meetings

Meetings with the classroom teacher will be most useful and productive if you are well-prepared and if you document what occurs during the meeting. Later, as you address issues of concern with your student, being able to look back at your notes and refer to specific things the teacher has said will greatly enhance your ability to achieve positive results.

The form on page 276 provides questions you might wish to ask the teacher as well as space to take notes. Before meeting with the teacher, go over the questions with your student. Ask your student what he or she thinks the teacher will have to say in response to each of the questions. During your meeting, you will notice that what the teacher is saying is either consistent with or inconsistent with what your student has to say. Your observations will be important for developing a plan of action that will ensure student success.

F

Effective In-Home Time Management

The three R's of student success—rituals, routines, and redirections—will help students complete their school work while maintaining opportunities for personal, unstructured time.

Rituals Rituals are specific ways that tasks are done regularly and that do not vary or change. Because they are consistent and familiar, students do not need to think about them and can focus their attention on other, more complex matters. The rituals of successful students include

- maintaining a sufficient amount of necessary school supplies;
- packing all books, notebooks, and other supplies, which will be necessary for any class or activity;
- writing their names first on all papers or other work that will be turned in and keeping all work in the same place (an astonishing number of students receive no credit for work they have completed because they fail to write their name on it or because they misplace it);
- adhering to reminder systems they have set up for themselves (i.e., looking at schedules and "To Do" lists each day at certain times, always writing assignments in the same place, and so on.).

Routines Routines vary but generally encourage regularity and consistency. Before, during, and after school, students tend to follow routines of some sort. Successful students establish routines that allow them time to complete their work *and* for recreation, personal preferences, and self-expression. A lack of balance is likely to lead to difficulties. The routines of successful students include

- recharging the mind and body daily with adequate sleep and healthy eating habits;
- being aware of what will be happening each day and establishing and referring to reminder systems that will ensure adequate preparation;
- attending to responsibilities first.

For teaching tips and how-to lessons go to

TEACHING TODAY

at **teachingtoday.glencoe.com**

F

Redirections The temptation to communicate with, socialize with, and otherwise engage peers during work time can seem irresistible for middle- and high-school students. Even the most serious students can find themselves ignoring what they know they should be doing. In addition, the distractions of television, video and computer games, the Internet, and pleasure reading exert a strong pull away from studies. As a result, each student must devise a set of personal strategies to redirect attention from such distractions. Learning partners need to be understanding of a student's need to devote time to self-chosen activities. In turn, they need to help students develop plans for reducing distractions and refocusing their attention when it strays from work. Such strategies might include

- set aside "down time" or a debriefing period between the end of the school day and the beginning of homework time;
- agree to keep the television, the computer, and similar appliances off during the time that your student sets aside each day to complete homework;
- establish a regular, quiet, comfortable place where homework can be done;
- encourage your student to include a picture or other item in the work area to serve as a visual reminder of some pleasurable experience he or she anticipates having once school work is completed;
- provide a snack or a ten-minute break when your student completes half the work or when some other natural stopping point occurs;
- make it a habit to "work together" whenever your student feels that working alone is an isolating or otherwise unpleasant experience.

As people mature, they gradually replace external controls with internal ones. You will find that the gentle reminders and pushes you frequently provide will become less necessary, but also less effective, as your student matures. For this reason it is important for learning partners to impress good study habits early. The important thing is to avoid a power struggle, and by acknowledging the dual importance of school and personal pursuits, you lay the foundation for a responsible, self-determining student who will feel comfortable balancing duty and pleasure.

F

Contracts and Written Agreements v. Plans and Schedules

Sometimes, a learning partner finds it useful to set up a contract or written agreement with his or her student who is struggling academically. Approached in the right spirit, such a document can be a helpful tool for keeping a student on track and for measuring progress and improvement.

Before you establish a contract, it is a good idea to develop a schedule or time plan to see if this simpler strategy sufficiently addresses the particular concerns. Students, whether they are struggling or not, can most efficiently maximize their learning experiences if they plan their time and maintain a written schedule. For this reason, all students should either fill out the **Time Planner** form on the following page or use it as a basis for creating a personalized written schedule that they share with their home learning partner. You can, of course, adjust the schedule as necessary, and it can be one of the factors students and their learning partners consider as they gauge academic progress.

On page 273 you will find a model contract between a student and a learning partner. This contract is for those students who might work best with a system that involves promises and incentives, or for whom the **Time Planner** does not adequately address individual needs. Students and learning partners can use this contract as is, or they can modify it to address specific concerns.

F

Time Planner

Name of Student _____

	Time to get up: Time to leave for school: Time to arrive at school: Time(s) for any special responsibility before the school day:	School day: Time(s) for any special responsibility during the school day:	Time(s) to get home or arrive at after-school program: Time for school work: Time for personal activities:
Monday			
Tuesday			
Wednesday			
Thursday			
Friday			
Saturday			
Sunday			

F

Student and Learning Partner Contract

This contract, entered into between _____ , the student, and

_____ , the learning partner, serves as a promise that:

- _____ will arrive at class on time each day with all necessary materials;

- _____ will follow directions and complete in-class assignments during class;

- _____ will complete out-of-class assignments according to directions, following this work schedule for their completion:

Day	Hours to be spent on out-of-class work
Monday	
Tuesday	
Wednesday	
Thursday	
Friday	
Saturday	
Sunday	

- If _____ fulfills the promises listed above, according to classroom teacher reports and the learning partner's observations, then the learning partner agrees to do or to provide the following:

_____

_____

_____

_____

_____

_____   _____
Student's signature   Date

_____   _____
Learning Partner's signature   Date

F

Sample Letters from Learning Partner to Teacher

Student Performance Communication 1

Date: _____

TO: _____
                        Classroom Teacher

FROM: _____ PHONE: _____
                  Learning Partner

I am writing to ask how my student, _____ , is doing in your class. Would you please take a few moments to respond to the following questions?

Are homework and class work assignments up-to-date?
- ○ Yes, my student has turned in all assignments.
- ○ No, the following work is missing: _____

_____

Is work quality satisfactory?
- ○ Yes, work quality is satisfactory.
- ○ No, there are concerns about work quality: _____

_____

Are classroom behavior and work habits appropriate?
- ○ Yes, classroom behavior and work habits are appropriate.
- ○ No, learning partner should give attention to the following: _____

_____

Thank you for your attention to my questions. Please call me if we need to communicate further.

Request for Extra-Curricular Enhancement Opportunities

Date: _____

TO: _____
                        Classroom Teacher

FROM: _____ PHONE: _____
                  Learning Partner

My student, _____ , seems to be doing well in your class, and I am interested in providing enrichment opportunities to enhance what my student learns at school. Would you please take a few minutes and write on the lines below any videos, museum exhibits, or other interesting things related to current or future science studies that are accessible and would be beneficial for my student? Thank you for your extra efforts.

_____

_____

_____

_____

Request to Meet with Teacher

Date: _____

TO: _____

Classroom Teacher

FROM: _____   PHONE: _____

Learning Partner

My student, _____ , seems to be having difficulties in your class. I would like to meet with you to discuss how we can improve the situation. The following dates and times would work well for me.

Date: _____   Time: _____   ◯ yes   ◯ no

Date: _____   Time: _____   ◯ yes   ◯ no

Date: _____   Time: _____   ◯ yes   ◯ no

If these dates and times do not work for you, please call me so that we can agree on a date and time that will work for both of us. Thank you for your attention to my request.

Planned Student-Absence Notification

Date: _____

TO: _____

Classroom Teacher

FROM: _____   PHONE: _____

Learning Partner

_____ , will not be in school on the dates below because

[reason for absence] _____ :

From _____ , 20 _____   to _____ , 20 _____

To prevent falling behind, it would be helpful to know what material will be covered in class during those dates, what homework assignments you will give, and so on. Please indicate on the lines below what work my student should complete. It will then be possible for me to ensure that school responsibilities are kept up to date.

_____

_____

_____

_____

_____

I apologize for any inconvenience my request might cause. Thank you in advance for your attention.

Student Performance Communication

Does my student consistently...	Classroom Teacher's Comments
get to class on time?	
show up with required materials?	
begin work at the start of class without extra prompting?	
follow directions?	
participate actively in class and in labs?	
behave in a positive, polite manner?	
pay attention to class work and avoid unnecessary socializing and other distractions?	
complete all class work?	
perform well on tests, labs, projects, and other assessments?	
complete all out-of-class work and/or homework?	
take initiative and show interest in being a responsible, independent learner?	
demonstrate an ongoing understanding of what is learned in class and retain skills and information over time?	
experience difficulties with others?	
need special attention or consideration?	
Action Plan:	

F

Effective Communication with the Community

The Value of Community Involvement

Studies reveal a strong correlation between community involvement and student performance. Home and community involvement for a science student is important because science involves cooperative, real-world-based learning. Science teaches students about inquiry: how to ask questions, form ideas, and understand the work of others. A student's community can help extend the inquiry that takes place in the classroom and outside of it. This section can help you forge a connection between students and the community. It offers specific information that will help you customize your approach based on your own particular goals and your students' needs.

What You Can Do

- Realize the importance of home and community partnerships.
- Understand the barriers to potential partnerships.
- Involve local businesses and organizations in helping students learn.
- Create opportunities for community organizations to spend more time at the school.
- Enlist the community as a resource for science education.

F

Community Involvement

A Resource for Learning

Communities have an interest in the education of our nation's young people; after all, they are the workers of the future. Since the community is a resource for learning, a natural partnership exists between schools and communities. Community partnerships can help bring science to life for students. As career mentors, classroom participants, and project sponsors, members of the local community can show your students a classroom outside of school.

Establishing partnerships within your neighborhood and community is as essential as establishing a good relationship with learning partners. And like learning partners, the community faces its own barriers that can keep its leaders and members away from the classroom. It's important to create a welcoming environment. Encourage the school to participate in community forums and town meetings. Public discussion of educational issues creates ownership and connectivity.

Experts say that local businesses are becoming more active in public education. This is probably because a public education-community partnership is a mutually beneficial one. Students become active, productive members of the community and learn about career choices. Business owners reap numerous rewards, including improving public relations and getting well-trained workers in the future.

Here are a few ways the community can become involved:

- donate materials
- provide advice and assistance with projects
- give field experiences and facility tours to students
- pool resources to sponsor after-school science programs
- establish company policies and programs that support the effort of employees who are learning partners
- provide information and expertise through the company Web site, mentors, and classroom visits

In addition, there are many excellent opportunities for community involvement and sponsorship in your classroom and with your school. If you would like to launch a partnership activity, read on for more details.

Careers in Science

"When am I ever going to use this stuff?" Have you heard this complaint in your class? One way to help your students understand the importance of science is to show how it can be useful to them in the future. Today, business and industry leaders are requiring many of the same problem-solving skills that your students use as young scientists.

Because business leaders find these skills to be very important, they often are eager to provide students with field experiences and facility tours, and are willing to make special presentations for the classroom, offer career information, and assist in curriculum development. Following are some additional ways to involve business and industry in your classroom.

F

Field Experiences/Facility Tours Ask local businesses or corporations to provide students with field experiences. These vary from short visits at corporate sites where students get an overview of how the facility uses science to longer, multiple-visit sessions in which students experience a deeper understanding of the role of scientific concepts in the workplace.

Special Presentations Invite role models to come into your classroom to talk about how they use various scientific concepts. Encourage speakers to bring equipment or exhibits to demonstrate the many uses of science in their fields.

Science Career Day Project As an extension of special presentations, host a formal Science Career Day. The goal of a Science Career Day is to have students gather information. This makes the students more proactive in asking questions and makes the professionals more comfortable since they don't have to stand in front of a classroom talking about what they do.

Ask students to learn as much as they can about a career. Then have them interview a professional in that career and write a report or give an oral presentation. Have them summarize their research, the interview, and how this career matches their goals for the future. More importantly, have them explain how much science is necessary for this career choice.

You might want to ask the language arts teachers to explore the students' career interests. Because students often are interested in similar careers, you can place them in groups according to their career interests. The language arts teachers can help students research careers and develop a set of general questions for interviews with professionals. After the interviews, they can help students with the drafts of their reports. As the science teacher, you can help students investigate how these professions use science and develop specific questions for their science career interviews.

It is important to invite professionals that reflect the gender and ethnic makeup of your students. Generally, learning partners and local businesses are good sources of career information. Have students write letters to invite the professionals to the school for Science Career Day (a sample letter is provided on page 281). On Science Career Day, students will interact personally with the professionals in small-group interview sessions.

When planning a Science Career Day, you will find that there are many careers among the physical, Earth, life, and health sciences. But many students might not be interested in a career in a field that has science as a major focus. However, many careers, including those in technology, involve more science than students might be aware of. Have students investigate those careers and the ways science is involved in them.

F

Other Ideas that Foster Community Relationships

In addition to facility tours and Science Career Days, there are many other ways you can partner with your local community.

- Encourage community members with strong science backgrounds to serve as tutors.
- College students, as well as senior citizens, can serve as science mentors to your students.
- Recruit community members who use science in their careers to visit the classroom, provide lessons, or work with students on projects.
- Plan for students to study science issues important to the local community, such as pollution, water treatment, or severe weather preparation, and encourage them to volunteer for community service projects.
- Set up school-business partnerships with local facilities that deal with the sciences, such as water treatment centers, hospitals, or power plants.
- Get local chapters of organizations to sponsor and facilitate community-based student clubs.
- Help students find sponsorship for and enter into local, regional, or national science events.
- Get parents, local business owners, or other members of the community to participate in job shadowing.

F

Sample Science Career Day Letter

You might wish to send a short letter inviting speakers to your class to discuss their occupations. A sample letter is provided below.

Dear (name of person),

My students at (name of school) will be hosting a Science Career Day on (day and date). Several of them are interested in (profession), and I would like to invite you to come to our class to answer some questions about this profession.

Before sharing your career with my class, I hope that you will agree to an interview with a small group of my students. The interview is one part of their career project report for science class. The objective is to learn how important science is to this career. The students look forward to learning as much as they can about this career by interviewing a professional in the career. After the conclusion of the interview, they will write reports or give oral presentations that summarize what they learned and how this career relates to their goals for the future.

I would like to schedule a group of (number) students to interview you informally. They will use questions that they have prepared. I can send the questions to you beforehand. One group member will then call you to discuss your Science Career Day project.

Please let me know if you can assist my class with its Science Career Day project.

Sincerely,
(your name)
[contact information]

F

The Community Partnership

The following chart displays some of the benefits that result when students, families, schools, and communities interact. Opening up schools during non-school hours will allow community access and accomplish many of the goals of the school-community partnership. The second chart gives examples of possible community partners for the school.

Benefits

For Students	For Families	For Schools	For Communities
student awards, incentive programs, scholarships, field trips, tutors, mentors, facility tours	learning-partner workshops, adult education classes, learning-partner incentives and rewards	lab equipment and materials, beautification, and repair; teacher incentives and awards; funding for science fairs and science programs; classroom assistance	community involvement, student exhibits and performances, charity and other outreach

Examples of Community Partners

Types of Community Partners	Example
Business/Corporations	local businesses, national corporations, and franchises
Universities and Educational Institutions	colleges, universities, trade schools
Health Care Organizations	hospitals, health care centers, mental health facilities, health departments, health foundations and associations
Government/Military Agencies	fire departments, police departments, chamber of commerce, city council, town council, community board
National Service and Volunteer Organizations	Rotary Club, Lions Club, Kiwanis Club, VISTA, Shriners, Boy and Girl Scouts, YWCA, United Way, Americorp, Urban League
Faith Organizations	churches, mosques, synagogues
Senior Citizen Organizations	nursing homes, senior volunteers, service organizations
Cultural and Recreational Institutions	zoos, museums, libraries, recreational centers, parks services

[Note: These charts are adapted from Sanders, M.G. (n.d.) "Collaborating for Student Success: A Study of the Role of 'Community' in Comprehensive School, Family, and Community Partnership Programs." *Nation Network of Partnership Schools.*]

F

Performance Assessment

Table of Contents

Introduction 286

Performance Assessment Toolbox

Observation and Questioning...290
Performance Report..292
Projects and Investigations...293
Sample Forms 297
Portfolios and Journals 298
Other Types of Assessment 304
Performance-Task Assessment Lists and Rubrics...............................307

Scientific Process

Make Observations and Inferences 309
Pose Questions 311
Form a Hypothesis...313
Design an Experiment..315
Collect Data..317
Analyze Data..319
Use Math in Science...321
Evaluate a Hypothesis...323
Assess an Experiment and Design a New Experiment 325
Conduct a Survey and Graph the Results......................................327
Complete a Data Table...329
Graph the Data..331
Summarize a Graph...333

Science Products

Develop a Consumer Decision-Making Study....................................335
Draw a Diagram..337
Design an Invention...339
Write a Lab Report..341
Draw a Map..343
Design a Data Table 345
Make and Use a Classification System 347
Design and Construct a Model 349
Design a Science Fair Display...351
Illustrate a Scientific Object 353

Communication Products Using Scientific Content

Design a Booklet or a Pamphlet 355
Plan and Display a Bulletin Board...357
Produce a Cartoon or a Graphic Novel..359
Design and Construct a Display..361
Investigate a Controversial Issue..363
Compose a Letter to an Editor...365
Write a Newspaper Article...367
Prepare and Give an Oral Presentation.......................................369
Write a Poem..371
Create a Poster 373
Write a Research Report 375
Write and Perform a Skit..377

G

Table of Contents

Prepare a Slide Show or a Photo Essay 379
Compose and Perform a Song with Lyrics 381
Write a Summary...383
Construct a Time Line 385
Produce a Video..387
Write a Fictional Story..389
Write a Nonfictional Story 391

Graphic Organizers for Science Content
Plan and Draw a Concept Map 393
Sequence an Events Chain 395
Classify with a Spider Organizer 397
Compare and Contrast Using a Venn Diagram 399

Other Products
Engage in Group Work 401
Develop a Performance-Task Assessment 403
Prepare a Management Plan 405
Maintain a Science Journal..407
Compile a Science Portfolio 409
Rubric Scoring Systems..411
Assessment for the Use of Scientific Methods 412
Self-Assessment of Classification Techniques 413
Self-Assessment 414
Journal-Assessment Checklist..415
Group Work Rubric and Checklist 416
Reports and Presentations Rubric 417
Sample Rubric 418
Areas to Evaluate Rubric 419
Bibliography 420

Digital Resources for Teachers

 Professional Development **mhpdonline.com** *These PD modules address both teaching strategies and science content.*

✓ Literacy Strategies: Reading, Writing, Listening, and Speaking
✓ Differentiate Instruction
✓ English-Language Learners
✓ Standards-Based Instruction
✓ Assessment Strategies and Rubrics

✓ Teaching Energy
✓ Teaching Mitosis and Meiosis
✓ Teaching Moon Phases
✓ Teaching Photosynthesis
✓ Teaching Physical and Chemical Change
✓ Teaching Weather Concepts

TEACHING TODAY **teachingtoday.glencoe.com**
A no-fee professional development Web site where you will find resources for:

✓ Lesson plans with downloads for newsletters, parent conference letters
✓ How-to articles sorted by discipline, grade level, and instructional type

✓ Teaching tips
✓ Math support
✓ Demonstration videos

G

Introduction

Assessing student performance in science without first understanding the goals of science education is a bit like trying to fit a square peg in a round hole—it just doesn't work. Since 1985, a major effort has been underway to redefine goals and promote reforms to K–12 science education. Project 2061, the long-term initiative of the American Association for the Advancement of Science (AAAS), recognizes that students will experience a multitude of scientific and technological changes in the twenty-first century. AAAS created Project 2061 in order to recognize that for students to make sense of our world, they will need to think critically and independently through recognizing and weighing alternative explanations of events, constructing and executing trade-offs, and dealing sensibly with problems that involve evidence, numbers, patterns, logical arguments, and uncertainties. To prepare students for these challenges, AAAS developed a helpful set of benchmarks to improve science, mathematics, and technology literacy. You can find these online at http://www.project2061.org. The information that follows provides you with ideas that can help you modify the benchmarks to suit your own assessment needs and ensure a comprehensive assessment.

Science Standards

Science standards help define the science that all students should know and be able to do. Science education should provide students with tools to

- inquire;
- know and understand scientific facts, concepts, principles, laws, and theories;
- reason scientifically;
- incorporate science when making personal decisions and taking positions on social issues;
- communicate effectively about science.

Understanding the fundamental concepts of life, physical, and Earth sciences remains essential to learning science. However, sequencing and connecting concepts across the sciences are necessary skills as well. In addition, students should integrate basic and higher-level science process skills with conceptual knowledge. Such complex behaviors help students acquire higher-order thinking and problem-solving skills that will enable students to thrive in our constantly changing world.

Assessment standards provide the criteria needed to judge progress toward the science education vision of "science for all." These standards can be used equally in the assessment of students, teachers, and programs. The assessment of student work should include both a study of a final product, such as a poster or a research report, and the processes that lead to it, such as a descriptive journal or science log.

Defining Assessment

Assessment is the practical means by which a teacher can gauge a student's perception, expertise, and proficiencies. To make meaningful assessments, collect information from students in a variety of forms. Paper-and-pencil tests are useful for measuring a student's knowledge about a particular subject or process, but assessment encompasses other methods also.

For Standards-Based Instruction go to

TEA⁺CHING TODAY

at **teachingtoday.glencoe.com**

For Assessments and Rubrics go to

TEA⁺CHING TODAY

at **teachingtoday.glencoe.com**

G

Assessment

Assessment focuses on measuring procedural knowledge. It includes a range of assessments that you can use to gather information about what a student knows, believes, and can do. It focuses on a student's growth over time and emphasizes his or her strengths. It also gives consideration to individual learning styles and various skill levels. You can measure a student's growth using many different methods, such as diagnostic, formative, formal, informal, and summative types of assessment.

Authentic Assessment

Authentic assessment engages students in real-world situations. It presents authentic problem-solving tasks that students might encounter in or out of school. Further, it engages students in inquiry and projects that are relevant for them. Examples of authentic assessment might include everyday observations in the classroom or independent projects; or tasks, such as filling out job applications, writing letters to a corporation or politician, or analyzing a television commercial. *Authentic assessment* is a term that is used less and less because all assessments are authentic, given the constraints of the assessment type. Tests are a genre that students will encounter throughout their lives, and therefore are authentic in that context.

Performance Assessment

Performance assessment measures a student's performance in creating a particular product or exhibiting information. It can help measure content knowledge, but it also incorporates higher-order thinking and processing skills. Performance assessment enables students to apply their knowledge to a specific problem or goal and often links to other content areas. Unlike traditional testing, it can provide feedback at various stages during the assessment process.

You can break a performance task down into a process that requires the following action skills:

Step in Process	Action Skills Used
1. Get the information.	find, complete, count, collect, read, listen, define, describe, identify, list, match, name, observe (using all the senses), record, recite, select, scan
2. Work with the information.	compare, contrast, classify, sort, distinguish, explain, infer, sequence, analyze, synthesize, generalize, evaluate, make analogies, make models, reason
3. Judge the quality of information.	evaluate whether the information source is likely to be biased or objective, evaluate whether the information itself is accurate and complete
4. Use the information for a purpose.	inform, persuade, motivate, entertain
5. Use the information to craft a product/presentation.	speak, debate, sing, write, survey, design, draw, compute, construct, demonstrate, act

G

Goals of Assessment

Plan and choose your means of assessment carefully. The outcomes of each student's assessments should allow you to

- gauge the level of scientific reasoning;
- improve the ability to apply scientific knowledge and reasoning;
- improve the ability to communicate effectively about science;
- identify learning styles, as well as strengths and weaknesses;
- identify areas of instruction that need more or less emphasis;
- promote self- and peer-assessment;
- promote independent learning;
- promote authentic learning.

Partner with Formal or Summative Testing

Formal or summative testing consists of multiple choice, true/false, matching, and short-answer questions that result in an assessment based on recalling facts and basic skills. In contrast, performance assessment provides an opportunity to evaluate how well students use one or more elements of literacy.

Each teacher must balance formal or summative testing and performance assessment. You might try using formal or summative testing first to ensure that your students have enough accurate information before you use performance assessment. Sometimes it is better to utilize performance assessment first as a strategy to engage students in learning.

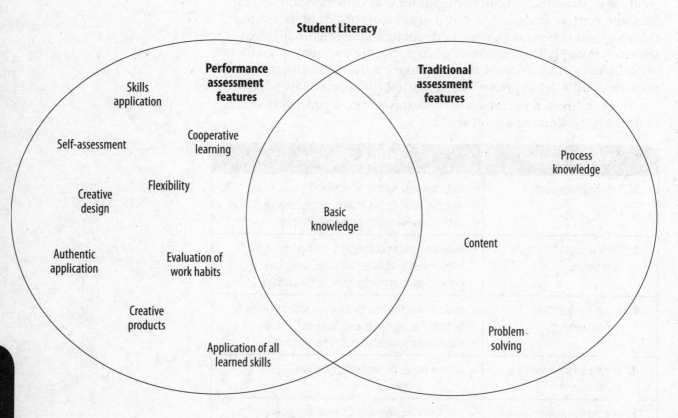

Student Literacy

HOW CAN I IMPLEMENT THIS SYSTEM?

SELECT
an appropriate Performance-Task Assessment List for the student product or process.

MODEL
through discussion and presentation of excellent work that is similar to but not the same as the current task. Relate elements of these models to the elements listed on the Performance-Task Assessment List.

PRODUCE
the completed task guided by the Performance-Task Assessment List.

SELF-ASSESS
the products or processes using the Performance-Task Assessment List.

REVISE
their work using their self-assessments.

TEACHER-ASSESS
the students' products, processes, and self-assessments using the Performance-Task Assessment List.

DISCUSS
the assessments with the students individually.

SCORE WITH RUBRICS
periodically to assess the overall quality of students' work. Performance-Task Assessment Lists may be used in assigning and explaining the Rubric scores.

FIND AND USE INFORMATION

UNDERSTAND THE TASK
- What is a reasonable topic?
- Who is the audience for my product?
- What kind of product will I make?
- What effect do I want my product to have on my audience?

SURVEY WHAT I KNOW AND WHAT I NEED TO FIND OUT
- What do I really know about this topic?
- What do I know about my audience?
- What do I need to find out?
- Where and how will I get this information?
- When is my product due?

REACH
- Are these information sources objective?
- Is this information factual or opinionated?
- How shall I save and organize this information?

REACH A SPECIFIC AUDIENCE
- What is the best way to communicate my purpose to my audience?

LOOK BACK AT THE PROCESS
- What are the strengths and weaknesses of the process I used?
- What are the strengths and weaknesses of my product?
- What goals do I need to set to improve my work the next time I do such a project?

USE MATHEMATICS TO SOLVE PROBLEMS

IDENTIFY THE PROBLEM
- What part of this problem can I solve by using math?

UNDERSTAND THE PROBLEM
- What exactly am I trying to solve?
- What do I really know?

FIND THE NECESSARY INFORMATION
- What information do I need to find?
- Where will I find it?

DECIDE ON THE TOOLS TO USE
- How will I collect the information I need?
- How can computers and/or calculators help?

COMMUNICATE THE RESULTS
- How shall I display my results?
- How do I convince my audience that I have found a reasonable answer?

Performance Assessment Toolbox

Tools vary for judging the performance of a task. Remember, your choice of assessment should be consistent with what you want to measure. This section presents ideas about different assessment tools you can use.

Observation and Questioning

What is it?

The assessment techniques of observation and questioning are not new to science teachers. In every science classroom, teachers observe students' behaviors and performances on scientific tasks, and question them about their work. During the introduction to a new topic or a review of previously taught material, use questions to check student understanding. Depending on students' responses, you should make appropriate adjustments in your instructional approach.

The emerging process goals of science instruction, however, imply that teachers need to re-examine the techniques of observation and questioning to make sure they are using the techniques effectively to assess the new goals. In other words, new curriculum standards require new or revised assessment methods.

How can you evaluate a student's performances on laboratory tasks or probe critical-thinking and problem-solving skills? How do you assess a student's knowledge of scientific connections? The following paragraphs provide answers to these questions.

What do I do?

Traditionally, teachers assign students science problems and then grade their written work on the basis of correct or incorrect answers. This procedure has serious shortcomings and often reveals little useful information. For example, a student might understand how to solve a problem, but a misconception might produce an incorrect answer and lead a teacher to think otherwise. A more powerful way to assess problem-solving competence is to ask students questions about how they tried to solve a problem. Listening to a student's descriptions of his or her thinking and observing his or her written work provide a more accurate assessment of problem-solving abilities than simply grading answers on tests.

Think, Communicate, and Make Connections

Questioning students in a problem-solving context reveals not only how they think but also their ability to communicate ideas clearly. You observe by listening, asking questions, and evaluating responses. Such a procedure enables you to change the direction of the questions in order to pursue other ideas or thoughts the students might have expressed, thus giving them a fuller and deeper understanding of the process. Asking the right questions can also reveal how students make connections about what they know.

Use Open-Ended Questions

An open-ended question is the best type of question to ask students when you assess their knowledge of science processes

For more information on English-Language Learners visit

Professional Development

at **mhpdonline.com**

G

because it does not have one answer. Open-ended questions provide students with opportunities to think for themselves and to demonstrate their understanding of a problem or other situation. Asking open-ended questions can reveal interesting information about what students understand. They also enable students to express their originality and creativity. Open-ended questions are incompatible with the erroneous notion that science consists of only memorizing responses to questions that have one correct answer. Open-ended questions enable students to see and understand that science is a logical and connected body of ideas that has great practical significance in understanding the world.

Examples of Open-Ended Questions

Open-ended questions often involve the use of words such as the following:

- describe
- explain
- compare
- tell
- analyze
- examine

- demonstrate
- sketch
- explore
- illustrate
- express
- contrast

- investigate
- prove
- show
- model
- predict
- define (operationally)

Now You Try It

Implementing the questions is an integral part of the instructional process. You can direct questions toward individual students, small groups, or the whole class. You can then use students' responses for assessment purposes, to guide instruction, or to identify problems.

Observe Student Performances

You can observe students working as individuals, in small groups, or within a class setting. Observations are useful for determining the level of student understanding (so you can take remedial action, if needed), guiding students working in a small group toward the goals of the group, or giving instructional feedback as students participate in class work. Use students' responses to modify instruction as it is taking place.

Observing students at work is a natural part of the classroom process. Very often, these informal observations are unplanned, and no one attempts to record what has been observed. However, to understand how students solve problems, closely observing their attempts to solve problems is critical.

The same is true for evaluating critical-thinking skills. Listen to students explain the reasons for their work. You can begin to understand how their minds work through their explanations. Of course, written work also can help you form a complete picture of scientific competence.

Observations are useful in assessing performance in the following areas:

- laboratory skills
- problem-solving approaches
- thinking processes
- understanding concepts

- communication skills
- small-group interaction
- making connections

G

Performance Report

Name _____

Time period _____

Class _____

———————————————————————————————

Description of work _____

_____

_____

Examples of significant work _____

_____

_____

Growth and improvement observed _____

_____

_____

Areas needing additional work _____

_____

_____

Group work _____

_____

_____

Attitude _____

_____

_____

Summary comments _____

_____

_____

G

Projects and Investigations

What is it?

Projects and investigations can involve individual students or small groups of two to four students working collaboratively. They should be long-term assignments and include a wide variety of concepts, basic and integrated process skills, problem identification, and solution techniques. Students involved in an ongoing task should be involved for at least two to three weeks.

Projects involving more substantial activities can last a month or more. Since students should be involved in more than a few projects during the course of a school year, the ideal duration of a project is about four to five weeks.

What do I do?

Projects are wonderful ways to involve students in extended problem-solving situations. These situations might be purely scientific, but most likely will relate to the real world or to other disciplines. Projects can involve students in open-ended situations that might have a variety of acceptable results. Or, they might be of such a nature that the problem situation leads students to formulate questions or hypotheses that require further investigation. Projects also provide opportunities for students to explore scientific ideas using physical materials or technology.

For Lesson Plans go to
TEA⁺CHING
TODAY
at teachingtoday.glencoe.com

Real-World Projects and Investigations

Projects and investigations can teach students how science is connected to everyday life. For example, you can construct projects that involve the use of science in the following areas:

- health
- population
- computers
- environmental issues
- agriculture
- careers and business
- cars, boats, airplanes (travel)
- sports
- recycling
- astronomy
- city issues
- international policy

Additionally, projects and investigations can show how science connects to other disciplines, such as mathematics, social studies, music, economics, computers, geography, and so on. All of these activities bring science to life for students by showing them the usefulness of scientific ideas and techniques in a wide range of practical activities.

G

When to Implement

You can, of course, assign projects and investigations at any time during the school year. However, you might want to wait until after the first three or four weeks of school before discussing the role of projects in the course. This gives students time to feel comfortable with the course content before they begin their first project.

The first few projects should be simple and straightforward. Some students might need your guidance to formulate their first plan for a project. As the year progresses, students should be able to work more independently.

How to Implement

Begin by talking to students about the idea of a project. Tell them that you will be using projects and investigations for both instructional and evaluation purposes.

Discuss the process goals of instruction—problem solving, communication, reasoning, and connections—and point out their important role in the study of science. Tell students that their projects should be problem-solving oriented and related to the content of the course.

At the beginning of the school year, the first projects that students work on most likely will relate to the content of the first or second chapter of their textbooks. In fact, you might be able to use the textbook as a source for project ideas.

More Specific Suggestions for Students

To help students get started on their projects, share with them some specific guidelines for using a student log for formulating, researching, and presenting projects.

First, students need to be able to write clear descriptions of what their projects are about. Review and critique these descriptions to make sure students have not taken on projects that are too difficult. Projects need to be doable, and they need to provide experiences that contribute to students' educational growth.

Second, students should state what procedures they intend to follow in the course of working on projects. Do they need to state and test a hypothesis? Do they have to make measurements or collect data? Will library research suffice? Do they have to conduct interviews? Is a computer necessary?

Third, students should keep written records or project logs of their work. They should write down the purposes of projects, the procedures they followed, and any materials they used. Also, they should record any questions that arose while working on projects, keep track of data, and make notes of their thoughts and ideas about projects. They should decide how to best communicate results using graphs, charts, tables, or illustrations.

Finally, students should record their results. They can present their final reports either orally or as written reports.

These steps can help students become successful investigators. They also provide important documents for you to use in assessing the educational outcomes of the projects and in shaping future projects.

Now you try it!

The use of projects in the science classroom can have many positive learning outcomes for students. In addition to developing scientific skills, projects provide opportunities for students to grow intellectually and socially. The following outcomes are a result of working on projects:

- define problems and conduct independent research
- work with others when doing a group project
- find out that real-world problems often are complex and require extensive effort over a long period of time
- see science as a practical, problem-solving technique
- acquire the ability to organize, plan, and pursue long-term objectives
- discover how to correctly use scientific materials
- practice writing reports of investigations

Scientific outcomes of projects are many and varied. No one list can encompass everything students could learn from doing projects. However, you can write a general list of outcomes. Projects can be of the utmost importance in developing scientific capabilities because they provide opportunities for students to

- solve and formulate problems in science and make applications to everyday life;
- use scientific language to communicate ideas;
- use analytical skills;
- apply reasoning skills;
- demonstrate knowledge of concepts, skills, and scientific theories and laws;
- make connections within the sciences and to other disciplines;
- develop an understanding of the nature of science;
- integrate scientific knowledge into a more meaningful set of concepts.

Project Evaluation

You need to evaluate project work by looking for evidence of the growth of scientific reasoning. If students have organized their projects according to the guidelines presented here, that is, if they have followed the steps of **(1)** writing descriptions of projects, **(2)** identifying the procedures they intend to follow, **(3)** keeping written records of their work, and **(4)** stating their results, then an evaluation of projects is not only possible, it's rather simple.

The description of a project will help you identify the key scientific growth areas. Of course, these should relate to problem solving, reasoning, communication, and making connections. The procedure to follow should help you identify more specific aspects of each growth area for evaluation. The written record and statement of results will let you see the student's thinking as he or she attempted to complete the project.

Evaluate each project on its own merit. You can use a written project to assess a student's writing skills. If the student presents the project to the class, assess oral communication skills. A proof or solution to a difficult or nonroutine problem provides evidence of

G

problem-solving abilities and reasoning skills. The collection, organization, and analysis of data provide evidence of problem-solving and thinking skills. The use of different techniques to represent or model a situation (diagrams, equations, or graphs) shows an understanding of scientific connections.

You can evaluate projects on either a holistic or an analytical basis. Holistic scoring is based on a project as a whole. For example, you can read and evaluate a sample of projects to determine a range of performance. Three to five categories can be established, and as you evaluate the rest of the projects, they can be placed in the established categories. After final adjustments, grades can be assigned.

Analytical scoring breaks down the project into specific elements or components and establishes point values for each one. For example, the following components and point values could be used to evaluate projects.

Element	Point Value
• Problem description	10
• Research method	10
• Project steps/work record	20
• Data	20
• Conclusions	20
• Project report	20
• Project grade	100 points

This analytical process provides checkpoints for individuals and groups undertaking long-term projects. One advantage of analytical scoring is that it allows for redoing and rewriting project elements, allowing students to receive maximum points on each element when they demonstrate mastery of the concepts and skills involved.

Productive Group Work

You can enhance students' understanding about science by having them work together in productive work groups. Working within a group enables students to pool their contributions to the implementation and outcomes of the project. However, the contributions of each individual could be lost unless someone keeps a record as to who has done what. This is important when you (or the students) evaluate group project work.

You should certainly evaluate the group's performance, but it is equally as important to assess what each individual has contributed to the group. You might accomplish this most easily by having a written log of group activities. Group members can rotate through roles such as investigator, materials manager, recorder, and maintenance director. After the group writes a final report, each student can participate in an oral presentation of the group's project.

G

Sample Forms

A log sheet like the one below can be used for cooperative group projects. A record of the project might require additional pages to adequately document information.

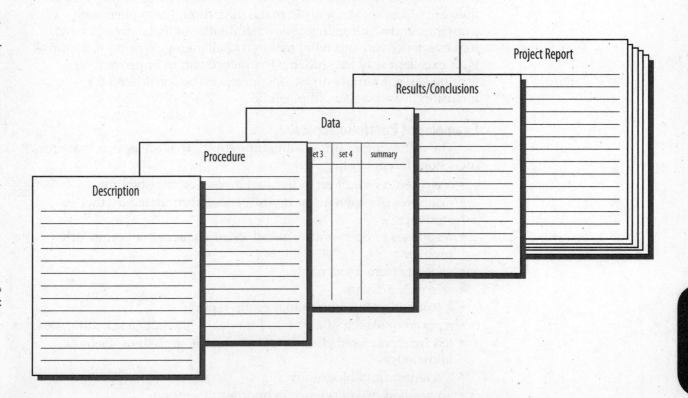

Group Log Sheet

Group members _____

Project _____

Date	Work done	Questions	Results

Description

Procedure

Data

| | | set 3 | set 4 | summary |

Results/Conclusions

Project Report

G

Portfolios and Journals

What is it?

A portfolio is a representative sample of a student's work collected over a period of time. It tells a story about a student's activities in science with a focus on problem solving, thinking and understanding, written communication, and science connections. A portfolio also can reveal a student's view of himself or herself as a science learner.

A portfolio is not just a folder of a student's work. The pieces of work in a portfolio have more significance than other work a student has done. They are chosen as illustrations of a student's best work at a particular point in time. Thus, each item in a portfolio should have a date on it. The range of items selected shows a student's intellectual growth in science over time.

You can use portfolios to assess student performance on a variety of science tasks during the school year. A student's work portfolio is usually a collection of his or her work over two or three weeks. A review of a work portfolio provides a basis for selecting items that will go into an assessment portfolio. Assist students with the review but do not direct the process. Students' actual selections will tell you which pieces of work they think are significant.

Students should submit written reflections on their portfolios, documenting their growth in science during the assessment period. Each student should include a summary of what he or she has selected and why. Student-selected items help you understand students' views of themselves as developing "scientists."

Journals present another opportunity for students to organize their thoughts. They are not lecture or laboratory notebooks; instead, they are places for students to make their thoughts explicit with drawings and writing. In journals, students can make note of what makes science fun and what makes it challenging. Writing in a journal is an excellent way for students to practice and to improve their writing skills. Journal entries, of course, can be considered for inclusion in an assessment portfolio.

Examples of Portfolio Topics

The following examples illustrate topics that are appropriate for inclusion in a portfolio:

- a written report of an individual project or investigation
- examples of problems or investigations formulated by the student
- responses to open-ended questions or challenging homework problems
- excerpts from a journal
- scientific artwork
- a student's contribution to a group report
- a photo or sketch of a physical model to illustrate a scientific idea
- teacher-completed checklists showing the growth of scientific knowledge
- a scientific autobiography
- an applied use of science in another discipline

G

Balance a Portfolio

The selection of work samples for a portfolio should be done with the goal of presenting a balanced portrait of a student's achievements. As students assemble their portfolios, remind students that the samples they select should be representative of growth in each of the following areas:

- problem-solving skills
- reasoning and critical-thinking skills
- communication skills
- scientific connections

Other important curriculum considerations for portfolio samples are

- statements on scientific attitudes, such as motivation, curiosity, and self-confidence;
- group skills acquired while working with others;
- use of technological tools.

Advantages of Using Portfolios

Using assessment portfolios in science has grown out of the need to align assessment tasks with emerging curricular standards. It has also resulted from teachers' frustration and dissatisfaction with paper-and-pencil testing. Advantages of using portfolios as assessment tools include

- getting a more complete picture of student achievement and growth;
- seeing complex and real-world tasks performed over a few weeks;
- involving students in the assessment process and encouraging self-assessment;
- motivating students to study and learn science;
- having an effective tool for learning partner-teacher communication;
- encouraging the development of writing skills.

Advantages of Using Journals

As students study science independently, writing in a journal can help develop their ability to reflect on their learning.

Types of journal entries include

- labeled drawings and sketches with comments;
- questions that occur to the student that he or she would like to be able to answer and the beginnings of answers to those questions;
- detailed observations;
- "What if . . . ?" questions that are the beginning of planning an experiment;
- sketches and notes about models and inventions;
- thoughts about what is interesting and enjoyable about science class;
- thoughts about what is difficult in learning science and how to overcome barriers to learning science;
- notes about interesting science items from newspapers, magazines, or television programs.

What do I do?

Use portfolios throughout the school year. Begin by discussing with students the idea of a portfolio. Use the procedures listed to help you and your class get started.

G

- Have students use file folders to collect their work for a portfolio.
- Ask students what they think should be included in an assessment portfolio.
- Discuss the format of a good portfolio. It should be neat, include a table of contents, and have a personal statement as to why the student included each piece of work.
- Provide variety in assignments so the portfolios can reflect this variety—group work, projects, investigations, journal entries, and so on.
- Have students create their first assessment portfolios from their work portfolios.
- Have students review others' portfolios so they can see their classmates' work.
- Discuss how you will evaluate the assessment portfolios.

Discuss each student's portfolio with him or her in preparation for developing the revised portfolio. The initial implementation of portfolios will be a learning experience for you as well as for your students. As you both gain experience in using portfolios, their effectiveness in guiding instruction and for assessment purposes will be greatly increased. At first, the use of assessment portfolios might seem like extra work. However, their continued use will enrich both your teaching and your students' learning processes.

Assess a Portfolio

In portfolio assessment, keep in mind that students individually chose the work in their portfolios as representations of their best efforts. Thus, a portfolio is essentially a self-evaluation by the student who created it. Your goal in assessing a portfolio is to help the student gain additional insights into his or her scientific performance on the tasks exhibited in his or her portfolio. These insights involve growth in the understanding of science, strengths and weaknesses of approaches and procedures, and an analysis of both the kinds of decisions made and the final outcomes of the activities in the portfolio.

Ideally, you will establish assessment criteria that you can share with your students. Both you and your students should understand and agree on the criteria of establishing and assessing a portfolio. It is these criteria that form the basis for the assessment comments you make on the work in the portfolio. When creating a portfolio, a student follows the criteria already established. He or she selects work to represent the key goals of instruction.

School districts and science classrooms across the country are establishing assessment criteria for portfolio evaluation. However, you might have to develop your own criteria. In so doing, you can develop criteria that are important to you and your students. The following section lists some ideas that can provide the basis for establishing your own assessment criteria.

Assessment Criteria

You can organize the assessment criteria for a portfolio into categories that align with the curriculum goals you are implementing. You can look for the overall quality of a piece of work rather than specific information or following the "right" steps, or you can give a fixed grade for completing the portfolio process.

G

Allow students the option of redoing certain elements of their portfolios in order to gain all possible points.

Assessment criteria should help you make judgments about your students' work. The criteria also should help you give fair and consistent evaluations to all portfolios.

Problem-Solving Criteria

Problem-solving criteria can help you evaluate to what degree your students

- understand problems;
- use various strategies to make a plan for solving problems;
- carry out plans using models or technology;
- analyze results, including statistical procedures;
- formulate problems;
- approach complex problems creatively.

Language Criteria

Use language criteria to assess how well your students use language to express themselves scientifically. Students should be able to

- use correct terminology;
- write clearly to express ideas;
- organize written work and journals well;
- explain results;
- summarize key topics;
- reflect on scientific ideas;
- ask questions.

Reasoning Criteria

Reasoning criteria will help you comment on the ways in which students

- identify variables;
- make hypotheses;
- conduct inquiries;
- document results;
- analyze results;
- critique ideas and procedures;
- construct, extend, and apply ideas.

Other Criteria

These criteria can help you make a comprehensive assessment of your students' performance. Comment on the ways in which they

- relate science to the real world;
- make connections within science;
- develop positive attitudes;
- value science;
- use self-assessment and self-correction of work;
- work as a group;
- use different scientific representations or models;
- interpret ideas;
- use technology;
- apply concepts and procedures.

G

Assessment of Portfolio

Student _____

Teacher _____

Date _____

_____

1. Concepts, procedures, process skills explored _____

_____

_____

2. Areas of growth in understanding _____

_____

_____

3. Unfinished work or work that needs revision _____

_____

_____

4. Assessment of the following areas:

  a. Problem-solving work _____

  _____

  _____

  b. Reasoning and critical thinking _____

  _____

  _____

  c. Use of language _____

  _____

  _____

  d. Other _____

  _____

  _____

G

Other Types of Assessment

What is it?

In addition to the major models of assessment, you can use the following techniques to assess student performance:

- interviews and conferences
- student self-assessment
- student-constructed tests
- homework

Interviews and Conferences

Interviews and conferences provide an opportunity for you and your students to meet one-on-one to discuss science. This personal meeting can be a powerful motivating experience for many students. It also can provide you with useful information about how your students think and feel about science.

An interview is a formal discussion that you can structure around questions that relate to a specific scientific topic. For example, a problem-solving interview would pose a problem for a student to solve. Working from a planned set of questions, you learn how a student goes about solving the problem. The student explains his or her choice of models and strategies to solve the problem, the procedure followed, and the meaning of the solution. Questions from you and verbal responses from the student are key ingredients of an interview.

A conference is not quite as focused as an interview. A conference is an informal discussion between you and a student. Although a conference always should have a purpose—for example, to review and discuss a student's portfolio—it need not stay with that purpose exclusively. Let the student talk, ask questions, and discuss what is important to him or her. Appropriate comments and questions from you can elicit valuable assessment information that might be impossible to get any other way.

Helpful Hints for Interviews and Conferences

The following helpful hints have been suggested by the National Council of Teachers of Mathematics:

- Prepare questions before the interview or conference.
- Put students at ease.
- Explain that you are looking for creative thinking.
- Pose a problem.
- Take notes.
- Be a good listener.
- Be nonjudgmental.
- Do any instructional intervention in a separate setting.

For Assessments and Rubrics go to

TEACHING TODAY

at **teachingtoday.glencoe.com**

G

Student Self-Assessment

One of the real benefits of using performance-assessment tasks is the opportunity to have students take part in the assessment process. When teachers view assessment as an integral part of the instructional process, its focus shifts from giving tests to helping students understand the goals of the learning experience and the criteria for success.

Implicit in all alternate methods of assessment is the idea that these methods can work most effectively when students know the goals of instruction and the criteria for measuring success against those goals. Knowing the goals and the criteria for success enables each student to monitor his or her own progress.

What do I do?

In order to help each student learn how to monitor his or her progress, explain the goals of instruction and the criteria for evaluating performances against the goals. Display the major instructional goals for the year in the classroom, and give copies to each student. You also need to discuss with students how you will judge their work. Students need to know that even though right and wrong answers have importance, there are some new criteria for being successful in science that show signs of growth in understanding and the ability to think, communicate, and solve problems.

Encourage students to question their works, strengths and weaknesses, accomplishments, work habits, goals, and attitudes. Periodically, ask students to tell you what they have done that shows progress toward achieving their goals. Ask them also to evaluate their own reports, journals, and portfolios and to provide evidence for their evaluations. All of these methods can help students learn how to assess their own work.

Use Self-Assessment Forms

One device that you can use for self-evaluation is a self-assessment form. You and your students can design such a form together. Then, every three or four weeks, students can complete the forms and give them to you. Typical questions include:

- What new understanding of science have you learned recently?
- Which topic is causing you difficulty at this time?
- Have you found any new topics that really interest you? Describe them.
- What do you enjoy and what do you not enjoy about working in groups?
- How do you feel about science now?
- What progress do you think you have made in science during the past few weeks?
- What can we do to improve our science class?

Goals of Self-Assessment

As students take a more active part in assessing their own work, they become more mature and responsible learners. Self-assessment helps students work and think independently, set goals and priorities, and learn how to achieve success both in school and outside of school.

G

The goals of self-assessment in learning science are more modest than those stated above, but no less important. Through self-assessment, each student takes part in the instructional process by evaluating his or her own performance. Students' subsequent actions should result in learning more science, correcting errors or misconceptions, improving performances on more challenging tasks, and gaining deeper insights into the nature of science itself.

Varied Test Formats

For evaluation of basic skills and of factual knowledge, written tests are still an effective means of assessing performance.

Student-Constructed Tests

As an alternative to your regular tests, you might want students to take tests made of student-constructed test problems. Assigning students to construct their own test problems gives them a sense of participation in the assessment process. They usually enjoy conceiving the problems and generally are very interested in the solutions.

You can form small groups of three or four students. Obviously, the test problems need to represent the content they study. Choose items from each student group to include on the test. It is important that all students contribute to the test. You might need to edit some problems but leave the essence of student-generated items intact. When discussing correct responses, contributing groups can offer study suggestions for their test problems.

Take-Home Tests

To add variety and interest to written tests, assign students take-home tests. Some college instructors practice this, but middle- and high-school teachers usually do not, so it will provide an interesrting change of pace for your students. Take-home tests can challenge students with more open-ended questions or nonroutine problems. Time is not a major factor because students have more than just class time to complete the test. Take-home tests can be teacher- or student-constructed.

Practical Tests

Practical tests offer yet another way to modify the test-taking regimen. These tests make use of physical materials and have students answer questions or perform various tasks that relate to the science content. They can be teacher- or student-constructed, and you can administer them to individuals or small groups of two or three students.

Homework

Teachers often assign homework and review it in class the next day. However, it often is overlooked as a means of assessing student performance. This does not have to be the case. Some teachers have success with assigning fewer homework papers but requiring that the assigned homework be included in the work or assessment portfolio. You could review and evaluate certain carefully selected homework assignments on a periodic basis. Skill types of problems or exercises could be included for evaluation; however, the emphasis should be on thought-provoking questions. In these ways, homework can play a more important role as an assessment technique.

G

Interview Scoring Form

Name:	Date:	Score
Explanation of problem to be solved		
Explanation of strategies to solve problem		
Explanation of procedures followed		
Explanation of the solution		
Verbal responses to teacher questions		

Scoring:

1 = needs improvement   2 = improving   3 = good   4 = excellent

Conference Form

Name: _____ Date: _____

Student questions: _____

_____

_____

_____

_____

Teacher questions and responses: _____

_____

_____

_____

_____

_____

G

Performance-Task Assessment Lists and Rubrics

Students perform numerous tasks when completing science assignments. This section provides checklists—Performance-Task Assessment Lists—that outline the elements or steps of the tasks identified. These lists will help you judge both the quality of the methods students use to complete the given tasks and the quality of the final product.

Rubrics for the given tasks follow each list. The rubrics provide a continuum of quality ratings (ranging from Excellent to Poor) suitable for judging the overall quality of the final product.

The Performance-Task Assessment Lists may be used as published in this book, or they may be tailored to specific tasks. Shortening the lists, combining them with other lists, or rewording them may allow clearer communication with a particular group of students. You might wish to prepare performance-task assessment lists and rubrics for other products and processes, following the model of those included in this book.

G

Performance-Task Assessment List

Make Observations and Inferences

Element	Assessment Points: Points Possible	Earned Assessment: STUDENT	Earned Assessment: TEACHER
Make Observations			
1 The student safely makes observations using all appropriate senses.			
2 Observations are quantitatively accurate and use metric measurements appropriately.			
3 Observations are qualitatively accurate.			
4 When necessary, the student makes scientific drawings. (See Performance-Task Assessment List for Illustrate a Scientific Object, page 353.)			
5 The student uses appropriate tools and materials to make observations.			
6 The student avoids personal opinions, conclusions, or inferences while making observations.			
7 The student records and organizes data appropriately and neatly. (See Performance-Task Assessment List for Complete a Data Table, page 329.)			
Make Inferences			
8 Inferences are reasonable given the observations made and the observer's prior knowledge.			
9 The student explains inferences and justifies them based on prior knowledge.			
Total			

G

Rubric
Make Observations and Inferences

	Rating
The student provided a well-organized list of quantitative (mathematical calculations) and qualitative (informed judgments) observations, showing that he or she put major effort into the study. Impressive drawings and diagrams accompanied the data. The student made carefully thought-out inferences and justified them by his or her observations and by prior knowledge.	
The student made detailed observations using all the appropriate senses safely. The student made both quantitative and qualitative observations accurately. The student showed skill in using tools and materials. Carefully drawn sketches or diagrams accompanied the data. The student recorded observations without making opinions, conclusions, or inferences. The records were organized and easy to read. The student made thoughtful inferences and justified them based on observations and his or her prior knowledge.	
The student made incomplete and/or inaccurate observations. The student did not use the metric system or used it inappropriately. The student did not use the tools or equipment well. Sketches and diagrams were missing, or they were poorly done. The list of observations was not well-organized and/or it contained personal opinions, conclusions, or inferences. Inferences were not thoughtfully justified based on the observations and/or on the student's prior knowledge.	
The student completed work very poorly or did not complete it at all.	

Note: For drawings, use the Performance-Task Assessment List: Illustrate a Scientific Object.

Comments:

G

Pose Questions

Element	Points Possible	Earned Assessment	
		STUDENT	TEACHER
Assessment Points			
1 The student asks thoughtful and relevant questions.			
2 Questions are well-crafted.			
3 Questions emerge logically from the observations made.			
4 Questions are descriptive.			
5 Questions interpret the observations.			
6 Questions analyze the observations.			
7 Questions lead to reasonable predictions.			
8 The student selects a question for investigation.			
9 The student gives a thoughtful justification for why he or she selected that question for further study.			
Total			

G

Pose Questions

	Rating
The student showed great insight by crafting thoughtful and interesting questions. The student clearly used higher-order thinking. The student gave persuasive explanations as to why he or she selected a particular question for further study.	
The student asked many questions that exhibited a thoughtful consideration of the observations. Questions included some higher-order thinking, such as interpretation, analysis, synthesis, and evaluation. The questions led directly to predictions that could become the basis for experiments. The student offered an adequate explanation for why he or she chose a particular question for further study.	
The list of questions showed little effort. The student did not use higher-order thinking. Some questions did not seem to be related to the observations. The student did not give a thoughtful explanation as to why he or she selected a particular question for further study.	
The student completed work very poorly or did not complete it at all.	

Comments:

G

Form a Hypothesis

Element	Assessment Points		
	Points Possible	Earned Assessment	
		STUDENT	TEACHER
1 The hypothesis is a simple explanation of observations.			
2 Predictions result from the hypothesis.			
3 The student makes a thoughtful justification for why the hypothesis and a more specific prediction can serve as the basis for an experiment.			
4 The predictions are useful in designing the experiment.			
Total			

G

Form a Hypothesis

	Rating
The student made a remarkably insightful hypothesis. The prediction was clearly testable, and the student provided a thoughtful explanation of how the hypothesis and prediction would provide the basis for designing an excellent experiment.	
The student made a clear, declarative hypothesis statement, which was followed by a prediction that related the independent variable (what the experimenter changes) to the dependent variable (how the thing responds). It was evident how the hypothesis and prediction flowed from the observations. The student justified how the hypothesis and prediction provided the basis for designing an experiment.	
The hypothesis and the prediction were unclear. It was also unclear how the hypothesis and prediction flowed from the observations. The student did not offer a thoughtful explanation about how the hypothesis and prediction would provide the basis for designing an experiment.	
The student completed work very poorly or did not complete it at all.	

Comments:

G

Performance-Task Assessment List
Design an Experiment

Element	Points Possible	Earned Assessment STUDENT	Earned Assessment TEACHER
1 The experimental design tests the prediction.			
2 The statement of the problem explains the need for the experiment.			
3 The methods and procedures follow a logical sequence.			
4 The experimental design includes appropriate safety concerns.			
5 The experimental procedure is complete and clear enough for another person to repeat the experiment.			
6 The student clearly identifies an appropriate independent variable.			
7 The plan provides for a control and accurate measurement of the independent variable.			
8 The student clearly identifies an appropriate dependent variable.			
9 The plan provides for the accurate measurement of the dependent variable.			
10 The student uses the metric system and SI units in the experimental design.			
11 The experiment includes proper controls.			
12 The student notes possible sources of experimental error.			
13 The student lists all required materials.			
14 The student describes an appropriate strategy to use repeated trials and measurements.			
15 The experimental report is neat and well-organized.			
16 The student writes the experiment using appropriate vocabulary, language mechanics, and complete sentences.			
17 The student provides instructions for proper cleanup and disposal of wastes.			
Total			

G

Rubric
Design an Experiment

	Rating
The experiment was exemplary in its clarity and completeness and showed an understanding of experimental methods. It had the potential to provide data that could be used to evaluate the hypothesis and its prediction. The procedural steps were logical and well-written. The student showed a clear understanding of the need for controls, the need to replicate the experiment, and the need for strategies to minimize experimental error. The student thoughtfully planned all safety and workstation precautions.	
The experiment tested the prediction. The sequence of steps was complete enough that another person could follow it. The student appropriately chose the independent and dependent variables and thoughtfully planned how to control and measure them. The student planned to use appropriate tools and materials. The student showed a good understanding of the need for controls, the need to replicate the experiment, and the need for strategies to minimize experimental error. The student planned safety precautions and strategies to deal with workstation care and waste disposal.	
The plan was incomplete and/or disorganized. The student chose the independent and/or dependent variables poorly or inappropriately, and they did not develop plans for measuring them. The student evidenced no clear understanding of controls or the need for replicating the experiment. The student did not describe strategies to minimize experimental error. Safety precautions were lacking or incomplete. The student made no plan to care for the workstation and dispose of wastes.	
The student completed work very poorly or did not complete it at all.	

Comments:

G

Performance-Task Assessment List
Collect Data

Element	Points Possible	Earned Assessment STUDENT	Earned Assessment TEACHER
1 The student selects appropriate tools and materials to collect the data.			
2 The student demonstrates skill in using the tools and materials to collect accurate data.			
3 The student takes and records repeated measurements.			
4 The student uses tools safely and properly.			
5 The student puts away materials and properly cleans the work area.			
6 The student utilizes strategies to minimize experimental error.			
Total			

G

Rubric
Collect Data

	Rating
The student showed exceptional skill in carrying out the experiment. Safety precautions were excellent. The student replicated the experiment and carefully minimized experimental error. The student maintained a clean workstation, stored equipment properly, returned materials to their proper locations, and disposed of wastes properly.	
The student followed the procedure for carrying out the experiment. The student safely used proper tools, equipment, and materials to carry out the procedure. The student replicated the experiment and employed strategies to minimize experimental error. The student cleaned the workstation and properly put away materials and tools. The student properly disposed of wastes.	
The student did not follow the procedure completely. The student showed little skill in using the tools, equipment, and materials. The student did not replicate the experiment and/or did not keep error to a reasonable minimum. The student did not properly clean the workstation. The student did not put tools, equipment, and materials away properly. The student did not dispose of waste properly.	
The student completed work very poorly or did not complete it at all.	

Comments:

G

Performance-Task Assessment List
Analyze Data

Element	Points Possible	Earned Assessment STUDENT	Earned Assessment TEACHER
1 The analysis is accurate and thoughtful.			
2 The student does not omit or ignore data for convenience of argument in the analysis.			
3 The student includes appropriate statistical procedures in the analysis.			
Total			

G

Analyze Data

	Rating
The student's analysis was excellent and showed great insight. The student used math correctly and extensively in the analysis.	
The student made use of all the data in the analysis and correctly used the appropriate mathematical procedures to analyze it.	
The student did not use all of the data in the analysis. The statistical procedures were not appropriate or they were not accurately carried out.	
The student completed work very poorly or did not complete it at all.	

Comments:

G

Use Math in Science

Element	Points Possible	Earned Assessment STUDENT	TEACHER
Assessment Points			

Understand the Problem

Element	Points Possible	STUDENT	TEACHER
1 The student clearly defines the problem.			
2 The student identifies the given information.			
3 The student lists the information that must be assumed.			
4 The student lists the information that must be obtained.			
5 The student draws a clear diagram that shows the important elements of the problem.			

Solve the Problem

Element	Points Possible	STUDENT	TEACHER
6 The student lists the algebraic formula(s) for the problem.			
7 The student rearranges the formula(s) correctly to solve for the unknown quantity.			
8 The student places values with appropriate units in the final formula.			
9 The student uses appropriate arithmetic operations accurately.			
10 All quantities have appropriate units.			
11 The sequence of arithmetic operations clearly displays the student's reasoning.			
12 The student uses the appropriate number of significant digits.			
13 The student uses scientific notation correctly.			
14 The answer is correct and includes the appropriate units.			
15 The answer is appropriate according to the assumptions and reasoning used.			

Communicate the Result

Element	Points Possible	STUDENT	TEACHER
16 The student makes a clear, concise statement of the problem, the strategy for the solution, and the answer. The student uses math vocabulary correctly.			
17 The student uses a labeled diagram to support the written statement.			
Total			

G

Rubric
Use Math in Science

	Rating
The student showed an especially thoughtful analysis of the problem and selected the correct formulas to solve the problem. The work was organized, complete, and easy to follow. The audience could understand the answer, which had the correct units and significant digits.	
The student showed that he or she understood the problem by paraphrasing it, identifying givens and information that must be assumed, and drawing a diagram to show the problem clearly. The student used formulas to solve the problem. The answers were accurate, had correct units, and had an appropriate number of significant digits. The student communicated the answer to the intended audience and thus demonstrated his or her ability to solve math problems.	
The student showed little understanding of the problem. The solution was faulty. The student used incorrect formulas, and the answer was incorrect. The student did not effectively communicate the answer to the intended audience.	
The student completed work very poorly or did not complete it at all.	

Comments:

G

322 | Blueprints for Success

Evaluate a Hypothesis

Element	Assessment Points		
	Points Possible	**Earned Assessment**	
		STUDENT	**TEACHER**
1 The student makes a clear statement about whether or not the hypothesis and the prediction are supported.			
2 The student justifies the evaluation of the hypothesis and the prediction.			
3 The student can make inferences and extrapolations, but clearly separates them from conclusions based on the data and their analysis.			
Total			

G

Evaluate a Hypothesis

	Rating
The student made a clear statement of the hypothesis and justified it in an analytical manner. The student supported the justification for the hypothesis and the prediction. Any inferences or estimations showed thoughtful insights. The data supported the conclusions well.	
The student made and supported a clear statement about whether the hypothesis and the specific prediction were supported. In the justification, the student tied the data and its analysis to the conclusion. If the student made inferences or extrapolations, he or she clearly identified them as such and did not confuse them with conclusions supported by data.	
The student did not make a clear statement as to whether the hypothesis and the specific prediction were supported. The student gave little justification for any conclusion reached. The student confused inferences or extrapolations with conclusions supported by the data or did not infer or extrapolate at all.	
The student completed work very poorly or did not complete it at all.	

Comments:

G

Performance-Task Assessment List

Assess an Experiment and Design a New Experiment

Element	Assessment Points		
	Points Possible	Earned Assessment	
		STUDENT	TEACHER
1 The student identifies the strengths and weaknesses of the experiment.			
2 The student identifies sources of experimental error.			
3 The student suggests applicable strategies for reducing experimental errors.			
4 The student states questions that arose during the experiment and presents options for further investigation.			
5 The student develops and states a question to use as the focus of the next experiment.			
Total			

G

Assess an Experiment and Design a New Experiment

	Rating
The student showed great insight in critiquing the experiment to identify its strengths and weaknesses and ways to improve it. The student included strategies to reduce experimental error. The student compiled a list of thoughtful questions for future investigations, and developed a question for the next experiment. The student clearly justified why that particular question should be investigated next.	
The student critiqued the experiment and identified its strengths and areas that need improvement. The student demonstrated understanding of experimental errors. The student proposed strategies to improve the experiment. The student listed questions that arose during the experiment that could be the basis for future experiments. The student developed and justified a question for future study.	
The student showed little thought while critiquing the experiment. He or she did not find strengths or identify areas that need improvement. The student demonstrated no understanding of how error entered the experiment. The student made few, if any, suggestions to improve the experiment. The student listed few questions for further study.	
The student completed work very poorly or did not complete it at all.	

Comments:

G

Performance-Task Assessment List

Conduct a Survey and Graph the Results

Element	Points Possible	Earned Assessment STUDENT	Earned Assessment TEACHER
1 The student clearly states the topic or question to be researched.			
2 The student selects the appropriate population to be surveyed on the topic or question.			
3 The student states survey questions clearly.			
4 Survey questions are relevant to the topic or question.			
5 The plan to collect data is well prepared, and will result in data that will be valid and reliable.			
6 The student organizes and appropriately labels the data from the survey.			
7 The student uses the appropriate type of graph (one that the audience will understand) to display the data. (See Performance-Task Assessment List for Graph the Data, page 331.)			
Total			

G

Conduct a Survey and Graph the Results

	Rating
The student masterfully conceived the survey. The student identified and carefully chose the target population. The strategy to conduct the survey was valid and reliable. The graph was accurate, visually appealing, and easy to understand. All graphing techniques were excellent. The student organized data from the survey into a clearly labeled chart or table. A key was present and easy to understand.	
The student chose an appropriate question or topic for the survey and stated it concisely. The student chose a target population, and the strategy to conduct the survey provided valid and reliable data. The student organized data from the survey into a labeled chart or table. The student accurately represented the data in an appropriate type of graph, which had clear labels and a title. The graph used visual techniques well, making it interesting and easy to understand. A key was present.	
The survey question or topic was neither clear nor on target for the assignment. The strategies to select a population and implement the survey were faulty and yielded data that were invalid or unreliable. The student did not organize data from the survey well. The student used an incorrect or inappropriate graph format. The titles, labels, and/or units were missing, unclear, or inaccurate. The graph appeared unorganized, too crowded, and/or sloppy.	
The student completed work very poorly or did not complete it at all.	

Comments:

G

Performance-Task Assessment List
Complete a Data Table

Element	Points Possible	Earned Assessment STUDENT	TEACHER
1 The data table includes the appropriate data.			
2 The student provides an appropriate title for the data table.			
3 The student appropriately organizes and labels the information in the data table columns.			
4 The student clearly indicates units of measurement for all variables.			
5 The student clearly shows data for the independent and dependent variables.			
6 The data have an appropriate number of significant digits.			
7 Accuracy of the data is appropriate to the measuring equipment or instrument being used.			
8 The student clearly shows data from multiple trials at each level of the independent variable.			
9 The data table is neat and legible.			
Total			

The assessment points header spans "Points Possible" and "Earned Assessment" (Student and Teacher).

G

Rubric
Complete a Data Table

	Rating
The student's data table was exceptionally well organized, clear, and concise. The data collected from the measuring equipment or instruments was accurate. The data showed an understanding of the procedures involved. The data had appropriate units of measurement and significant figures. The table was neat and legible.	
The student's data table was good. The data that the student collected from the measuring equipment or instruments was satisfactorily accurate. The data showed a basic understanding of the procedures involved.	
The student's data table showed inaccuracies related to the measuring equipment or instruments used. The data showed some problems related to the procedure involved. The table was unorganized and not done neatly.	
The student completed work very poorly or did not complete it at all.	

Comments:

G

Graph the Data

Element	Assessment Points		
	Points Possible	Earned Assessment	
		STUDENT	TEACHER
1 The student uses an appropriate type of graph.			
2 The student uses appropriate starting points and uniform intervals for each axis.			
3 The student chooses an appropriate scale for each axis, depending on the range of data for that axis.			
4 There is a title for the graph, which clearly states the relationship between the two axes.			
5 The student clearly labels axes.			
6 The independent variable data are on the x-axis and the dependent variable data are on the y-axis.			
7 The student plots data accurately.			
8 The graph reflects any uncertainty of measurement.			
9 Student indicates on the graph trends or lack of trends.			
10 The student employs colors, textures, labels, or other features to make the graph easier to read.			
11 If necessary, a key is given.			
12 The graph is neat and legible.			
Total			

G

Graph the Data

	Rating
The student clearly and accurately represented the data in an outstanding graph. The student placed the variables on the correct axes. The student used space masterfully and plotted all data correctly. The graph had a title, and all parts of the graph were accurately labeled. The student provided a clear key. The graph was neat and legible.	
The student selected an appropriate type of graph for the data. The variables are on the correct axes. The student used an appropriate scale with reasonable starting points and intervals on each axis so that the graph fit the space well. The student plotted the data correctly. The title was clear and described the two variables. The graph was neat and easy to read. The student provided a key.	
The student chose an inappropriate or incorrect type of graph. The student put the variables on the wrong axes. The student did not label the axes or labeled them inadequately. The scales were not appropriate, and the lines or bars did not fit the space well. The title was missing or inadequate. The graph was not easy to read or understand. The student provided an inadequate key or did not provide one at all.	
The student completed work very poorly or did not complete it at all.	

Comments:

Performance-Task Assessment List

Summarize a Graph

Element	Assessment Points: Points Possible	Earned Assessment: STUDENT	Earned Assessment: TEACHER
1 The summary gives a reasonable interpretation of the data.			
2 The data are the basis of results that answer the research question.			
3 The student references both independent and dependent variables.			
4 The student clearly and accurately describes the relationship between the dependent and the independent variables.			
5 The summary is concise.			
6 The summary includes appropriate vocabulary, grammar, and complete sentences.			
7 The summary is neat and legible.			
Total			

Rubric
Summarize a Graph

	Rating
The student's summary was accurate and precise. The student used descriptions of the graph that accurately correlated with the data. Language mechanics were excellent. The student reached a clear conclusion about the research question. The student identified any inferences as such.	
The student's summary clearly and accurately stated the relationship between independent and dependent variables. The student reached a conclusion about the research question. The summary was concise and neat. Language mechanics were satisfactory.	
The student's summary inaccurately or unclearly stated the relationship between independent and dependent variables. The student reached no conclusion about the research question. The summary mixed statements of fact with inferences. The summary was not well organized, and its language mechanics were poor.	
The student completed work very poorly or did not complete it at all.	

Comments:

G

Develop a Consumer Decision-Making Study

Element	Points Possible	Earned Assessment STUDENT	TEACHER
1 The student selects a consumer product type to evaluate. The student clearly states why he or she selects this product type.			
2 The student thoughtfully develops a set of criteria by which to judge the product.			
3 The student thoughtfully plans a strategy to collect valid and reliable data about each criterion for each product.			
4 The student uses scientific methods to collect data for some of the criteria.			
5 The student thoroughly constructs a scoring system to assess each criterion.			
6 The student considers and minimizes sources of error.			
7 The student collects data in an organized manner so that it can be used.			
8 The student makes a final presentation of the data in a format that clearly communicates the results of the study.			
9 The student reaches a clear conclusion and supports it with data from the research.			
Total			

G

Develop a Consumer Decision-Making Study

	Rating
The student's work was excellent. It showed careful thought in the explanation for the product-type selection. The student obviously took great care to collect appropriate, valid, and reliable data. The student used scientific methods where appropriate. The student thoughtfully considered potential sources of error and worked to reduce their effects. The final format to display the findings was creative and clear. The presentation format communicated the findings in an understandable manner for the intended audience.	
The student selected a consumer product type to assess and provided a clear explanation for the product-type selection. The student planned a strategy to collect valid and reliable data on each criterion. The student used scientific methods where appropriate. The student considered potential sources of error and worked to reduce their effects. The student organized the data in a useful manner. The final presentation of the data was in a format that clearly conveyed the results of the tests to the intended audience.	
The student did not provide a clear explanation for why the product was selected for assessment. The student selected an inadequate and/or inappropriate set of criteria to test each sample. The strategy was not adequate to collect valid or reliable data. The student did not use scientific methods in an appropriate manner while testing the sample. The data collected was poorly organized. The student did not thoughtfully consider and/or control sources of error. The student used an unclear and/or incomplete final format to present the data and findings.	
The student completed work very poorly or did not complete it at all.	

Comments:

G

Performance-Task Assessment List
Draw a Diagram

Element	Points Possible	Earned Assessment STUDENT	Earned Assessment TEACHER
1 The title contributes to the meaning or purpose of the object, event, or process depicted in the diagram.			
2 The diagram clearly outlines the most important parts of an object, event, or process and how they relate or work together.			
3 If a process is depicted, arrows, numbers, or other graphic devices indicate the sequence.			
4 The student shows the correct sequence and a consistent scale for diagrams involving a process of change over time.			
5 Details, both drawn and printed, are scientifically accurate.			
6 When appropriate, the student adds color, pattern, texture, labels, or other details to improve accuracy or to clarify the diagram's intent.			
7 The student uses a visual device to make any magnifications or callouts apparent.			
8 The diagram is neat and presentable.			
Total			

G

Rubric
Draw a Diagram

	Rating
The student's diagram was outstanding in detail and accuracy. The title clearly conveyed the content of the diagram or diagram sequence. It was evident from the diagram and labels that the student had a thorough scientific understanding of the object, event, or process. The relationships among the parts and how they work together was displayed clearly. The student drew and labeled the diagram neatly and exceptionally well.	
The student's diagram was acceptable and included the elements for drawing an accurate and understandable diagram. The student used labels and a consistent scale. The diagram was neat and presentable.	
The student's diagram needed to be substantially improved. The diagram did not show all of the important parts of the object, event, or processes, nor did it explain completely how the object, event, or process worked. Labels were incorrect or missing. The student did not draw the diagram to a consistent scale. The diagram was not neat or presentable.	
The student completed work very poorly or did not complete it at all.	

Comments:

G

Performance-Task Assessment List
Design an Invention

Element	Points Possible	Earned Assessment STUDENT	Earned Assessment TEACHER
1 The student clearly states the purpose of the invention.			
2 A design for the invention shows its dimensions and parts. The student uses metric measurements whenever possible.			
3 An explanation of the design describes how the parts function and what materials the student will use to make the invention.			
4 The invention performs its intended function very well.			
5 The invention is durable and functions reliably.			
6 The invention is safe.			
7 The invention gets a high "green" rating for its eco-friendliness.			
8 The invention appeals to those who would use it.			
9 The invention is original or is a marked improvement of a previous invention.			
10 The written directions for the invention are clear and easy to follow.			
Total			

G

Design an Invention

	Rating
The student's invention was remarkably creative and solved a problem or served the purpose for which it was intended. The plan for the invention was of high technical quality. The invention worked very well and was attractive, safe, sturdy, and reliable. It was very eco-friendly. The directions were written very clearly and were easy to follow.	
The student described the purpose for the invention. The student made a clear and neat plan that showed the dimensions and parts of the invention. The student used metric measurements. The plan also showed how the parts work and of what materials the parts are made. The actual invention was safe and reliably performed its intended function. It was eco-friendly. The student included a set of complete directions.	
The student did not define the problem or the purpose for the invention. The plan for the invention was incomplete. It did not show the dimensions accurately or completely. It did not clearly show the parts and/or how they work. The actual invention did not work well, or was not eco-friendly. The set of instructions was missing, incomplete, or difficult to follow.	
The invention was a copy, did not work, or was incomplete. There were no instructions given for the invention.	

Comments:

Performance-Task Assessment List

Write a Lab Report

Element	Points Possible	Earned Assessment STUDENT	TEACHER
Introduction			
1 The introduction states the independent and dependent variable without stating what the effect actually is.			
2 The student gives the name(s) of the experimenter(s).			
3 The student concisely summarizes the project, including the statement of the problem, the hypothesis, the procedures, the main results, and the conclusions (not to exceed 250 words).			
Statement of the Problem			
4 The student summarizes background information about the problem.			
5 The student cites relevant literature.			
6 The student states the hypothesis clearly. The hypothesis explains the influence of the independent variable on the dependent variable.			
Experimental Design			
7 Procedures for controlling and measuring variables through repeated trials are easy to follow. (See Performance-Task Assessment List for Design an Experiment, page 315.)			
Data Collection and Display			
8 Refer to the Performance-Task Assessment List for Complete a Data Table, page 329.			
9 Refer to the Performance-Task Assessment List for Graph the Data, page 331.			
Data Analysis			
10 Refer to the Performance-Task Assessment List for Analyze Data, page 319.			
Conclusion			
11 The student evaluates the hypothesis clearly.			
12 The student makes and justifies extrapolations from the data.			
13 The student makes connections to other studies, if appropriate.			
14 The student makes recommendations for further study.			
Total			

G

Write a Lab Report

	Rating
The student's lab report was excellent. It was well organized and thoughtfully presented. The statement of the problem included a description of how the problem was identified, a clear statement of the hypothesis, a more specific prediction of the relationship between the independent and dependent variables, if applicable, and a summary of relevant literature. The overall impression of validity and reliability was strong. It was clear that the student had masterful command of scientific methods. Language mechanics were excellent and the report was coherent and concise.	
The introduction to the student's lab report included the name(s) of the experimenter(s) and the title, the independent and dependent variables, if applicable, and a concise summary of the entire experiment. The statement of the problem included a description of how the problem was identified, a statement of the hypothesis, and a summary of relevant literature. Data was organized into charts and/or tables with correct titles and labels, and also was correctly put into graphs. It was clear that the student understood the science involved in the experiment and had a satisfactory command of scientific methods. Language mechanics were good and the report was presentable.	
The student's lab report included an incomplete or unclear introduction and summary. In the statement of the problem, the reason for the experiment was not clear and/or the hypothesis was inappropriate or awkward. The experimental design could not be duplicated from the information provided and/or there were significant errors in the experimental design. The data was poorly organized and/or it was used incorrectly in graphs that were poorly drawn. The student had a poor mastery of the science concepts and of scientific methods. Errors occurred in language mechanics. The student wrote a low-quality report.	
The student completed work very poorly or did not complete it at all.	

Comments:

G

Performance-Task Assessment List

Draw a Map

Element	Assessment Points: Points Possible	Earned Assessment: STUDENT	Earned Assessment: TEACHER
1 The title indicates the map's purpose.			
2 The legend includes all features and symbols that appear on the map.			
3 An arrow or compass rose indicates north and orients the viewer.			
4 A scale bar is present and labeled.			
5 The map itself includes only necessary details.			
6 Labels identify important features, which are accurately placed and spelled correctly.			
7 The student uses a scale to show accurate relationships among the map's components, such as the sizes of the states of the United States in relation to each other. The student also considers the scale of the map in relation to the size of the page and amount of information on it.			
8 If appropriate, the student accurately draws and labels lines of latitude and longitude.			
9 The student uses color, shading, or shapes to indicate land/water features, biomes, topography, or other features of importance.			
10 The overall design of the map is balanced, attractive, legible, and easy to read.			
Total			

Draw a Map

	Rating
The student drew an outstanding map. It was attractive and very easy to use and understand. The student included an appropriate amount of information and detail and made use of design elements that rendered the map attractive and useful.	
The student's map was adequate, using all or most of the elements listed on the assessment list.	
The student's map needed to be revised. The map included too much detail and was confusing and/or difficult to read or lacked detail and was not very useful. The scale bar or parts of the legend were missing. There were misspellings in the labels, or the labels were not placed correctly. The map was not attractive and did not make use of color, shading, shape, or other design elements.	
The student completed the map very poorly or did not complete it at all.	

Comments:

Performance-Task Assessment List

Design a Data Table

Element	Assessment Points: Points Possible	Earned Assessment: STUDENT	Earned Assessment: TEACHER
1 The table includes a title that indicates what information is presented.			
2 The table is organized in a way that is appropriate for the data being presented.			
3 The table is divided into columns and rows.			
4 The column headings indicate what items are being compared.			
5 Row headings, if used, indicate specific characteristics being compared in the items of the columns.			
6 The student records relevant data in the appropriate places of the table.			
7 The table is neat and legible.			
Total			

G

Design a Data Table

	Rating
The student's data table was excellent. The title, column, and row headings were clear and related to the data presented. The table headings and data were neat and legible.	
The student's data table was adequate. It included all elements and was neat and presentable. The title or headings might need to be revised to connect more closely with the data presented.	
The student's table was incomplete. Several elements were missing and/or were not specific or relevant. The student did not present the table neatly.	
The student completed work very poorly or did not complete it at all.	

Comments:

G

Make and Use a Classification System

Element	Points Possible	Earned Assessment STUDENT	TEACHER
1 The student begins the classification system with the most general characteristics and proceeds to the most specific characteristics.			
2 The chosen characteristics are part of the essential nature of the objects being classified.			
3 Several people can use the classification system with the same set of objects and classify them in the same way.			
4 New objects that are related can be classified using this classification system.			
5 The classification system can be modified to work with new classes of objects.			
Total			

G

Make and Use a Classification System

	Rating
The student's classification system used characteristics that are essential to the nature of the objects being classified. Classifications flowed smoothly from general to specific through a logical series of specifications. The classification system was especially easy to use. It also worked exceptionally well when classifying new and related objects.	
The student's classification system used characteristics that are necessary to the nature of the objects being classified. The steps flowed from general to specific through a logical series of decisions. Most people using this classification system independently classified objects in the same way. The classification system could be used with new objects and could be modified to better fit and expand the collection of objects classified.	
The student's classification system was only partially usable. Several people using the classification system made some similar decisions, but other classification decisions differed greatly. The final result was that objects were not classified in the same way.	
The classification system did not work or had not been completed.	

Comments:

Performance-Task Assessment List
Design and Construct a Model

Element	Assessment Points		
	Points Possible	Earned Assessment	
		STUDENT	TEACHER
1 The student gives a clear explanation of how the model demonstrates the science concepts it represents.			
2 The student draws a clear plan for the model. The plan shows dimensions and parts. The student uses metric measurements.			
3 The plan includes an explanation of how the model simulates the real item. The explanation includes a description of how the model differs from the real item.			
4 The constructed model is sturdy and simulates the elements of the real item.			
5 Color, labels, and other such devices enhance what the model is intended to show.			
6 The model is neat and presentable.			
7 The model is safe to use.			
Total			

G

Design and Construct a Model

	Rating
The student's model clearly and cleverly demonstrated the science concept(s) it was intended to show. The plan was of high technical quality. The model simulated extremely well the elements of the real item it was intended to demonstrate. The model was of very high artistic and technical quality. The model was safe and eye-catching.	
The student satisfactorily described the science concepts the model was intended to show. It was clear that the student understood the science concepts. The model simulated the elements of the real item it was intended to demonstrate. The constructed model was sturdy but lacked creativity. The model was safe and presentable.	
The student did not explain the science concepts that the model was intended to show. It was unclear how well the student knew the science concepts. The explanation of how the model is similar to and dissimilar from the real item was incomplete or inaccurate. The constructed model did not work well, if at all. The model was unsafe, and the presentation was careless.	
The student completed the model poorly and inaccurately or did not complete it at all.	

Comments:

G

Design a Science Fair Display

Element	Points Possible	Earned Assessment STUDENT	TEACHER
Background			
❶ The student concisely states the background for the problem.			
❷ The student clearly states the hypothesis and a prediction.			
Procedure			
❸ The student clearly describes the procedure and includes the following: identification of independent and dependent variables; description of how the independent variable changes and is measured; description of how the dependent variable is measured; strategy for keeping other factors constant; strategy for a control; strategy for repeated trials.			
Data			
❹ The student correctly draws charts and/or tables. (See Performance-Task Assessment List for Design a Data Table, page 345.)			
❺ The student correctly displays graphs. (See Performance-Task Assessment List for Graph the Data, page 331.)			
❻ The student summarizes data analyses. (See Performance-Task Assessment List for Summarize a Graph, page 333.)			
Conclusion			
❼ The student clearly states major findings.			
❽ The student accurately makes key points of interpretation.			
❾ The student states questions for further study.			
❿ The student provides a bibliography page in proper form.			
Other			
⓫ The narratives contain no grammatical errors.			
⓬ Graphics are attractive and legible.			
⓭ Props add to the clarity and interest of the display.			
⓮ The display is informative and attractive.			
Total			

G

Design a Science Fair Display

	Rating
The student's display was outstanding. It was informative and attractive. It clearly indicated that the student had mastered the science and the scientific methods involved. The statement of the problem, the hypothesis, specific predictions, an explanation of the design, and a display of data in charts and/or graphs helped the audience quickly understand the entire experiment.	
The student's display was eye-catching. It was attractive and all the parts seemed to fit together without being crowded. The student organized the statement of the problem, the hypothesis, the prediction, the summary of the experimental design, the data charts and/or graphs, and a good evaluation of the hypothesis so that the audience could understand the entire experiment quickly. It was obvious that the student had a basic knowledge of the science and scientific methods involved. The student provided examples of the experimental equipment to demonstrate elements and/or results of the experiment. These materials added interest and helped the audience learn more from the display.	
The student's display was unorganized and cluttered. It did not present a clear question, process, and resulting data. Some elements of the experimental design were missing or poorly represented. After several minutes of study, the audience was still unsure of the student's purpose and conclusions. There might have been flaws in the experimental design. Many mechanical errors existed in the narrative. Overall, the equipment displayed added little real information for the audience.	
The student completed work very poorly or did not complete it at all.	

Comments:

G

Illustrate a Scientific Object

Element	Points Possible	Earned Assessment STUDENT	Earned Assessment TEACHER
Assessment Points			
1 The student shows appropriate and accurate details of structure.			
2 The drawings show an appropriate number of views of the object, so that the object is represented in its entirety.			
3 All drawings use the same scale, which is shown clearly. The scale is metric.			
4 The student's illustration has accurate details of color, pattern, texture, and/or other physical characteristics.			
5 If appropriate, the student has accurately shown the relationship of the object to its surroundings.			
6 If appropriate, the student has accurately shown the relationship between the structure and function of the object.			
7 Text accompanies the drawing and explains the science that the drawing is intended to show.			
8 The student uses labels accurately.			
9 Drawings are neat and presentable.			
Total			

G

Rubric
Illustrate a Scientific Object

	Rating
The student's drawing was striking and realistic. The detail was meticulous. The student consistently used a very precise metric scale. The student drew enough views of the object to provide the audience with a complete picture of its structure. The student used labels to help convey information. The student employed principles of artistic composition well in the drawing.	
The student's drawing showed the details of the structure of the object. The student drew the object in a metric scale, which was clearly marked. Ample views of the object were drawn in order to provide the audience with an accurate picture of the structures under study. The student used labels to provide needed information. The drawing was neat and presentable.	
The student's drawing did not show much detail of the structure. It was not drawn to a consistent scale. The scale was not metric. The student did not use details of color, pattern, and texture well. Labels were incorrect or lacking. The drawing was not neat.	
The student completed work very poorly or did not complete it at all.	

Comments:

G

Design a Booklet or a Pamphlet

Element	Points Possible	Earned Assessment STUDENT	Earned Assessment TEACHER
Assessment Points			
1 There is a clear theme throughout the booklet or pamphlet.			
2 The student organizes chapters or sections to support the theme.			
3 Chapters or sections have clear main ideas.			
4 The student supports main ideas with details.			
5 It is clear that the student understands the science concepts relevant to the assignment.			
6 Original thinking is clearly evident.			
7 The student identifies information sources properly.			
8 Diagrams, pictures, and other graphics are well made, appropriate, and add to the overall effectiveness of the booklet or pamphlet.			
9 The student follows the proper format.			
10 The student produces high-quality writing.			
11 The work is neat, legible, and presentable.			
12 The work communicates well with the intended audience.			
13 The work is creative and interesting.			
Total			

G

Rubric
Design a Booklet or a Pamphlet

	Rating
The student produced exemplary work. There was a clear, focused theme for the entire work, and each component supported it well. The supporting details enhanced the quality of the main ideas and were woven skillfully into the work. The student properly referenced sources. The student followed the proper format. There were no grammatical errors.	
The student's work was satisfactory. There was a theme for the entire piece, and each component supported it. The supporting details added to the quality of the main ideas and did not appear to be "stuck on" or listlike. The student referenced appropriate information from a variety of sources. The student used the proper format. There were few grammatical errors.	
The student's work was weak. It did not accomplish its purpose well, nor did it communicate effectively with the intended audience. The theme was not clear. The components seemed "stuck on" or listlike. It was not clear if the student understood the science concepts related to this project. The student did not reference sources well. The student did not use the proper format. The work contained grammatical errors that interfered with the meaning.	
The work was very weak or was not completed.	

Comments:

G

Plan and Display a Bulletin Board

Element	Assessment Points		
	Points Possible	Earned Assessment	
		STUDENT	TEACHER
1 The theme of the bulletin board is immediately apparent.			
2 The student accurately states the appropriate science concepts.			
3 Adequate and accurate information supports the science concepts.			
4 The display works visually. It is not too crowded. It is organized, and it draws and holds the attention of the audience for which it was intended.			
5 If there is a sequence to see, it is easy to follow.			
6 Pictures, diagrams, graphs, and other visuals add to the quality of information. They are clear and easy to understand.			
7 Printed material is easy to read.			
8 The bulletin board is neat and presentable.			
Total			

G

Plan and Display a Bulletin Board

	Rating
The student's bulletin board was very attractive. Not only did the student present the science in an accurate, interesting, and understandable way, but it was also obvious that the student understood the science concepts and was able to expand on them.	
The student's bulletin board caught and held the attention of the audience for which it was intended. The audience could easily study the display. The information was appropriate to the task and showed that the student understood the basic science concepts.	
The student's bulletin board display was cluttered or otherwise unattractive. The theme was unclear and/or the science presented was inaccurate or incomplete. The visuals and text were unorganized or too small to be easily studied.	
The student completed work very poorly or did not complete it at all.	

Comments:

Produce a Cartoon or a Graphic Novel

Element	Points Possible	Earned Assessment	
		STUDENT	TEACHER
1 One or more characters portray important elements of the science lesson.			
2 The characters are interesting and appropriate to the topic.			
3 The theme is appropriate to the science topic and is clearly evident.			
4 Captions and dialogue present the science concepts and supporting information accurately.			
5 Drawings present the science concepts and supporting information accurately.			
6 The artwork is creative and interesting.			
7 The quality of the artwork is high.			
8 The story line, which is interesting to the intended audience, is based on valid science.			
9 The entire cartoon or graphic novel is appropriate, neat, and presentable.			
Total			

G

Produce a Cartoon or a Graphic Novel

	Rating
The student's cartoon or graphic novel was very well done. The central character(s) was both realistic and portrayed the central theme of this science lesson. The cartoon or graphic novel not only presented the science lesson in an accurate and interesting way, but all of the artwork was creative and well executed.	
The student's cartoon or graphic novel included an interesting character or characters. The characters portrayed central themes from the science lesson, though the connection was not always clear. The story included the essential science concepts that were conveyed through visuals, dialogue, and/or captions. The artwork was of acceptable quality. The work was appropriate and presentable.	
The student's cartoon or graphic novel character or characters did not have much depth. The science lesson was unclear and/or inaccurate. The story was weak and/or did not flow smoothly. The artwork was poorly executed. It was not neat, presentable, or appropriate.	
The student completed work very poorly or did not complete it at all.	

Comments:

G

Performance-Task Assessment List
Design and Construct a Display

Element	Points Possible	Earned Assessment	
		STUDENT	TEACHER
1 The display has a clear theme that encompasses the science concepts studied.			
2 The physical objects in the display coordinate well with the theme.			
3 The student clearly and accurately explains the science concepts with written descriptions.			
4 The graphics help convey the theme.			
5 The organization is clear, creative, and thoughtful. The student coordinates the physical objects and the graphics.			
6 The display is attractive and presentable.			
Total			

G

Design and Construct a Display

	Rating
The student's display was eye-catching and conveyed a strong message. The student's written descriptions clearly and accurately explained the science concepts involved. The physical objects were particularly well-suited to the theme. The graphics were done with artistic and technical skill. There was neither too much nor too little in the display.	
The student's theme for the display was appropriate to the science concepts shown. The student selected and arranged the physical objects that enabled observers to recognize the theme. Written descriptions accurately explained the science concepts involved. The student thoughtfully organized and coordinated the physical objects and the graphics. The display accomplished its purpose with the intended audience.	
The student's theme was not appropriate to the science concepts assigned. The selection and organization of physical objects showed little thought or effort. The student did not write descriptions, or the descriptions the student did write did not clearly and accurately explain the science concepts involved. The display was neither neat nor presentable. The display did not accomplish its purpose with the intended audience.	
The student completed work very poorly or did not complete it at all.	

Comments:

G

Performance-Task Assessment List

Investigate a Controversial Issue

Element	Points Possible	Earned Assessment	
		STUDENT	TEACHER
1 The student clearly states the alternative positions.			
2 The student clearly states the criteria for choosing his or her position.			
3 The student considers the audience when making the list of criteria.			
4 The student thoroughly researches each position.			
5 The student thoughtfully states support for his or her argument.			
6 The student evaluates information sources for objectivity and accuracy.			
7 The student properly references information from research.			
8 The student thoughtfully states his or her reasons for not supporting an opposing position.			
9 If working in a group, each person studying the controversial issue understands the reasons for and against each position.			
10 The student uses an appropriate form of discussion, negotiation, and compromise.			
11 The student presents the alternative positions for each criterion.			
Total			

Copyright © Glencoe/McGraw-Hill, a division of The McGraw-Hill Companies, Inc.

G

Rubric
Investigate a Controversial Issue

	Rating
The student researched the positions exceptionally well. The student gave a thoughtful analysis for each position and prepared arguments for each position. The student strongly and eloquently supported the chosen position. If group work was involved, everyone understood the arguments for each position and was able to expand on them.	
The student stated the position in the controversy and made a thoughtful list of criteria to evaluate each position. The student researched each position and prepared information to support each position but sometimes misstated the argument. The student evaluated the quality of the information sources and clearly selected both objective and accurate information. If two or more people were involved in the work, each understood the arguments involved.	
The student did not clearly state the positions. The list of criteria to evaluate each position was incomplete and/or not fully appropriate. The student did not explore the positions adequately. The student used biased or unreliable information. If two or more people were involved, they did not use decision-making strategies.	
The student completed work very poorly or did not complete it at all.	

Comments:

Performance-Task Assessment List
Compose a Letter to an Editor

Element	Points Possible	Earned Assessment	
		STUDENT	TEACHER
1 The letter includes facts and information that demonstrate knowledge of science concepts.			
2 The student maintains a balance and avoids extreme positions or overstatements.			
3 The letter anticipates and responds to opposing viewpoints.			
4 The student's research goes beyond the scope of classroom activities.			
5 The student clearly states the main idea.			
6 The student gives accurate and forceful supporting details and information.			
7 The student uses and correctly references unbiased sources.			
8 The student's references for sources of information adds emphasis and effect.			
9 The letter's tone is rational and logical.			
10 The student consistently maintains the style of the letter throughout.			
11 The letter effectively gets the attention of the audience.			
12 There are no grammatical errors.			
13 The letter is well organized.			
Total			

G

Compose a Letter to an Editor

	Rating
The student's letter was impressively written and well crafted. The letter was scientifically accurate. The writer was able to capture and maintain the audience's attention. The student provided insights that went beyond the material read and discussed in class. The letter was concise and grammatically error-free.	
The student's letter was well crafted. The student demonstrated a basic knowledge of the science concepts discussed. The writing was organized around a central issue connected to the problem. The student included facts to support arguments. The writer was able to capture the attention of the audience and was effective in establishing a position through the use of facts and logic. The letter was mostly free of mechanical errors.	
The student had not mastered or used more than one or two of the elements of a good letter. The work contained generalizations that were not supported. The student made no attempt to give the science behind the issue. The student did not have a grasp of the issue nor a clear position to argue. There were multiple grammatical errors and flaws in organization.	
The letter was replete with scientific errors and/or misinformation or was not completed.	

Comments:

G

Performance-Task Assessment List

Write a Newspaper Article

Element	Assessment Points: Points Possible	Earned Assessment: STUDENT	Earned Assessment: TEACHER
1 All facts, general and scientific, are correct.			
2 Quotes are accurate.			
3 The student uses quotes but does not build the article on them.			
4 The writing flows well. It does not read like the minutes of a meeting.			
5 The focus of the article is evident from the first paragraph.			
6 The article immediately captures a reader's interest.			
7 The student writes concisely. There is as much news as possible in as little space as possible.			
8 The student includes enough details to sufficiently support the article.			
9 The student writes to communicate with the appropriate audience.			
10 The student uses humor appropriately and positively.			
11 The writer is truthful.			
12 There are no grammatical errors.			
13 The headline is both catchy and appropriate to the article.			
14 Photographs or other images relate to the article and enhance its message.			
15 The captions for the images are accurate, correctly formatted, and properly placed.			
Total			

Write a Newspaper Article

	Rating
The student wrote an exceptional article. It conveyed the story in a smooth and engaging style. It held the reader's interest throughout. The student worked especially appropriate quotes and details seamlessly into the article. Photographs were informative, added much to the story, and showed active rather than passive poses. The headline was memorable.	
The student wrote an interesting and concise article. The theme was apparent, and the article flowed smoothly as it developed. Appropriate details supported the theme. It was clear that the student had a basic knowledge of science concepts. Photographs were clear and interesting. The headline was appropriate to the story and captured the reader's attention.	
The student's article did not read smoothly and did not keep the reader's attention. The theme was unclear, and the article was not organized well. Details were missing or inappropriate. The student applied science concepts incorrectly. Photographs were uninteresting and of poor quality. The headline was not memorable.	
The student completed work very poorly or did not complete it at all.	

Comments:

G

Prepare and Give an Oral Presentation

Element	Points Possible	Earned Assessment STUDENT	Earned Assessment TEACHER
Contents			
❶ The student uses science concepts accurately.			
❷ Accurate supporting details explain the concepts.			
❸ The student uses vocabulary appropriate to both the science content and the audience.			
❹ The student uses visuals, including pictures, diagrams, photographs, videos, flow charts, and props appropriately to support the presentation.			
❺ There is a clear introduction, an organized body, and a concise conclusion.			
Presentation			
❻ The student masterfully employs vocal qualities, such as speaking rate, volume, articulation, and inflection.			
❼ The student uses humor appropriately and positively.			
❽ The student effectively uses body language, such as eye contact, posture, and gestures.			
❾ When necessary, the speaker uses appropriate pauses and gives the audience time to think.			
❿ The speaker responds well to questions.			
Total			

G

Prepare and Give an Oral Presentation

	Rating
The student made an excellent presentation. He or she had extensive knowledge of the science content and used superb oral presentation skills to demonstrate it. The student's strategies, such as visual aids, props, and/or humor, were especially effective. The speaker involved the audience and interacted with it at the appropriate times.	
The student clearly knew the subject matter. The student used science concepts correctly. Everyone in the audience could see the visual aids, which were interesting and clear. The speaker was enthusiastic, spoke audibly, and used eye contact and other body language to increase the effectiveness of the presentation. The speaker involved the audience and paced the presentation well.	
The student did not have a strong command of the topic. The student did not use science concepts well, and the presentation lacked supporting details. Visual aids were poor or lacking. The presentation was more like a reading than an oral presentation. The student did not employ characteristics like volume, inflection, and body language. The student did not involve the audience in the presentation.	
The student completed work very poorly or did not complete it at all.	

Comments:

G

Write a Poem

Element	Points Possible	Earned Assessment	
		STUDENT	TEACHER
1 The science topic of the poem is evident.			
2 The poem's title connects to the lines which follow it.			
3 If the student uses line breaks, they help give the poem special interest or meaning.			
4 The poem uses specific details that create pictures with words.			
5 If the poem is traditional, the student arranges words to emphasize certain sounds, such as repeated consonant or vowel sounds, repeated words or word phrases, or rhyming words.			
6 The poem flows and uses poetic techniques that typically appear in the form of poetry chosen; e.g., alliteration, assonance, consonance, meter, rhythm, verse, rhyme, refrain, simile, metaphor, line breaks, and other techniques.			
7 The poem, if handwritten, is legible.			
Total			

G

Rubric
Write a Poem

	Rating
The student wrote an exceptional poem. The student expanded on the scientific topic throughout the poem. The student carefully selected powerful, appropriate, or interesting words, phrases and lines for the poem. The student effectively used words to create mental pictures. Lines had the appropriate rhythm, rhyme, or syllable count of the chosen poetry form. The student wrote neatly, if the poem was handwritten.	
The student wrote an excellent poem that reflected the scientific topic throughout. The student followed the appropriate rhythm, rhyme, or syllable count for the chosen poetry form. If the poem was handwritten, the student wrote neatly.	
The student needed to revise the poem substantially. Although there was a topic, it was either unclear or was not carried throughout the poem. There were few details, or the poem did not read well. The student did not attempt to use imagery or other poetic techniques. If the poem was handwritten, the student did not write neatly.	
The student completed work very poorly or did not complete it at all.	

Comments:

G

Create a Poster

Element	Assessment Points		
	Points Possible	Earned Assessment	
		STUDENT	TEACHER
1 A title helps to identify the theme, though it is clear without the title.			
2 Appropriate and accurate main ideas support the theme.			
3 Appropriate and accurate details support the main ideas.			
4 There is a wholeness about the poster. It does not seem like a collection of random information.			
5 The information in the poster is accurate and shows that the student thoroughly understands the science concepts.			
6 Space, shapes, textures, and colors provide information and add to the overall effectiveness of the poster.			
7 Pictures, photographs, drawings, diagrams, graphs, or other visual devices add to the overall effectiveness of the poster.			
8 The poster's format is appropriate to the task and to the audience for which it is intended.			
9 The poster accomplishes its purpose with its intended audience.			
10 The poster is creative and interesting.			
11 The poster is neat, legible, and presentable.			
Total			

G

Create a Poster

	Rating
The student's poster was creative, and it communicated information to the audience in an excellent manner. Appropriate details supported the main ideas. Information was complete and accurate. All visuals added clarity and information. The work was very neat and organized.	
The student's poster demonstrated a clear theme. The details supported the main ideas. The student used concepts and information that showed the student understood the science concepts related to the project. Visuals added clarity and information. The work was neat.	
The student's poster was difficult to understand even when the student explained its purpose. The poster seemed like a collection of pieces without a main idea to link them together. The student did not demonstrate a mastery of the core curriculum related to the project. The student did not use visuals or used them inappropriately. The work was not neat.	
The student completed work very poorly or did not complete it at all.	

Comments:

G

Write a Research Report

Element	Assessment Points		
	Points Possible	**Earned Assessment**	
		STUDENT	**TEACHER**
1 The report includes a title page and an outline.			
2 The introductory paragraphs state and define the topic clearly.			
3 The body of the report includes facts that support the topic.			
4 The student uses a variety of sources of information.			
5 The student quotes and cites information directly from sources.			
6 If the student uses the opinions or ideas of others, they are cited.			
7 If the student uses charts or diagrams, they help explain or clarify main points of the report.			
8 The student cites the sources of all statistical information.			
9 The student organizes and presents information in a clear, logical, and engaging manner.			
10 The student uses subheadings to show the report's organization.			
11 The closing paragraphs summarize the main points and draw conclusions based on presented research.			
12 The bibliography is complete and follows guidelines for citing books, periodicals, online sources, and other information sources.			
13 The report uses correct spelling, grammar, and punctuation.			
14 The student uses a word-processing program for the report and follows formatting specifications.			
Total			

G

Write a Research Report

	Rating
The student's research report was superior. It was highly organized, included detailed explanations, and was well written. The topic was thoroughly covered, with supporting information from a variety of sources. The ideas flowed smoothly and the writing style was engaging. The text showed an excellent command of grammar, spelling, and punctuation. It adhered to the guidelines for citing and documenting sources. The student's report was neat and followed formatting specifications.	
The student's research report was very good. It was well organized. The topic was covered, but the student used only a limited number and variety of sources. The text was well written with few errors in grammar, spelling, punctuation, or source documentation. The student's report was neat and followed formatting specifications.	
The student's research report was incomplete and needed to be revised substantially. There were problems with organization. The student did not sufficiently support ideas with sources or did not explain ideas well. There were weaknesses in grammar, punctuation, spelling, and sentence structure.	
The student completed work very poorly or did not complete it at all.	

Comments:

G

Write and Perform a Skit

Element	Assessment Points		
	Points Possible	Earned Assessment	
		STUDENT	TEACHER
1 The central theme of the skit is a science concept that is appropriate to the assignment.			
2 The student presents the science concept accurately.			
3 The actors' parts convey important science concepts and information.			
4 The story line of the skit is interesting and helps to present the science concepts.			
5 Each actor's actions help convey the science concepts accurately.			
6 The student chooses props and/or costumes well. They support the characters and enhance the presentation of the science concepts.			
7 Music and other sound effects support the story line and help present the science concepts.			
8 Dialogue supports the development of the characters, the story line, and the presentation of the science concepts.			
9 It is evident that the skit was rehearsed sufficiently.			
10 The audience could easily hear and see the actors in the skit.			
11 The skit is entertaining to the audience.			
Total			

G

Write and Perform a Skit

	Rating
The student's skit was very well done. The student used dialogue to support the characters' development and to present science information. The skit showed that the student clearly understood the science concepts related to the project.	
The student's skit had a central science theme that was evident from the story. The student used dialogue both for character development and to present the science information. The skit was entertaining to its intended audience.	
The student's skit lacked structure. Its science theme was unclear and/or inaccurately or poorly developed. The story strayed off-topic or was mundane. It appeared as though little thought or rehearsal went into the skit.	
The student completed work very poorly or did not complete it at all.	

Comments:

G

Prepare a Slide Show or a Photo Essay

Element	Assessment Points		
	Points Possible	Earned Assessment	
		STUDENT	TEACHER
1 The student composes each photo carefully to clearly show what he or she intends.			
2 Each photo is well focused and properly exposed.			
3 The photos have a clear theme.			
4 The student organizes the sequence of photos logically			
5 The photos have the intended effect on the audience.			
6 The student understands the science concepts related to the topic and chooses photos appropriately.			
7 Titles and captions contribute to the theme and purpose of the set of photos.			
8 For the photo essay, the student mounts and displays photos attractively and effectively.			
Total			

Prepare a Slide Show or a Photo Essay

	Rating
The student's slide show or photo essay was organized well and sequenced smoothly. The technical quality of the photos was excellent. The theme was precisely and engagingly presented. It was clear that the student understood the science concepts. For the photo essay, the student mounted and displayed the photos attractively.	
The student's slide show or photo essay offered a good presentation of the theme. The photos clearly showed what the student intended. The photos were organized and sequenced and contained a clear theme. The student clearly had a basic understanding of the science concepts of the theme. For the photo essay, the student mounted and displayed the photos satisfactorily.	
The student took photos that did not show the intended theme. The photos were not well organized. It was not clear that the student understood the science concepts. The student did not choose photos to present the theme to the intended audience. For the photo essay, the student did not mount and display the photos attractively.	
The student completed work very poorly or did not complete it at all.	

Comments:

G

Compose and Perform a Song with Lyrics

Element	Assessment Points		
	Points Possible	Earned Assessment	
		STUDENT	TEACHER
1 The melody is clear and distinct.			
2 If the student uses harmony, it supports and enhances the melody.			
3 Any rhythmic element present is on beat.			
4 The rhythmic element contributes to the song.			
5 The lyrics contain a main theme.			
6 Details in the lyrics support the main theme.			
7 The lyrics convey accurate scientific concepts.			
8 The song is appropriate for the intended audience.			
9 The singer remembers the lyrics and melody.			
10 The volume is reasonable.			
11 The student communicates the lyrics effectively through appropriate phrasing and dynamics.			
Total			

G

Rubric
Compose and Perform a Song with Lyrics

	Rating
Composition	
The student's music and lyrics had a main theme and were outstanding. The lyrics conveyed accurate scientific concepts. If the student used rhythmic elements, they were on beat and contributed to the overall mood and style of the song. The song was appropriate for the intended audience.	
The student's lyrics had a main theme. If the student used rhythmic elements, they contributed to the overall mood and style of the song. The lyrics conveyed accurate scientific concepts. The song was appropriate for the intended audience.	
The student's melody and lyrics did not contain main themes. The student used rhythmic elements, but they were offbeat and detracted from the song. The scientific content of the lyrics was inaccurate. The music and lyrics did not work well together.	
The student completed work very poorly or did not complete it at all.	
Performance	
The student's singing was exceptional. The student clearly conveyed the scientific meaning through the phrasing and style of the song.	
The student's singing was average. The student generally conveyed the scientific meaning through the song. The song was well-received.	
The student's singing was poor. It seemed that the song was not rehearsed. The phrasing or style of the song did not convey the meaning of the song.	
The student completed work very poorly or did not complete it at all.	

Comments:

G

Performance-Task Assessment List
Write a Summary

Element	Points Possible	Earned Assessment STUDENT	Earned Assessment TEACHER
1 The summary includes all of the main points and omits nonessential details.			
2 The student states the main idea in the first sentence and supports it with the sentences that follow.			
3 The student arranges main points logically.			
4 The student states important ideas in his or her own words, not the author's.			
5 The summary includes correct use of spelling, grammar, and punctuation.			
6 The concluding sentence ties the summary together and is an effective end.			
7 The student presents the summary well.			
Total			

G

Rubric
Write a Summary

	Rating
The student's summary was exemplary. The summary was brief, yet it presented all of the main scientific concepts and vocabulary clearly, logically, and in the writer's own words. The reader could easily understand the scientific concepts presented in the summary. The student presented the summary well.	
The student wrote a high-quality summary. The student presented all of the main scientific concepts in his or her own words. There were a few grammatical errors, but they did not interfere with the meaning of the summary. The student presented the summary well.	
The student's work was weak. The student did not include all main scientific concepts or vocabulary words. There was too much detail for some concepts or not enough detail for others. The student did not present the main ideas logically. The reader would have difficulty understanding the scientific concepts from the summary. The writing was not neat, or there were numerous errors in spelling, grammar, or punctuation.	
The student completed work very poorly or did not complete it at all.	

Comments:

G

Construct a Time Line

Element	Assessment Points		
	Points Possible	Earned Assessment	
		STUDENT	TEACHER
1 The time line includes a title that is appropriate for the entries listed.			
2 The time line is divided into the correct number of equal segments.			
3 The student labels dates on the correct segments of the time line in a left-to-right sequence.			
4 Dates and captions are accurate.			
5 If the student included illustrations, drawings, or photos, they contribute to an understanding of the text.			
6 The time line is neat, legible, and presentable.			
Total			

G

Construct a Time Line

	Rating
The student's time line was very well done. It gave a complete chronological history of the scientific topic presented in the title. The information was accurate, concise, and well written. The student used photographs or other illustrations to enhance the meaning of the entries and add interest. The product was neat and presentable.	
The student's time line was adequate. Although the student included many accurate entries, he or she might have omitted some or made others more concise. The product was neat and presentable.	
The student's time line needed to be substantially improved. The time segments were not of equal length. Although the entries of the time line were accurate, the student omitted major scientific events. Some entries were out of sequence or were not clear. The product was not neat or presentable.	
The student completed work very poorly or did not complete it at all.	

Comments:

G

Performance-Task Assessment List
Produce a Video

Element	Assessment Points		
	Points Possible	Earned Assessment	
		STUDENT	TEACHER
① The video has a clear science theme.			
② The video has a purpose; e.g., to inform, persuade, or provoke a reaction.			
③ The science concepts are appropriate to the topic.			
④ The student uses accurate information to support the science concepts.			
⑤ The scenes are appropriate to the theme.			
⑥ The scenes flow together and do not seem like a series of unconnected pieces.			
⑦ If the student uses music, titles, and special effects, they strongly support the theme and purpose of the video and help connect the scenes.			
⑧ The sound quality of the video is excellent.			
⑨ The video quality is excellent.			
⑩ The video is creative and interesting.			
⑪ The video achieves its purpose with the intended audience.			
Total			

G

Produce a Video

	Rating
The student's video effectively accomplished its purpose with the intended audience. The science concepts and supporting information were superb. The video was creative, interesting, informative, and technically excellent.	
The student's video was a good presentation of a science theme. The science concepts and supporting information were accurate. The video flowed smoothly and provided introductory and guiding information. The video was interesting and informative.	
The student's video had serious technical flaws. The video was disjointed; it seemed more like a series of pieces rather than a smooth story. The video did not accomplish its purpose with the intended audience.	
The student completed work very poorly or did not complete it at all.	

Comments:

G

Write a Fictional Story

Element	Assessment Points		
	Points Possible	Earned Assessment	
		STUDENT	TEACHER
1 There is a clear theme to the story.			
2 Science concepts in the story are accurate.			
3 The plot centers around, develops, and resolves a problem.			
4 The story has an engaging, interesting conflict that captures and holds the attention of the reader.			
5 Each event or episode is important to the plot.			
6 The plot develops logically.			
7 The student uses relevant details that enrich the story.			
8 The characters are consistent and believable.			
9 Characters develop through "showing" rather than "telling."			
10 The story has a consistent point of view.			
11 The writer describes the setting through believable details.			
12 The setting enhances the story.			
13 The title is appropriate, meaningful, and interesting.			
14 The writing is grammatically correct.			
15 The student provides evidence that he or she wrote substantial revisions.			
16 The work is neat and legible.			
Total			

G

Write a Fictional Story

	Rating
The student wrote a superior story. It was unusually eloquent, complete, and creative. The plot created and resolved a problem. The plot was logically sequenced. The story had a believable and detailed setting that included the theme. There was evidence of substantial revision. If handwritten, the story was very neat and legible.	
The student wrote an excellent story. The plot introduced and resolved a problem. The plot was sequenced, and each event was important to the meaning of the story. The story had a believable setting that enhanced the theme. There was evidence of revision.	
The student's story needed to be improved. Although there was a plot, it did not adequately introduce and/or resolve a problem. There were serious gaps in the plot, and the events were not arranged in a clear and logical order. The setting was incomplete or irrelevant to the plot. There was no clear theme, point, or message to the story. If handwritten, the story was not neat or legible.	
The work was very poorly done, did not have a plot, or was not completed.	

Comments:

G

Performance-Task Assessment List
Write a Nonfictional Story

Element	Points Possible	Earned Assessment STUDENT	Earned Assessment TEACHER
1 The introduction clearly states the thesis.			
2 The introduction clearly introduces the main ideas.			
3 The student uses concepts that are appropriate and accurate.			
4 Each paragraph has a topic sentence that is one of the main ideas.			
5 Each paragraph has appropriate and accurate supporting details.			
6 The conclusion sums up the story's points in an interesting, thoughtful, and unique manner.			
7 The student's own voice and style are evident throughout the story.			
8 The title is clear and informative.			
9 The writing is grammatically correct.			
10 The student uses visuals such as drawings, diagrams, or pictures in an appropriate way to add information and interest.			
Total			

G

Write a Nonfictional Story

	Rating
The student's writing was unusually insightful. It showed an exceptional grasp of the topic, task, audience, and purpose. The student used visuals to create interest and to give further information. The student's style was evident throughout the writing. The student used language extraordinarily well.	
The student's writing was excellent. It was clear that the student understood the task, audience, and purpose of the writing. The student used concepts that were appropriate and accurate. The reader could grasp the student's style throughout the writing. The student used visuals to add information. The writing was grammatically correct.	
The student's writing needed to be improved. Although the student attempted to complete the task as given, it was not entirely clear that he or she fully understood the task, audience, or purpose of the writing. The student remained focused on a single topic throughout much of the piece, but he or she had difficulty developing his or her thesis. The student might have included inappropriate or inaccurate supporting details. There were many mechanical errors.	
The student's writing was very poor, showing little attempt to complete the task given. There was an overall lack of focus, elaboration, organization, or the work was not completed.	

Comments:

G

Plan and Draw a Concept Map

Element	Assessment Points		
	Points Possible	Earned Assessment	
		STUDENT	TEACHER
❶ The set of concept words in the ovals is appropriate to the science topic.			
❷ The student organizes the set of concept words from most general to most specific.			
❸ There is an appropriate number of levels that correspond with the hierarchy (general to specific) of concept words.			
❹ The student uses linking words on the lines to connect concept words and to reflect the relationships among those concept words.			
❺ The student makes valid cross-links among concept words in different parts of the concept map.			
❻ The concept map has an appropriate title.			
❼ The concept map is easy to follow.			
❽ The student indicates prior knowledge and new knowledge.			
❾ The concept map is neat and legible.			
Total			

G

Plan and Draw a Concept Map

	Rating
The student's concept map was excellent, thoughtfully organized, and connected the concepts. There was an appropriate number of levels to the concept hierarchy, and there were some especially insightful cross-links. The student was very clear about which parts of the concept map represented his or her new learning. The map was easy to follow, neat, and legible.	
The student selected an appropriate set of concept words to include in the concept map. These concept words were arranged in a hierarchy from most general to most specific. There was an appropriate number of levels of this hierarchy. There were cross-links among concept words in different parts of the hierarchy. The student indicated which parts of the concept map represented his or her new learning. The map was neat, legible, and easy to follow.	
The student used some concept words inappropriately. Some important concept words were missing from the map. The hierarchy of the list of concept words had only a few levels. While the student made some connections correctly, the linking words the student used to show connections among concept words indicated incorrect connections. There were few, if any, cross-links. The concept map was not easy to follow, and it was not neat and presentable.	
The student completed work very poorly or did not complete it at all.	

Comments:

Performance-Task Assessment List

Sequence an Events Chain

Element	Assessment Points		
	Points Possible	Earned Assessment	
		STUDENT	TEACHER

Items in an Events Chain

1 The student includes scientifically accurate items.

2 The collection of items shows thoughtful selection of the most important elements.

3 The student states each item clearly.

4 The sequence is chronological and/or logical.

5 The title captures attention and accurately conveys the purpose of and information in the events chain.

6 Geometric forms, colors, textures, arrows, and other techniques add meaning and clarity to the events chain.

7 The events chain is neat and legible. It is not overcrowded, nor is it too sparse.

8 The events chain communicates well with its intended audience.

Written Explanation of Each Element of an Events Chain

9 The student states the main idea clearly.

10 Sufficient supporting details explain the main idea.

11 The student uses language correctly.

12 The writing is neat, legible, and concise.

Total

G

Sequence an Events Chain

	Rating
The student's events chain clearly and completely communicated its purpose to its intended audience. The student thoughtfully selected the collection of elements. The title attracted attention and conveyed the content of the events chain. Visuals added meaning and clarity to the events chain. Overall, it was very attractive, neat, and legible.	
The student used most of the elements involved in making a good events chain. The student selected the collection of items with a purpose in mind. The title attracted attention and conveyed the content of the events chain. Visuals added to the chain, but they could have been neater and more presentable.	
The student's events chain presented inaccuracies and/or misstated processes. The events chain was difficult to follow because of problems, such as overcrowding the page with ideas or misplaced elements. The student did not use visuals well. The events chain did not convey its intended message to its audience. It lacked organization and neatness.	
The student completed work very poorly or did not complete it at all.	

Comments:

G

Classify with a Spider Organizer

Element	Assessment Points		
	Points Possible	**Earned Assessment**	
		STUDENT	**TEACHER**
1 The student uses geometric shapes. There is a large central shape. Other shapes surround it.			
2 The student uses geometric shapes throughout the spider organizer to convey relationships among elements.			
3 The topic and main ideas are clear.			
4 The student lists the topic in the central shape and places main ideas connected to the topic in surrounding shapes.			
5 An appropriate number of details supports each main idea.			
6 The student includes enough information to indicate that he or she understands the concepts.			
7 The information is accurate.			
8 Space, shapes, textures, and colors provide information and add to the effectiveness of the organizer.			
9 Pictures, drawings, designs, and other graphics provide information and add to the effectiveness of the organizer.			
10 The spider organizer is neat, clear, and legible.			
Total			

G

Rubric
Classify with a Spider Organizer

	Rating
The student's spider organizer was outstanding. The appropriate geometric figures displayed the main topic, ideas, and details clearly. The details for each qualifier supported the main ideas effectively. Visuals added clarity and information. The spider organizer was immaculate, very clear, and presentable.	
The topic and main ideas of the student's spider organizer were clear. The geometric figures displayed the main topic, ideas, and details clearly. The details for each qualifier supported the main ideas. The student used concepts and information to show that he or she understood the assignment. The organizer was clear, neat, and presentable.	
The student's spider organizer was difficult to understand. It seemed either overcrowded or sparse. The main ideas did not seem to connect to the topic or were not similar in value. Some information was incomplete or inaccurate. There were no visuals. The work was not clear, neat, or presentable. There were many mechanical flaws.	
The student completed work very poorly or did not complete it at all.	

Comments:

G

Performance-Task Assessment List

Compare and Contrast Using a Venn Diagram

Element	Assessment Points: Points Possible	Earned Assessment: STUDENT	Earned Assessment: TEACHER
1 The student clearly identifies the two objects or events to compare and contrast.			
2 The student makes a thoughtful list of characteristics unique and important to the first object or event. The student uses appropriate and accurate information to make this list.			
3 The student makes a thoughtful list of characteristics unique and important to the second object or event. The student uses appropriate and accurate information to make this list.			
4 The student chooses characteristics that show a clear understanding of the science involved to contrast the two objects or events.			
5 The student makes a list of important characteristics common to both objects or events. The student uses appropriate and accurate information to make this list.			
6 The student chooses a common set of characteristics that shows a clear understanding of the science involved.			
7 There is an order within the lists that shows a priority for the most important characteristics.			
8 The Venn diagram is neat and legible.			
Total			

Note: This Performance-Task Assessment List for a Venn diagram can be adapted for use as a Pro/Con Graphic Organizer.

G

Compare and Contrast Using a Venn Diagram

	Rating
The student thoughtfully selected and stated the characteristics that distinguish and identify commonalities of the two objects (or events). The overall science concepts were clear. The order of the lists demonstrated a strong understanding of the science involved.	
The student showed that he or she understood the science by selecting a set of unique characteristics for each object (or event). A set of characteristics common to the objects (or events) revealed a basic understanding of the science. The Venn diagram was neat and legible.	
The student chose characteristics to compare and contrast the objects (or events) that showed little understanding of the important science concepts. The lists seemed unorganized and/or randomly organized.	
The student completed work very poorly or did not complete it at all.	

Comments:

G

Engage in Group Work

Element	Points Possible	Earned Assessment	
		STUDENT	TEACHER
1 The student comes to the group prepared to cooperate and contribute.			
2 As a member of the group, the student completes all assigned individual tasks on time and shows good workmanship.			
3 The student participates in a constructive manner.			
4 The student encourages others to participate in a constructive manner.			
5 The student is a good, active listener.			
6 The student strongly and thoughtfully supports positions.			
7 The student disagrees with other group members courteously and respectfully.			
8 The student compromises well.			
9 The student shares responsibility while helping the group get the job done on time and according to directions.			
10 The student promotes positive interactions in the group.			
Total			

The table above has the heading **Assessment Points** spanning the Points Possible and Earned Assessment columns, with **Earned Assessment** spanning STUDENT and TEACHER.

G

Rubric
Engage in Group Work

	Rating
The student had highly developed group work skills. The student showed responsibility by being well prepared. The student contributed during discussions and actively listened to others. The student strongly supported his or her own opinions. The student promoted positive interactions within the group.	
The student showed responsibility by being prepared for group work and completing individual tasks on time. The student listened to others and was tolerant of divergent views. The student supported his or her own opinions and worked with the group. The student promoted positive interactions within the group.	
The student was not prepared for group work and did not complete individual tasks on time and/or with quality. The student contributed too little or excessively dominated group work. The student did not support his or her own position or was not willing to listen to others. The student was a poor team player and did not work to develop and carry out a plan to accomplish a task. The student did not promote positive interactions in the group.	
The student was a very poor group worker or did not participate at all.	

Comments:

Performance-Task Assessment List

Develop a Performance-Assessment Task

Element	Points Possible	Earned Assessment	
		STUDENT	TEACHER
1 The student assesses important concepts.			
2 The student assesses important process skills.			
3 The background statement is friendly and gives an interesting context for the task.			
4 The statement of the task describes the type of product(s) to make. The product is authentic, like one found in the real world.			
5 When the product is such that reasoning would not be clear, some preliminary work, such as making a graphic organizer, is part of the required task.			
6 The student provides Performance-Task Assessment Lists for the processes and products of this task. The student writes these lists with appropriate detail.			
7 The student regards self-assessment as an important part of the task.			
8 The student identifies a specific audience for the product. The audience has a real interest in the product.			
9 The purpose of the task encompasses what the product intends to accomplish for the student and/or for the audience of this product.			
10 The procedure provides appropriate structure to this task.			
11 The student allocates reasonable time to the task.			
12 The student properly addresses safety issues.			
Total			

G

Develop a Performance-Assessment Task

	Rating
The performance task engaged the student in a thoughtful, active project. It required the student to use important concepts, process skills, and work habits. It was clear that the assessor would be able to determine the student's competencies. The task was authentic because the student's products and/or performances and the processes used are like those in the real world.	
The student's concepts, process skills, and work habits were important. The task clearly defined the type of product or performance to be crafted. The purpose of the task clearly stated what the product was intended to accomplish. The student listed the procedure in appropriate detail and might have included reference to the Performance-Task Assessment Lists the student should use. The student addressed safety and time issues and made materials available.	
It was not clear that this task would allow the assessor to get a clear picture of how well the student could use concepts, process skills, and work habits. The products of the task were not well defined, and/or the goals were not well described. The procedure was not at the correct level of specificity for these students. The student did not adequately address safety, and materials were not appropriate or not available.	
The task was very poorly constructed and would not work or was not completed.	

Comments:

Performance-Task Assessment List
Prepare a Management Plan

Element	Assessment Points		
	Points Possible	Earned Assessment	
		STUDENT	TEACHER
1 The student completes the heading properly.			
2 The student writes a complete list of tasks.			
3 The tasks are specific.			
4 The target dates for completing all tasks are appropriate.			
5 The student thoughtfully considers a description of the barriers to successfully completing the project.			
6 The student thoughtfully considers a description of strategies for overcoming those barriers.			
7 The plan is neat and legible.			
Total			

G

Rubric
Prepare a Management Plan

	Rating
The student's management plan was highly organized and detailed. The student defined the barriers especially well, and action plans to overcome or avoid the barriers were clearly feasible. Because the student listed the elements in proper order and with complete details, it was clear that the student thought the project through.	
The student's management plan was organized and complete. The student listed the elements in order and detailed them sufficiently. The student thoughtfully considered potential barriers and planned to overcome each one. The plan was neat.	
The student's management plan was incomplete. Elements were missing and/or were not specific. The student might have listed elements in an incorrect order. The student did not identify barriers, and/or did not think about how to overcome them. The plan was not prepared neatly.	
The student completed work very poorly or did not complete it at all.	

Comments:

Copyright © Glencoe/McGraw-Hill, a division of The McGraw-Hill Companies, Inc.

Performance-Task Assessment List
Maintain a Science Journal

Element	Assessment Points		
	Points Possible	Earned Assessment	
		STUDENT	TEACHER
1 The student lists his or her name.			
2 The student dates all entries.			
3 The student explores many science concepts.			
4 Diagrams, sketches, and drawings indicate logical thought.			
5 The student organizes and writes observations in complete sentences.			
6 Questions show higher-order thinking such as analysis, synthesis, and evaluation.			
7 "What if . . . ?" statements show that the student considers relevant and interesting independent and dependent variables.			
8 Sketches of inventions and models show that the student understands science concepts.			
9 The student uses graphic organizers to structure observations.			
10 The student identifies problems and concerns, and provides possible solutions.			
11 The student identifies interesting and enjoyable elements and gives reasons for them.			
12 The student shows exploration as a learner.			
13 The student sets goals to improve study habits.			
14 The student includes lists of interesting information and ideas from sources, such as newspapers, magazines, television and the Internet.			
Total			

G

Maintain a Science Journal

	Rating
The student's science journal showed that he or she thoughtfully considered many elements of science and tackled some very tough concepts. The student revisited unanswered questions as he or she constructed answers. It was clear that the student was able to see himself or herself finding and solving problems and striving to improve work habits.	
The student's science journal was organized and complete. Many science concepts appeared in it, and it was clear that the student spent time and effort exploring ideas and phenomena through graphics and writing. The student evidenced good, clear thinking throughout. The student showed some ability to explore how he or she went about learning and set and followed some goals for improvement.	
The student's science journal was incomplete. There was little effort to include details. Little higher-order thinking was evident. There was not much evidence that the student understood himself or herself as a learner. The student did not explore his or her strengths and weaknesses.	
The student's science journal was incomplete and/or unorganized.	

Comments:

G

Performance-Task Assessment List
Compile a Science Portfolio

Element	Assessment Points		
	Points Possible	Earned Assessment	
		STUDENT	TEACHER

Categories for the Contents of the Portfolio

Element	Points Possible	Student	Teacher
1 *Range of thinking and creativity in science*—the collection of science items demonstrates thinking skills and creativity.			
2 *Use of scientific methods*—the collection of items shows that the student understands how to use scientific methods.			
3 *Models and inventions*—the collection of items shows quality models and inventions.			
4 *Connections between science and other subjects*—the collection of items demonstrates how the student makes thoughtful connections between science and other school subjects.			
5 *Reading or viewing materials related to science*—the collection of items shows that the student regularly reads or views materials related to science.			

The Portfolio as a Whole

Element	Points Possible	Student	Teacher
6 The portfolio has a clearly labeled cover that includes the student's and teacher's names.			
7 The collection of items in each category shows a wide range of work.			
8 The index for each category is clear.			
9 The self-reflective narrative in each category addresses strengths and weaknesses in that area.			
10 The self-reflective narrative in each category outlines plans for further development in that area.			
11 The portfolio shows an understanding of the concepts, skills, and work habits important in science class.			
Total			

G

Compile a Science Portfolio

	Rating
The student's science portfolio showed a command of the concepts, skills, and work habits important to science class. A wide range of quality work demonstrated that the student had a high level of science literacy and was setting challenging personal goals for learning. The index did an excellent job of guiding the reader through the items in each category. The self-reflective narratives focused on the individual's learning process and work habits.	
The student's science portfolio had a collection for each of the five categories. The collection worked as a whole to show a well-rounded exhibition in that category. The index guided the reader through the items. The self-reflective narrative showed thoughtful insight into the student's strengths and weaknesses, areas of growth, and goals for further growth.	
The student's collections for each category showed poor-quality work. The collection was limited in scope. Some categories might have been missing. The index might have been unorganized, incomplete, or unclear. The self-reflective narratives showed that the student had very little insight into his or her strengths and weaknesses. Learning goals were missing or showed little thought.	
The student's portfolio was poorly done. It was unorganized or incomplete.	

Comments:

Rubric Scoring Systems

The rubrics have an open column under the "Rating" head that allows you to customize your scoring or ranking based on your particular needs or your students' needs. You can express scores or ranks as words, letters, numbers, or with symbols, as described below.

Words:

- Excellent—Very Good—Acceptable—Unacceptable
- Demonstrates high proficiency—Clearly demonstrates proficiency—Demonstrates progress toward proficiency—Demonstrates strong need for proficiency
- Exceeds expectations—Meets expectations—Approaches expectations—Below expectations
- Exemplary—Proficient—Satisfactory—Insufficient
- Distinguished—Competent—Developing—Inadequate

Numbers:

- (highest) 4 3 2 1 0 (lowest)
- (highest) 10 9   8 7 6   5 4 3   2 1 0 (lowest)
- 100 percent   90 percent   80 percent   70 percent or lower

Letters:

- (highest) A B C D F (lowest)
- If you want to avoid using customary letter grades (A, B, C, D, F) choose another series of letters, such as V, W, X, Y, Z.

Sample Rubrics and Checklists

In addition to the rubrics and checklists presented in the previous section, samples of other types of assessment lists follow on pages 412–419. You can use these samples to customize individual or group assessment in your classroom.

G

Assessment for the Use of Scientific Methods

Scientific Methods	4	3	2	1
Investigation question	Appropriate and fully stated in correct terms	Appropriate and fairly well-written	Somewhat workable, is poorly stated, or is incomplete	Unclear or unanswerable
Hypothesis	Well-written explanation, fully stated in clear terms with justification	Acceptable explanation with a good justification	Weak or unclear explanation; no justification	Illogical or does not apply to the investigation
Investigation plan	Good and fully explained; includes steps, materials, and variables; easy to understand what the student did and how it was done	Good; workable; most of the steps, materials, and variables are included	Sketchy; somewhat workable; important steps, materials, and variables are not included	No steps listed or is totally unworkable
Data collection and organization	Recorded and organized into charts, graphs, sketches, and so on, that are complete and easy to read; results are well-summarized in a written statement	Recorded and organized well; results are summarized	Partially recorded and/or organized ineffectively; results are not summarized	Not recorded in an acceptable manner; not organized in any way
Conclusions	Logical and well-stated with a good comparison of results to the original hypothesis; clearly the student learned something	Fairly well-stated with acceptable comparisons between results and hypothesis	Fairly logical, but not explained well; no comparison of results with hypothesis	Totally illogical or not supported by the investigation
Writing mechanics	Work is legible and in final copy form; follows writing conventions (punctuation, capitalization, spelling, and grammar)	Errors are few and do not interfere with the communication and understanding of concepts	Several errors are made that interfere with the communication and understanding of concepts	Multiple errors are made that interfere with the communication and understanding of concepts

Comments:

G

Self-Assessment of Classification Techniques

Classification Assessment	4	3	2	1
Item selection	I selected important and interesting items to classify. They might be difficult to classify.	I selected items that are important and that made me think when I classified them.	I selected items that were not very important or that were too easily put into categories.	I selected items that were unimportant or that had nothing to do with the classification.
Identify categories	I identified categories that are meaningful and important to the items' classifications.	I identified categories that made me think about the important characteristics of the items.	I identified categories that do not reflect the most important characteristics of the items.	I identified categories that used only trivial characteristics of the items.
Item placement	I placed all 10 items into logical categories.	I placed at least 8 of 10 items into logical categories.	I placed at least 6 of 10 items into logical categories.	I placed 5 or fewer items into logical categories.
Written explanations	I clearly and completely described how and why I selected the 10 items. I also discussed some of the difficulties I faced in classifying them.	I described how I selected the items. I attempted to discuss some of the difficulties I faced in classifying them.	I described how I selected the items, but my description is incomplete or confusing.	My explanations are incomplete or very confusing.
Writing mechanics	My written work is legible and follows standard writing conventions (punctuation, capitalization, spelling, and grammar).	My writing errors are few and do not interfere with the communication and understanding of concepts.	I made some errors that distract from the communication and understanding of concepts.	I made many errors that interfere with the communication and understanding of concepts.

Comments:

G

Self-Assessment

Name _____ **Date** _____

1. New science concepts or information that I have learned recently are _____
   _____
   _____
   _____

2. Topics that cause me difficulty at this time are _____
   _____
   _____
   _____

3. The progress I have made in science over the past few weeks involves _____
   _____
   _____
   _____

4. The topics that interest me and that I would like to study further are _____
   _____
   _____
   _____

5. My feelings about science are _____
   _____
   _____
   _____

6. To improve our science class, we should try _____
   _____
   _____
   _____

G

Journal-Assessment Checklist

_____ detailed observations

_____ questions students would like to be able to answer and possible answers to those questions

_____ labeled drawings and sketches with comments

_____ "What if . . . ?" questions

_____ sketches and notes about models and inventions

_____ notes about interesting science items from newspapers, magazines, and other media

_____ thoughts about what is interesting and enjoyable about science class

_____ thoughts about difficulties in learning science and how to overcome the difficulties

_____ writing skills improving

_____ communication skills improving

_____ showing a relationship between science and the real world

G

Group Work and Rubric Checklist

Group Work Checklist	Excellent	Good	Fair	Poor
Stayed on task				
Worked together/cooperated				
Handled materials well/cleaned up				
Completed the task				

Note: Put a check mark or write an explanation in the appropriate box.

Reports and Presentations Rubric

Reports and Presentations	4	3	2	1
Scientific thought				
Oral presentation				
Exhibit display				
Written report				

G

Sample Rubric

Category	Criteria	Rating

Note: Use a number or letter in the ratings box.

G

Areas to Evaluate Rubric

Areas to Evaluate	20	15	10	5	1

G

Bibliography

1. Airasian, P.W. (1991). *Classroom Assessment*. New York: McGraw-Hill, Inc.

2. American Association for the Advancement of Science (1989). *Project 2061: Science for All Americans*. Washington, D.C.: American Association for the Advancement of Science.

3. Arter, J., and Spandel, V. (1992). "Using Portfolios of Student Work in Instruction and Assessment." *Educational Measurement: Issues and Practice*, 11, 1:36–44.

4. Barnes, Lehman W. and Marianne B. Barnes (1991). "Assessment, Practically Speaking. How Can We Measure Hands-on Science Skills?" *Science and Children*, 28, 6:14–15.

5. Carin, Arthur A. (1993). *Teaching Science Through Discovery*. New York: Merrill.

6. Champagne, A.B., Lovitts, B.E. and Clinger, B.J. (1990). *Assessment in the Service of Science*. Washington, D.C.: American Association for the Advancement of Science.

7. "From Teachers Who Know: Assessment for Maximum Teaching and Learning (1999)." *OASCD Journal*, Spring: 7–12.

8. Gronlund, N.E. (1993). *How to Make Achievement Tests and Assessments*. Boston, MA: Allyn and Bacon.

9. Ham, Mary and Dennis Adams (1991). "Portfolio Assessment. It's Not Just for Artists Anymore." *The Science Teacher*, 58, 1:18.

10. Kulm, G. and Malcom, S.M. (1991). *Science Assessment in the Service of Reform*. Washington, D.C.: American Association for the Advancement of Science.

11. Raizen, Senta A. et al. (1989). *Assessment in Elementary Science Education*. Colorado Springs, CO: The National Center for Improving Science Education.

12. Stiggins, R.J. (1987). "Design and Development of Performance Assessments." *Educational Measurement: Issues and Practice*. 6, 3:33–42.

13. Vermont Department of Education. (1992). *Looking Beyond "The Answer:" The Report of Vermont's Mathematics Portfolio Assessment Program, Pilot Year 1990–1991*. Montpelier: Department of Education.

14. Wangsatorntanakhun, Jo Anne. (1999). *Designing Performance Assessment: Challenges for the Three-Story Intellect*. Ruamrudee International School: 1–2.

15. Wiggins, G. (1989). "A True Test: Toward More Authentic and Equitable Assessment." *Phi Delta Kappan*, 70, 9: 703–713.

For Assessments and Rubrics go to

TEACHING TODAY

at **teachingtoday.glencoe.com**

G